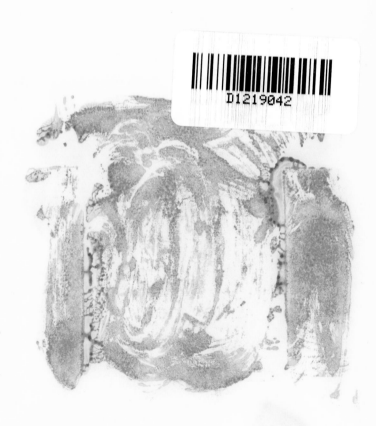

D1219042

Introduction to solids

McGRAW-HILL SERIES IN MATERIALS SCIENCE AND ENGINEERING

Editorial Board
Michael B. Bever
M. E. Shank
Charles A. Wert
Robert F. Mehl, *Honorary, Senior Advisory Editor*

AZÁROFF, *Introduction to Solids*
ELLIOTT, *Constitution of Binary Alloys, First Supplement*
PAUL AND WARSCHAUER, *Solids under Pressure*
SHEWMON, *Diffusion in Solids*
WERT AND THOMSON, *Physics of Solids*

Introduction to solids

LEONID V. AZÁROFF

PROFESSOR OF METALLURGICAL ENGINEERING
ILLINOIS INSTITUTE OF TECHNOLOGY

54B
Az16i

McGRAW-HILL BOOK COMPANY

New York   Toronto   London

1960

INTRODUCTION TO SOLIDS

Copyright © 1960 by McGraw-Hill, Inc. Printed in the United
States of America. All rights reserved. This book, or parts
thereof, may not be reproduced in any form without permission
of the publishers. *Library of Congress Catalog Card Number* 59-15044

6 7 8 9 – M P – 9 8 7 6

02668

THE MAPLE PRESS COMPANY, YORK, PA.

21863

The John J. Wright Library
LA ROCHE COLLEGE
Allison Park, Pennsylvania

10.35

4-61   B+1

Dedicated To

Carmen

Preface

There once was a time when it was possible for a scientist not only to master his own field but also to have a working knowledge of all related fields. With the growth of scientific knowledge it became increasingly necessary to specialize until, today, very few are able to master even a single field completely. So it has come to pass that chemists are often unaware of the physical properties of the compounds that they analyze, physicists do not fully appreciate the crystallography of the crystals whose properties they study, mineralogists fail to appreciate the full potential of the minerals they seek, and engineers are only partly aware of the nature of the materials that they use. In keeping with this trend, chemists, electrical engineers, metallurgists, mineralogists, physicists, and many, many others who constantly deal with solids have tended to become familiar with only one aspect of solids, as if each part were independent of the whole. Most textbooks written to date also reflect this trend so that it is difficult for even the willing student to obtain the broadening he seeks. This book represents an attempt, therefore, to provide the necessary broad background on a sufficiently elementary level to be useful to all who are interested in solids.

In constructing such a synthesis, it becomes necessary to decide what to include and what to omit without destroying the book's purpose. The one thing that the majority of solids of practical importance have in common is that they are crystalline. An attempt has been made, therefore, to use the crystallinity of solids as a framework in discussing their nature and properties. In keeping with this it is necessary, first of all, to define what crystals are and how they are distinguished from other kinds of matter. Once the geometry and atomic composition of solids is understood, their properties can be considered. Here, again, a choice has to be made in selecting the properties to emphasize. In order not to limit the usefulness of this book to a few specialists, only the commonest kinds of properties are considered in detail. Thus organic solids have been completely omitted because their appreciation requires a familiarity with organic chemistry that few nonchemists possess. For similar reasons, the properties of surfaces have not been considered, and so on.

An attempt has been made, nevertheless, to include more material than can normally be covered in a single college course. This has been done for two reasons. It allows the teacher to select for emphasis in class those parts that he deems most appropriate. On the other hand, it provides the student with an opportunity to find supplementary material within the same book. To this end, the literature sections at the end of each chapter contain lists of references where the interested student can find further elaboration of the subjects that interest him most. Similarly, the exercises at the end of each chapter have been designed, in part, to serve as a review of the subject matter discussed, to introduce some concepts not enlarged in the text, and to illustrate some applications of the principles learned. In doing this, mathematical complexity has been intentionally kept to a minimum. Where absolutely necessary, mathematical expressions are introduced to illustrate the principles involved. The actual manipulation of all equations used, however, rarely requires more than a familiarity with elementary mathematics. Thus the notes on which this book is based have been found to be equally useful in solid-state courses for students of physical science and of engineering.

In order to help the reader visualize the three-dimensional aspects of crystalline solids, the text is profusely illustrated. All drawings appearing in this book have been especially prepared for it. In some cases, ideas for drawings were borrowed from various sources used in writing this book. In addition, a number of colleagues have been very kind in supplying photographs of actual examples, and a number of publishers gave permission to reproduce material previously published. In particular, thanks are due for the following illustrations:

Chapter 1: Fig. 1, W. A. Bentley and W. J. Humphreys, *Snow crystals* (McGraw-Hill Book Company, Inc., New York, 1931); Fig. 2, M. J. Buerger, Massachusetts Institute of Technology, Cambridge, Mass.

Chapter 5: Fig. 3, J. W. Menter, Tube Investments Research Laboratories, Cambridge, England; Fig. 16, F. Lincoln Vogel, Bell Telephone Laboratories, Murray Hill, N.J.

Chapter 6: Fig. 12, W. C. Dash, General Electric Research Laboratory, Schenectady, N.Y. Reprinted with permission from *Journal of Applied Physics*, vol. 27 (1956), no. 11.

Chapter 7: Fig. 10, David R. Boyd and Y. T. Sihvonen, General Motors Research Laboratories, Detroit, Mich.

Chapter 8: Fig. 27, Robert F. Mehl, Carnegie Institute of Technology, Pittsburgh, Pa. Reprinted with permission from *Progress in metal physics*, vol. 6 (Pergamon Press Ltd., London, 1956).

Chapter 10: Fig. 23, R. V. Coleman and G. G. Scott, General Motors Corporation, Detroit, Mich.

Chapter 11: Figs. 6, 19, 13, 15, and 18, Max Hansen, *Constitution of binary alloys* (McGraw-Hill Book Company, Inc., New York, 1958).

Chapter 14: Fig. 5, Donald P. Cameron, International Business Machines Research Center, Poughkeepsie, N.Y.

A large number of my colleagues were very kind to read and criticize those parts of this manuscript in which they had special knowledge; for this I am very grateful. In addition, thanks are due to Drs. C. S. Barrett, J. J. Brophy, M. J. Buerger, I. Fankuchen, and B. Post who reviewed major portions of the manuscript. Although I assume full responsibility for all statements made, the suggestions received were invaluable in forming this book. Thanks are also due to Mrs. Doris Ahles, who spent many a weekend preparing the typescript, and to my wife, who spent many lonely hours waiting for me to complete it.

Leonid V. Azároff

Contents

1

Introduction

It is the nature of man to study his environment and to seek to understand the many processes that it manifests. Even the most casual observer soon becomes impressed by how orderly these processes are. In the cosmos, the distant stars and the nearby planets appear to follow the same orbits year after year, a movement that knows no equal in regularity or endurance. On earth, the rhythmic sequence of tides, of lunar cycles, and of just cycles all testify to the simple elegance of the basic patterns to which nature conforms. The natural patterns of many solids are obvious to the unaided eye; the lustrous, systematically arrayed faces of single crystals of minerals such as quartz or garnet are common examples. The name *crystal* comes from the Greek word krystallos, meaning clear ice, and was first applied to describe the beautiful transparent quartz "stones" found in the Swiss Alps. The choice of this particular name was prompted by the mistaken belief that these stones were formed from water by extremely intense cold. By the seventeenth century, however, the name crystal was extended to other manifestations of solids that bore the relation to the original rock crystal of being bounded by many flat shiny faces, symmetrically arrayed.

Other kinds of patterns formed by solids are best seen with the aid of magnification by, say, an ordinary microscope. Figure 1 shows two magnified pictures of ordinary snowflakes. The regularity of this form of solid H_2O is not unlike that displayed by natural crystals of other compositions, and, indeed, a snowflake *is* a crystal of ice. In their book *Snow crystals*,† Bentley and Humphreys show hundreds of photographs of snowflakes. It is somewhat surprising to read that they never encountered two snowflakes that looked exactly alike although many of them look very similar. On the other hand, all the snowflakes exhibit the same high degree of symmetry that can be seen in two of the illustrations reproduced

† Mc-Graw-Hill Book Company, Inc., New York, 1931.

1

Fɪɢ. 1.   Snowflakes or single crystals of ice.   (Photographed by W. A. Bentley and W. J. Humphreys.)

from their book in Fig. 1.   Although originally the name crystal was incorrectly applied to quartz specimens found among the rocks in mountains, in view of the millions of true crystals that descend from the sky on this earth each winter, it is difficult to think of a more suitable name to describe these highly symmetrical manifestations of solids.

The symmetrical patterns revealed by the microscope persist down to much smaller dimensions in solids as well.   If it were possible to look at atoms in crystals directly, they would be found in symmetrical arrays like the ones shown in Fig. 2.   As will become clearer in later chapters, it is not possible to "look" at atoms directly.   When one examines the workings of a microscope, however, it becomes apparent that a subterfuge can be employed to attain the same end result.   A microscope forms a magnified image essentially by the following process.   The object is viewed with the aid of light rays which are first reflected from the object toward a series of lenses.   Each lens in turn breaks up the bundle of light rays into separate rays (this process is called diffraction) and recombines them in such a way that the object appears to be much larger than it really is. Now, it is possible to obtain a diffraction picture of a crystal by using x-rays, although it is not possible to refocus the diffracted x-rays with the aid of any lens as yet devised.   On the other hand, if this diffraction picture is viewed in a suitably constructed instrument with the aid of visible light, an actual picture of the atoms results.   The two-wavelength microscope, as such an instrument is called, can thus produce magnifications of

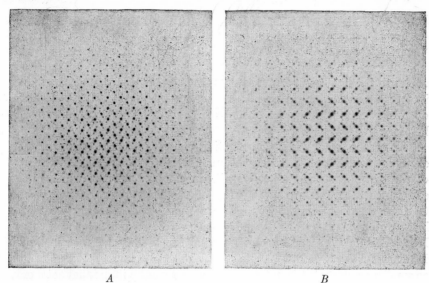

A   B

FIG. 2.   Atomic arrays in two crystalline forms of FeS_2.   The large circles are iron atoms, and the small circles are sulfur atoms, magnified slightly over 5,000,000 times. (Photographed by M. J. Buerger.)

A. Marcasite, FeS_2, looking along the crystallographic *c* axis.

B. Pyrite, FeS_2, looking along the crystallographic *a* axis.

a hundred million times, as compared with 10,000-fold enlargements attainable with microscopes using visible light only.

Figure 2 shows two pictures obtained with the two-wavelength microscope.   Both are of crystals composed of the same kinds of atoms, namely, iron and sulfur in the ratio of one iron atom to two sulfur atoms.   As can be seen, the iron disulfide molecules look alike in both crystals but the over-all arrangement of molecules is somewhat different.   These two different arrangements, or *crystal structures*, are the structures of two distinct minerals, marcasite and pyrite.   Two or more crystals having identical atomic compositions but different arrangements or structures are called *polymorphs*, derived from a Greek word meaning many forms.   The different structures of polymorphous compounds produce two or more kinds of crystals differing not only in their appearance but in other properties as well.   It turns out, in fact, that many physical properties are more markedly affected by differences in crystal structure than they are by differences in atomic or so-called chemical compositions.

The atoms shown in Fig. 2 all appear to be at rest in their very symmetrical arrays.   In an actual crystal, however, the atoms are in constant motion.   Now it may seem strange, at first thought, to picture a solid, say this book, as a beehive teeming with activity.   This difficulty is due only to man's lack of familiarity with this type of activity, caused by his inability to see it directly. Yet there are many visible manifestations of such activity and motion in everyday objects. For example, take the "running" stream which "rotates" the wheels of a dynamo, which "produces" the electricity, which "rushes" through miles and miles of cables to the light sources, which "light up" and turn the evening hours into day. Moreover, this process goes on constantly and regularly all over this earth without the benefit of direct intervention by any living being.

The process of artificial illumination can also be cited as a common example of the law of the conservation of energy. The mechanical energy of the distant rotating wheel results in electrical energy which in the end is transformed into the energy of the light given off in a room. Observe that nowhere in this entire sequence is any energy created or lost, which is the principle of conservation required by the above law. This fact in itself is evidence of the orderly manner in which inanimate objects function. This functioning, of course, takes place on so small a scale that it is not possible to observe the individual acts, only the sum total as the actions of the whole.

In order to understand the functions or actions of the whole, however, it is necessary first to understand the actions of each part. To help him do this, man has devised some very ingenious tools such as the two-wavelength microscope, for example. These have enabled him to peer inside an inanimate object and to discern its minutest parts. It is from such observations, which showed that solids were composed of spherical atoms in regular arrays, that the final proof came to substantiate the atomic theory of matter. As the tools of research became successively more powerful, it was discovered that the atom in turn consists of a central nucleus surrounded by a number of electrons. These electrons are in constant motion and are responsible for most of the external activity exhibited by solids. In fact, this motion is so persistent and so rapid that no kinds of magnification schemes devised to date have been able to arrest the speed of the electron long enough actually to see it. Thus man knows of the electron's existence only by the tracks it leaves as it moves, like a furtive mouse whose tracks of the previous night's repast are found the following morning on the pantry shelf.

The nucleus is much heavier and more sedate and, therefore, it moves relatively little. (Since the nucleus is several thousand times larger than an electron, it virtually *is* the atom.) Its motion in solids is restricted to small vibrations about a mean position, and for most purposes the nucleus can be considered as being at rest. This quiescent state of the nucleus or of the atom is, in fact, the structural feature that distinguishes solids from liquids. In the latter form of matter, the atoms are much more free to move about and are in constant motion. They are still attracted to each other, as they are in a solid, and thereby give the liquid its cohesiveness. On the other hand, their ability to move freely is the reason why a liquid can be poured from one container to another.

It appears from the above that it should be possible to transform a liquid to a solid by decreasing the motion of the atoms or to reverse the process by increasing their motion. This can indeed be done. When the temperature is lowered sufficiently, a liquid freezes and a solid results. As the temperature is raised, the atoms become increasingly more mobile until their motion becomes so great that the orderly array in the solid disintegrates and it becomes a liquid. If the process is carried far enough, the liquid can be transformed into a gas, which is nothing more than a state in which the atoms have gained so much freedom of motion that they no longer bother to stick together at all.

When the liquid cools, two types of solids can form. If the liquid cools sufficiently slowly for the atoms to assume orderly arrangements like the ones shown in Fig. 2, a crystal results. On the other hand, if the temperature is dropped abruptly, arresting the motion of the atoms before they can reorganize themselves, then a mixed-up structure called a *glass* or an *amorphous* solid may result. Such a glass, when reheated, does not melt in the abrupt sense that at one instant it is still a solid and in the next it is a liquid but it simply softens gradually and continuously until it is so soft that it is again a liquid. As with most properties of solids, the explanation of the difference in the behavior of glasses and crystals when heated is determined by the difference in their atomic arrangements or structures. In a crystal, the atoms are arranged like soldiers on a parade ground, in well-defined columns and rows (Fig. 2). When the command "Dismissed!" is shouted, the individuals dash off in every direction, and instantaneously the orderly array has disappeared; it may be said that the ranks have melted. In a glassy substance, the atoms never had a chance to organize themselves into orderly arrays in the first place. Hence, in a glass it is not possible to distinguish the solid from the liquid state except by the relative motions of the atoms, a property described by the term viscosity.

The basic feature of all crystals is the regularity of their atomic arrangement, already encountered above. If the magnified views of the two structures shown in Fig. 2 are examined carefully, it becomes apparent that there is a basic unit in each structure that when systematically repeated reproduces the whole structure. Thus the first notable feature of the regularity of crystal structures is the *periodicity* of their patterns. Now, periodic patterns are not the exclusive property of crystals. The beauty of such patterns was recognized by man a long time ago. The friezes adorning the most ancient temples of the East and West are some of the earliest encountered examples of periodicity in one dimension. The patterns on wallpapers or dress materials, the designs found in men's ties, as well as many others can be cited as examples of modern-day patterns that are periodic in two dimensions.

In addition to periodicity, most crystal structures possess the property of *symmetry*. There are several kinds of symmetries possible. A frequently encountered one is the symmetry of rotation. It can be seen in Fig. 1, for example, that each snow crystal can be rotated about its center six successive times without repeating the same movement (the angle of rotation each time is 60°), and each time it is rotated, the crystal looks the same as it did before rotation. Other symmetries are also possible and, of course, combinations of symmetries are possible. It might appear from this that a large number of different kinds of structures are available to accommodate the extremely large number of different kinds of solids known to exist. Actually, only 230 different combinations can be formed in three dimensions, a conclusion independently arrived at by three men: the Russian crystallographer Federoff, the German mathematician Schoenflies, and the English physicist Barlow. It is interesting to note that a large fraction of these possible symmetries have already been discovered to exist among the several thousand crystals examined so far.

A proper introduction to solids, therefore, must begin with a study of the rules that govern the formation of crystal structures. These rules constitute a branch of man's knowledge commonly called *geometrical crystallography*. Fortunately, this subject is no more complex than solid geometry and is easily mastered. It is possible to consider next the way that atoms arrange themselves in crystals in conformity with these crystallographic requirements. Crystals can form from a gas by *sublimation* or from a liquid by *crystallization*. When a crystal forms from a vapor or a liquid, its continued growth depends on the presence of a sufficient supply of growth units, that is, the atoms required to make up its structure. If the supply is overabundant, the crystal may grow extremely fast, in many directions at once, and it develops a branchlike appearance or *habit* (Fig. 1). Conversely, if the supply of atoms decreases below a certain value, the crystal stops growing and may actually start to redissolve. Many other fates can befall a crystal during growth and also after growth is completed. Because nothing is ever quite perfect, crystals contain many kinds of imperfections. Crystals may absorb foreign atoms during their growth or forget to include others that rightfully belong. Furthermore, it may happen that the atoms which assumed one structure while the crystal grew rearrange themselves to form another structure long after growth is completed. These variations from an ideal structure have a marked influence on the properties of crystals. The plan followed in this book, therefore, is to introduce the constitution of crystals first and then to discuss their properties. The common features and properties of all crystals are described in the first part of the book. The last six chapters are devoted to a somewhat more detailed discussion of specific crystal types.

The vagaries in the "life" of a crystal have been described by the nineteenth-century English writer John Ruskin.

And remember, the poor little crystals have to live their lives, and mind their own affairs, in the midst of all this, as best they may. They are wonderfully like human creatures—forget all that is going on if they don't see it, however dreadful; and never think what is to happen tomorrow. They are spiteful or loving, and indolent or painstaking, with no thought whatever of the lava or the flood which may break over them any day; and evaporate them into air-bubbles, or wash them into a solution of salts. And you may look at them, once understanding the surrounding conditions of their fate, with an endless interest. You will see crowds of unfortunate little crystals, who have been forced to constitute themselves in a hurry, their dissolving element being fiercely scorched away; you will see them doing their best, bright and numberless, but tiny. Then you will find indulged crystals, who have had centuries to form themselves in, and have changed their mind and ways continually; and have been tired, and taken heart again; and have been sick, and got well again; and thought they would try a different diet, and then thought better of it; and made but a poor use of their advantages, after all.

And sometimes you may see hypocritical crystals taking the shape of others, tho they are nothing like in their minds; and vampire crystals eating out the hearts of others; and hermit-crab crystals living on the shells of others; and parasite crystals living on the means of others; and courtier crystals glittering in the attendance upon others; and all these, besides the two great companies of war and peace, who ally themselves, resolutely to attack, or resolutely to defend. And for the close, you see the broad shadow and deadly force of inevitable fate, above all this: you see the multitudes of crystals whose time has come; not a set time, as with us, but yet a time, sooner or later, when they all must give up their crystal ghosts—when the strength by which they grew, and the breath given them to breathe, pass away from them; and they fail, and are consumed, and vanish away; and another generation is brought to life, framed out of their ashes.

Suggestions for supplementary reading

Sir Lawrence Bragg, *The crystalline state*, vol. 1, *A general survey* (G. Bell & Sons, Ltd., London, 1949).

Jacob Porter Frankel, *Principles of the properties of materials* (McGraw-Hill Book Company, Inc., New York, 1957).

2

Geometrical crystallography

Periodicity in crystals

The principles of geometrical crystallography are quite general and can be applied to many different systems. In this chapter, the specific principles that apply to crystals are developed in just enough detail to permit the understanding of the structures and properties of crystals that must conform to them. The basis on which crystals are distinguished from noncrystals is that the atoms in crystals are arranged in the form of a *periodic array*. Such an array consists of a representative unit of the structure, usually a group of atoms or molecules, repeated in space at regular intervals. The representative unit can be repeated in many different ways and still satisfy the basic requirement of periodicity. It is natural, therefore, first to inquire into the different ways of periodically repeating an object. The study of the different possibilities and laws that govern them is called *pattern theory* or *geometrical crystallography*.

Representation of a pattern. Provided only that the pattern is periodic, the laws of geometrical crystallography are independent of the detailed nature of the pattern to which they are applied. In illustrating these laws, therefore, it is possible to select any motif to represent the basic unit whose periodic repetition constitutes the pattern. In order to maintain complete generality, it is advisable to select a motif that is unsymmetrical. For example, consider an ordinary boot shown in Fig. 1. It is interesting to note that a boot can exist in two different forms, namely, one that fits the left foot and one that fits the right foot. A pair of such boots is shown in Fig. 2A and B. To distinguish the two forms, one is usually called *left-handed* and the other *right-handed*. It should be realized that any asymmetric object can exist in both a left-handed and a right-handed form. A pair of objects thus related are said to be *enantiomorphous*.

8

Repetition of an object. A symbol that is almost as unsymmetrical as a boot and much easier to draw is the number seven. Figure 3 shows an enantiomorphous pair of sevens, one on each side of a vertical line. Note that, whereas a single seven is unsymmetrical, the representation in Fig. 3 is symmetrical in that each side of the figure looks like a mirror

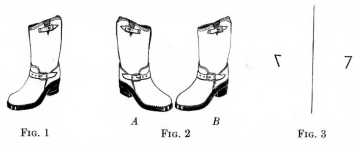

FIG. 1   A   FIG. 2   B   FIG. 3

image of the other reflected across the vertical line. In fact, such a *reflection* of an object across a *symmetry line* is one of the possible operations of repetition.

A very simple operation of repetition consists of taking one of the representations in Fig. 3 and repeating it without change after translating it a distance t. If this *translation* t is repeated continuously, a sequence of periodically spaced sevens obtains (Fig. 4) quite similar to a row of evenly spaced pickets in a fence.

Another way of repeating a seven is to rotate the seven about a point, as shown in Fig. 5. The simplest way to picture this operation is to think of an *axis* passing through the center of Fig. 5 and to represent the repetition by a *rotation* through an angle φ about this axis. It should be noted that, if it is desired that the repeated object return to

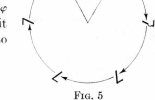

7 7 7 7 7 7 7

$\xrightarrow{\ t\ }$

FIG. 4   FIG. 5

self-coincidence after an integral number of rotations n, then φ must be an integral submultiple of a complete revolution, that is,

$$\varphi = \frac{360°}{n} \qquad n = 1, 2, 3 \ldots . \tag{1}$$

Translation periodicity. The single translation in Fig. 4 produces an infinite linear array of the repeated object. If such a translation, t_1, is combined with another, noncollinear translation, t_2, then a two-dimensional array (Fig. 6) obtains as follows: The entire linear array due to translation t_1 (Fig. 4) is repeated an infinite number of times by the second

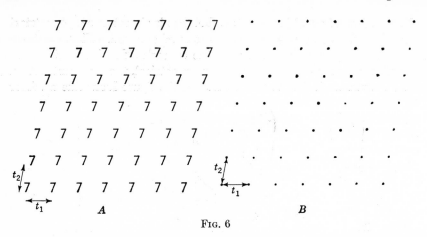

translation t_2. Another way of looking at this is to say that the linear array due to t_2 is repeated by t_1.

Since the nature of the repeated objects in Fig. 6A does not affect the translation periodicity, it is conventional to represent this periodicity by replacing each object in the array with a point. The resulting collection of points shown in Fig. 6B is called a *lattice*, in this case, a two-dimensional or *plane lattice*. It should be remembered that a point is an imaginary, infinitesimal spot in space, and, consequently, *a lattice of points is imaginary* also. On the other hand, the array of sevens in Fig. 6 is real. It is *not* a lattice of sevens, because a lattice is an imaginary concept; instead it is correctly called a *lattice array* of sevens.

It is possible to add a third translation to the plane lattice in Fig. 6B or to the lattice array in Fig. 6A. In each case, the third translation repeats the entire plane at equal intervals t_3. This third translation thus produces a *space lattice* (Fig. 7B) or a *three-dimensional lattice array* (Fig. 7A). Because it is easier to draw a plane lattice than a space lattice on a sheet

7^{7^7} 7^{7^7} 7^{7^7} 7^{7^7} 7^{7^7}

7^{7^7} 7^{7^7} 7^{7^7} 7^{7^7} 7^{7^7}

7^{7^7} 7^{7^7} 7^{7^7} 7^{7^7} 7^{7^7}

7^{7^7} 7^{7^7} 7^{7^7} 7^{7^7} 7^{7^7}

$7^{7^7}_{t_3}$ 7^{7^7} 7^{7^7} 7^{7^7} 7^{7^7}

A   B

FIG. 7

of paper, wherever possible plane lattices are used in this book. The extension of the principles illustrated to three dimensions follows directly from the above discussion.

Representation of a lattice. It has been shown above that two noncollinear translations define a plane lattice and three noncoplanar translations define a space lattice. It is natural to ask, therefore, given a particular lattice, which pair (or which triplet) of translations does one choose to describe it? Actually, there exists an infinity of choices for each translation because a line joining any two lattice points is a translation of the lattice. Figure 8 shows a plane lattice and some of the choices

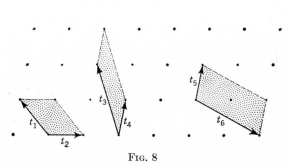

Fig. 8

that exist. If pairs of translations such as t_1, t_2, or t_3, t_4 are chosen, they are said to define a *primitive cell*, so called because *one* lattice point is associated with each cell. This can be seen in two ways:

1. Consider each lattice point as belonging equally to four adjacent cells in Fig. 8; thus only a part of each point belongs to any one cell. Since each cell has four corners, it contains four such parts, whose total "area" adds up to one whole point.

2. Alternatively, displace slightly any one of the shaded primitive cells in Fig. 8. It becomes immediately obvious that only one lattice point can lie within the area of any one primitive cell.

On the other hand, the cell defined by t_5 and t_6 contains a lattice point within the cell in addition to the one shared at the corners and is called a *multiple cell*. Several kinds of multiple cells are possible, namely, *double cells*, *triple cells*, etc., depending on whether they contain two, three, or more lattice points, counting all the corner points together as one point and adding one for each point contained in the interior of the cell. The translations that define a primitive cell are called *conjugate translations*.

Either a primitive or a multiple cell can be selected as a *unit cell* of the lattice. The unit cell is so called because the entire lattice can be derived by repeating this cell as a unit by means of the translations that serve as the unit cell's edges. The choice of a unit cell is dictated by convenience and convention to be that cell which best represents the symmetry of the lattice, as discussed in a later section. The three translations selected as the edges of the unit cell are called the *crystallographic axes a, b, c,* and the angles between them α, β, γ (Fig. 9), where

α is the angle between *b* and *c* (opposite the *a* axis).
β is the angle between *c* and *a* (opposite the *b* axis).
γ is the angle between *a* and *b* (opposite the *c* axis).

The three crystallographic axes can be thought of as three noncoplanar vectors defining a lattice. Any other translation in the lattice, therefore,

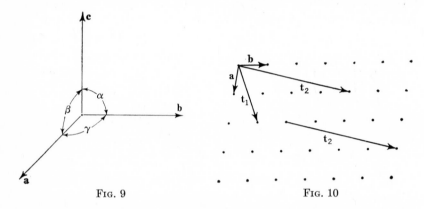

FIG. 9   FIG. 10

can be represented by the appropriate vector sum of these three axes. Figure 10 shows two such translations in a two-dimensional lattice,

$$\mathbf{t}_1 = 2\mathbf{a} + 1\mathbf{b}$$

and
$$\mathbf{t}_2 = 1\mathbf{a} + 4\mathbf{b}. \tag{2}$$

Note that any translation parallel to $\mathbf{t}_2$ is also the translation $\mathbf{t}_2$ regardless of its point of origin.

In three dimensions, any translation in a lattice can be represented by the vector sum

$$\mathbf{t} = u\mathbf{a} + v\mathbf{b} + w\mathbf{c}. \tag{3}$$

Since, in a given lattice, **a, b, c** remain unchanged, the translation direction **t** can be specified by the three integral coefficients in equation (3): *u, v,* and *w.* It is conventional to use the shorthand notation [*uvw*] to specify a translation direction in a lattice.

Notation of planes in a lattice. It is often convenient to consider a stack of parallel planes passing through a lattice. The designation of these planes is slightly more complicated than the designation of directions. Figure 11 shows the projection of a lattice along its *c* axis which is perpendicular to the *ab* plane. Consider a plane that is parallel to the *c* axis and is represented in an edge view by the heavy line in Fig. 11. The translation periodicity of the lattice, of course, requires that a parallel plane pass through every lattice point (light lines in Fig. 11). The intercepts of the plane first considered are two units along the *a* axis, three along *b*, and ∞ along *c* since the plane is parallel to this axis. Now, consider the intercepts of the parallel plane lying nearest to the origin. This plane has the intercepts ⅓ along *a*, ½ along *b*, and ∞ along *c*. Since all the parallel planes are exactly alike, it is convenient always to consider the plane nearest to the origin. In order to avoid using fractions in its designation, the reciprocals of the intercepts are used instead. The resulting integers are named after their inventor, the *Miller indices* of the plane.

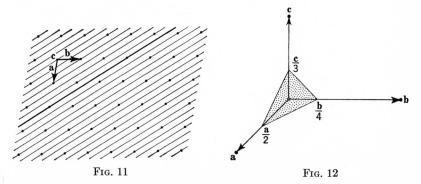

FIG. 11   FIG. 12

The procedure for obtaining the indices of any plane is summarized below for the plane shown by the heavy line in Fig. 11.

Procedure	a	b	c	
1. Determine intercepts	2	3	∞	
2. Note their reciprocals	$\frac{1}{2}$	$\frac{1}{3}$	$\frac{1}{\infty} = 0$	(4)
3. Clear fractions	3	2	0	

It is conventional to represent the indices of a plane by enclosing them in parentheses: (*hkl*). The meaning of these indices is that the set of parallel planes (*hkl*) cuts the *a* axis into *h* parts, the *b* axis into *k* parts, and the *c* axis into *l* parts. As an illustration, the (243) plane nearest the origin is shown in Fig. 12.

A special case of indexing arises when a lattice can be described by a unit cell having two equal axes inclined at 120° and a third axis that is orthogonal to the plane of these two axes (Fig. 13). As can be seen in Fig. 14, the plane of the two equal axes contains a third axis that is equal in length to the other two. It will be shown later in this chapter that this type of lattice occurs in the *hexagonal crystal system*, in which case the three coplanar axes are equivalent by symmetry. There is some advantage to displaying this symmetry equivalence in the indices. If the four *hexagonal axes*, or Bravais-Miller axes $\mathbf{a}_1$, $\mathbf{a}_2$, $\mathbf{a}_3$, $\mathbf{c}$, are used, then the corresponding *hexagonal indices*, or Bravais-Miller indices, are $(hkil)$. It is

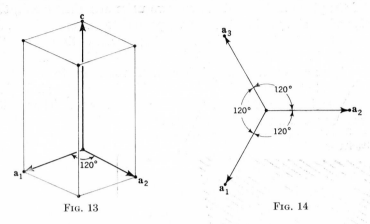

FIG. 13   FIG. 14

easy to show that the relationship between the three equivalent axes is

$$\mathbf{a}_1 + \mathbf{a}_2 = -\mathbf{a}_3 \tag{5}$$

and between the corresponding indices,

$$h + k = -i. \tag{6}$$

A negative index is written with a bar over it; that is, $(11\bar{2}1)$ means $(1,1,-2,1)$. Since the relationship in equation (6) is easily remembered, the i is sometimes replaced by a dot when the hexagonal indices $(hk\cdot l)$ are used.

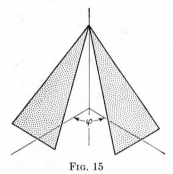

FIG. 15

Relationships between planes. It has been shown in Fig. 11 that the plane (hkl) is merely one of an infinite set of parallel planes related to each other by the translations of the lattice. A plane can be related to one or more other planes in the lattice by other operations of repetition also. For example, Fig. 15 shows two planes related by a rotation of amount φ. Such sets of symmetry-related planes are said to constitute a *form*. The indices of the various planes belonging to a form are readily determinable, and it is sufficient to use the indices of any one plane to represent the symmetry-related set. When this is done, the indices are placed inside double parentheses; that is, a symmetrical set of planes is designated $((hkl))$.†

Another collection of planes of frequent interest is a set of planes that have one direction in common. This common direction is the direction along which the planes intersect and is called a *zone axis*. The planes that share this zone axis are said to belong to the same *zone*. The indices of a zone axis $[uvw]$ and a plane (hkl) in this zone must obey the relation

$$uh + vk + wl = 0. \tag{7}$$

As a simple example of planes belonging to a zone, consider the [001] zone axis and all the planes that have indices $(hk0)$.

The zone axis $[uvw]$ of two intersecting planes $(h_1k_1l_1)$ and $(h_2k_2l_2)$ can be determined as follows:

$$\begin{aligned} u &= k_1l_2 - k_2l_1 \\ v &= l_1h_2 - l_2h_1 \\ w &= h_1k_2 - h_2k_1. \end{aligned} \tag{8}$$

Symmetry elements

The operation of rotation. It has already been shown that an object can be repeated periodically by the operation of a translation. It also has been shown that an object can be repeated by a rotation about an axis. In each of these cases the character of the object did not change; that is, a right-handed object repeated as a right-handed object and a left-handed object repeated as a left-handed object. The objects forming such a set are said to be *congruent*.

In the case of repetition by rotation, the axis about which the rotation takes place is called a *rotation axis*. If the operation of rotation results in a congruent set, it is called a *proper rotation*, and the rotation axis is called a *proper rotation axis*. It is also possible to have a rotational operation which relates enantiomorphous objects; that is, a right-handed motif becomes left-handed upon repetition and vice versa. Such an operation is called an *improper rotation*, and the corresponding symmetry element is called an *improper rotation axis*.

† This designation follows one proposed by M. J. Buerger on page 114 of *Elementary crystallography* (John Wiley & Sons, Inc., New York, 1956). In this convention, symmetrical sets of planes are designated $((hkl))$ instead of $\{hkl\}$, and symmetrical sets of directions or lines are designated $[[uvw]]$ instead of $\langle uvw \rangle$. Although very rarely used, a lattice point is designated by $\cdot uvw\cdot$ instead of the previously used designation $[[uvw]]$, and a symmetrical set of points is then designated $:uvw:$ As can be seen, this convention has the great advantage that an element and its symmetrical set are represented in a parallel manner.

Proper rotation axes. Successive rotations by an amount φ eventually lead to the superposition of the repeated object upon the initial one if

$$\varphi = \frac{360°}{n} \qquad n = 1, 2, 3 \ldots \ldots \tag{1}$$

The rotation angle φ is called the *throw* of an axis, and the number of successive rotations, n, required to cause superposition is sometimes called the *fold* of an axis.

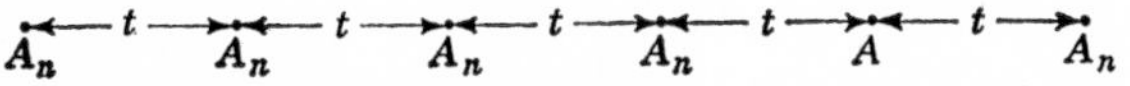

$$\overset{\longleftarrow t \longrightarrow}{A_n} \quad \overset{\longleftarrow t \longrightarrow}{A_n} \quad \overset{\longleftarrow t \longrightarrow}{A_n} \quad \overset{\longleftarrow t \longrightarrow}{A_n} \quad \overset{\longleftarrow t \longrightarrow}{A} \quad \overset{}{A_n}$$

FIG. 16

A rotation axis is said to exist when *all of space* around it has the property of rotational symmetry about this axis. For example, a tulip is said to have 3-fold symmetry because the petals and other parts of the flower grow in sets of three about the floral axis. Similarly, the floral axis of a columbine is 5-fold; that is, the "flower space" is divided into five equivalent parts. In general, a rotation axis can be 3-fold or 5-fold or n-fold, depending entirely on the symmetry of the space surrounding the axis. In crystals, on the other hand, the throw of an axis is limited by the fundamental requirement of translation periodicity.

To discover the permissible throws that rotation axes can have, start with the row lattice shown in Fig. 16 and place an n-fold axis A_n at each lattice point. Since n rotations by an amount φ cause superposition, it does not matter whether the rotations proceed in a clockwise or counterclockwise manner. Accordingly, two opposite rotations by an amount φ about two axes in Fig. 16 are shown in Fig. 17. The two new lattice

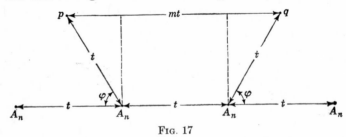

FIG. 17

points thus produced, p and q, must be equidistant from the original row lattice by construction. Hence, the line joining p and q is parallel to the translation t and must be equal to some integral multiple of t. If it is not, then the line joining the two lattice points p and q is not a translation of the lattice and the array is not periodic.

With the aid of Fig. 17, it is a simple matter to determine the possible values that φ can have in a lattice. According to the construction in

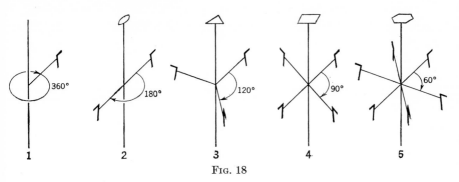

FIG. 18

Fig. 17,

$$mt = t + 2t \cos \varphi \qquad m = 0, \pm 1, \pm 2, \pm 3 \ldots \qquad (9)$$

and $\pm m$ is used depending on whether the translation is measured to the right or left. Dividing both sides of (9) by t and rearranging terms,

$$\cos \varphi = \frac{m-1}{2}. \qquad (10)$$

Finally, since m is an integer, $m - 1$ is also an integer, say N, and (10) can be written

$$\cos \varphi = \frac{N}{2}. \qquad (11)$$

It is now possible to construct a table showing the solutions of (11) for different integral values of N. Table 1 shows all solutions for $-2 \leq N \leq 2$ corresponding to the range $-1 \leq \cos \varphi \leq 1$. Magnitudes of N greater than 2 lead to an impossibility since the magnitude of the cosine of an angle cannot exceed unity. Consequently, there are only five possible solutions of (9), and only five kinds of axes are compatible with a lattice. These axes are shown in perspective in Fig. 18. The symbol for a proper rotation axis is an integer corresponding to the number of repetitions in 2π. Thus a 2-fold axis is called a 2, a 4-fold is called a 4, etc.

Table 1
Determination of rotation axes allowed in a lattice

N	$\cos \varphi$	φ (deg)	n
-2	-1	180	2
-1	$-\frac{1}{2}$	120	3
0	0	90	4
$+1$	$+\frac{1}{2}$	60	6
$+2$	$+1$	360 or 0	1

Improper rotation axes. As stated earlier, an improper rotation axis repeats a left-handed object from a right-handed one, and vice versa. One symmetry operation already encountered that produces such enantiomorphous sets is the operation of reflection. If a rotation is combined with a reflection into a single hybrid operation, the resulting operation is called *rotoreflection*. The corresponding symmetry element is called a *rotoreflection axis*. There exists a rotoreflection axis corresponding to each of the five proper axes. To distinguish the two kinds of axes, a *tilde* is placed over the numerical symbol of the corresponding rotation axis: $\tilde{1}$, $\tilde{2}$, $\tilde{3}$, etc.

As an illustration of a rotoreflection axis, consider $\tilde{1}$, pronounced "one-tilde." The proper rotation 1 rotates an object representing all of space through an angle of 0 or 360°, leaving it unchanged. The rotoreflection axis $\tilde{1}$ combines this operation with a reflection to give the configuration

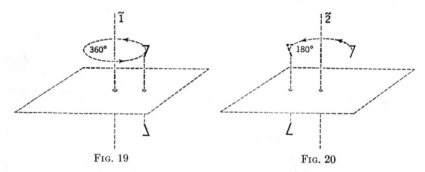

FIG. 19   FIG. 20

shown in Fig. 19. The enantiomorphous pair of sevens is not unlike the pair already encountered in Fig. 3. Accordingly, it can be said that the operation of $\tilde{1}$ is equivalent to a reflection through a plane, specifically, a *reflection plane* or *mirror plane* symbolically represented by the letter *m*.

To illustrate further the operation of a rotoreflection axis, Fig. 20 shows a perspective view of $\tilde{2}$. Remember that the operation of rotoreflection consists of two distinct parts. First, the seven in Fig. 20 is rotated by an "imaginary" 2 through an angle of 180°, but it is not left there. Instead, it is next reflected through an "imaginary" plane placed at right angles to the "imaginary" rotation axis. It should be emphasized that a 2-fold rotoreflection axis is neither a 2-fold axis nor a reflection plane but rather a hybrid combining the operations of both into a single operation.

A very useful method of displaying a symmetry element is to show a projection of the symmetry element along some convenient direction. In the case of rotation axes, it is convenient to project along the direction of the axis. Figure 21 shows such projections of the proper rotation axes and improper rotation axes. In illustrating the operation of an improper axis it is necessary to distinguish between an object lying above the

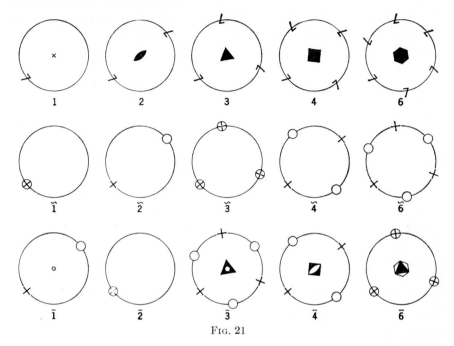

Fig. 21

imaginary reflection plane and one below it. If the axis is normal to the plane of the paper, the imaginary reflection plane lies in the plane of the paper. A cross is used to indicate an object lying above this plane, and a circle, an object below this plane. It should be realized that the cross and circle bear another important relationship to each other, namely, if the cross represents a right-handed object, the circle represents a left-handed object.

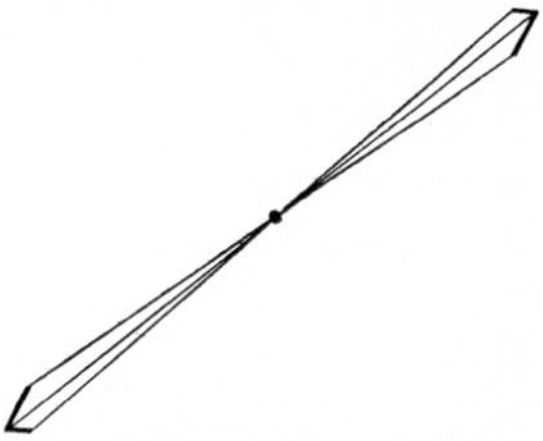

Returning to Fig. 20 for a moment, it can be shown that the enantiomorphous pair of sevens in that figure is related by an *inversion center* lying halfway between the two sevens. The inversion or *symmetry center* has the property of inverting all of space through a point, as illustrated in Fig. 22. Representing all of space by a seven, its inverted equivalent can be obtained

Fig. 22

by passing a construction line from each part of the seven through the inversion center and continuing each construction line until its length on both sides of the center is equal. An equivalent part of the seven is then placed at each end of each line until the enantiomorphous pair in Fig. 22 results.

It is possible to combine an inversion center with a rotation axis to produce a *rotoinversion axis* in an analogous manner to the formation of a

Table 2
Conventional designation of improper axes

Rotoinversion axis	Rotoreflection axis	Conventional designation
$\bar{1}$	$\tilde{2}$	Center of symmetry, $\bar{1}$
$\bar{2}$	$\tilde{1}$	Mirror plane, m
$\bar{3}$	$\tilde{6}$	3-fold rotoinversion, $\bar{3}$
$\bar{4}$	$\tilde{4}$	4-fold rotoinversion, $\bar{4}$
$\bar{6}$	$\tilde{3}$	6-fold rotoinversion, $\bar{6}$

rotoreflection axis. Again, it should be realized that a rotoinversion axis is a hybrid of the two operations and is neither a proper rotation nor an inversion center. The five rotoinversion axes of crystallographic interest are shown in Fig. 21. To indicate a rotoinversion axis a bar is placed over the corresponding proper axis symbol. For example, a 3-fold roto-inversion axis is designated $\bar{3}$, pronounced "three-bar."

If the five rotoreflection axes are compared with the five rotoinversion axes in Fig. 21, it becomes apparent that they are equivalent in pairs. In fact, one equivalence has already been illustrated in comparing Fig. 20 with Fig. 22 which showed $\tilde{2}$ and $\bar{1}$, respectively. Since the two kinds of improper axes are thus equivalent in pairs, it is sufficient to adopt only one kind to represent these symmetry operations. Accordingly, Table 2 lists the conventional designations for the equivalent pairs of improper axes.

Screw axes. Just as it is possible to combine a proper rotation with an inversion to produce a hybrid rotoinversion axis, it is possible to combine a proper rotation with a translation parallel to the rotation axis. This operation is shown in Fig. 23 where a rotation from e to f by an amount φ combined with a translation from f to g by an amount T is equivalent to a *screw motion* from e to g. The symmetry element that corresponds to such a motion is called a *screw axis*. In a lattice, an axis must be parallel to a translation direction. Therefore, after n rotations through an angle φ and n translations T are concluded, that is, after n translations along the screw axis, the cumulative translation distance in the direction of the axis must equal some multiple of the lattice translation mt. In other words,

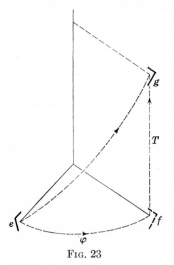

Fig. 23

$$nT = mt \qquad (12)$$

where n and m are integers. Equation (12) can be rearranged to determine the values that T can have:

$$T = \frac{mt}{n}. \tag{13}$$

According to (13), the different values that the translation component, or *pitch*, of a screw axis can have depend on the fold n of the axis. Since $m = 0, 1, 2, 3, \ldots$, the values that T can have, for the various axes, are those given in Table 3. Because $\frac{3}{2}t = t + \frac{1}{2}t$ and $\frac{5}{4}t = t + \frac{1}{4}t$, etc.,

Table 3
Possible values of the pitch T of a screw axis

Fold of axis	Possible values of the pitch T
1	$0t$, $1t$, $2t$, etc.
2	$0t$, $\frac{1}{2}t$, $\frac{2}{2}t$, $\frac{3}{2}t$, etc.
3	$0t$, $\frac{1}{3}t$, $\frac{2}{3}t$, $\frac{3}{3}t$, $\frac{4}{3}t$, etc.
4	$0t$, $\frac{1}{4}t$, $\frac{2}{4}t$, $\frac{3}{4}t$, $\frac{4}{4}t$, $\frac{5}{4}t$, etc.
6	$0t$, $\frac{1}{6}t$, $\frac{2}{6}t$, $\frac{3}{6}t$, $\frac{4}{6}t$, $\frac{5}{6}t$, $\frac{6}{6}t$, $\frac{7}{6}t$, etc.

the only unique screw axes according to Table 3 are 2_1, 3_1, 3_2, 4_1, 4_2, 4_3, 6_1, 6_2, 6_3, 6_4, 6_5, where the subscript is the value of m in equation (13). Note that $m = 0$ and $m = n$ correspond to pure rotations which can be thought of as special cases of screw axes. The eleven screw axes are shown in perspective in Fig. 24. It can be seen in this figure that pairs of axes such as 3_1 and 3_2, or 6_1 and 6_5, are identical except for the sense of the screw motion. Such pairs are therefore enantiomorphous; the individual axes are commonly distinguished as being left- or right-handed.

Table 4
Possible glide planes

Type of glide	Symbol	Translation component T
Axial glide	a	$\dfrac{a}{2}$
Axial glide	b	$\dfrac{b}{2}$
Axial glide	c	$\dfrac{c}{2}$
Diagonal glide	n	$\dfrac{a}{2} + \dfrac{b}{2}$, $\dfrac{b}{2} + \dfrac{c}{2}$, or $\dfrac{c}{2} + \dfrac{a}{2}$
Diamond glide†	d	$\dfrac{a}{4} + \dfrac{b}{4}$, $\dfrac{b}{4} + \dfrac{c}{4}$, or $\dfrac{c}{4} + \dfrac{a}{4}$

† The translation component T in the diamond glide is actually one-half of the true translation along the face diagonal of a centered plane lattice.

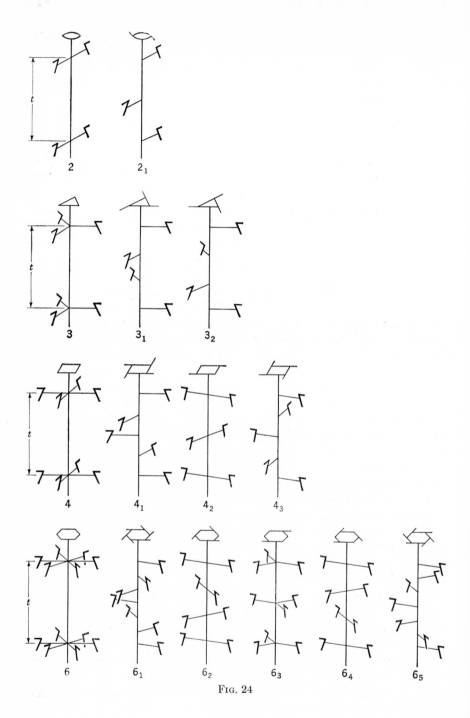

Fig. 24

22

Glide planes. It is possible to combine a reflection with a translation parallel to the reflection plane. Such a combination is called a *glide reflection*. The symmetry element relating the resulting pattern (Fig. 25) is called a *glide plane*. The translation component T of a glide plane is equal to one-half of the normal translation of the lattice in the direction of the glide. Thus a glide along the a axis has $T = \frac{1}{2}a$ and is called an a glide. Similarly, a diagonal glide can have $T = \frac{1}{2}a + \frac{1}{2}b$

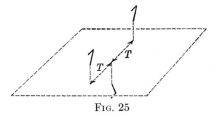

FIG. 25

or $\frac{1}{2}b + \frac{1}{2}c$, etc. The different possible glides and their translation components are listed in Table 4.

Symmetry groups

The symmetry elements described above are the only ways of repetition compatible with translation periodicity. Because this periodicity is the basis of all crystal structures, the atoms in crystals must be periodically arrayed. If the crystal also possesses symmetry, this means that the atomic arrays must have this symmetry. Normally, the crystal structure determines the external form or *morphology* of the crystal. Hence, it is natural that many crystals are found in nature whose morphology displays the presence of one or more of these symmetry elements. If symmetry axes are thought of as lines, and mirrors as planes, these elements appear to intersect at a common point at the crystal's center. The different possible combinations of symmetry elements at a common point are called *point groups*. The early crystallographers, who were limited to the observation of the morphology of different crystals, deduced their respective point groups and used them as a basis for classification. As a consequence, otherwise unrelated crystals exhibiting the same point-group symmetry are said to belong to the same *crystal class*. Thus the terms *point group* and *crystal class* are essentially synonymous.

The presence of screw axes and glide planes cannot be detected by examining the external appearance of a crystal. This is so because the translations that are part of their operation of repetition are too small (of the order of atomic dimensions) to be seen with even the most powerful microscopes. On the surface of an actual crystal, therefore, a screw axis appears simply as a rotation axis ($T = 0$) and a glide plane appears as a mirror plane. Another way to look at this is to remember that a point group describes the symmetry of crystal space about a point. Since a point cannot include a translation component, point groups cannot contain screw axes or glide planes.

It is possible to derive all possible combinations of symmetry elements in a straightforward formal manner by means of *group theory*. In order to understand how the various combinations arise, however, it is not necessary to resort to this branch of higher mathematics. Instead, it is possible to derive a few simple theorems, similar to the theorems used in geometry, and to proceed by considering all those combinations that are consistent with these theorems. Such a procedure is good enough to derive the thirty-two possible point groups. On the other hand, the combination of symmetry groups with two noncollinear translations in a plane, or with three noncoplanar translations in space, becomes rather

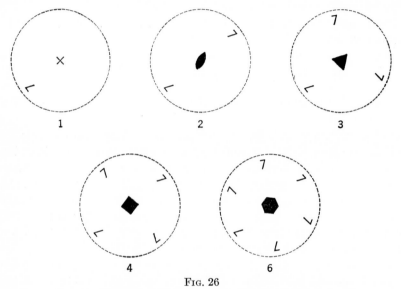

Fig. 26

cumbersome if carried out in this naive manner. Consequently, the discussion in this chapter is limited to indicating what some of these so-called *plane groups* and *space groups* are like, without attempting their systematic derivation.

Point groups. As already indicated, the symmetry of space about a point is uniquely described by a collection of symmetry elements at that point, called a *point group*. Generally, a point group can contain any operation of repetition, whether such operations are compatible with translation periodicity or not. For obvious reasons, only combinations of crystallographic symmetry elements that are compatible with translation periodicity are discussed in this book.

To start, all the symmetry elements already described that do not have translation components each constitute a possible point group. Accordingly, Fig. 26 shows the five point groups: 1, 2, 3, 4, and 6. Next, consider the possible ways that two axes can be combined at a point. Here, an important concept of group theory enters, namely, *when one symmetry operation is followed by another, a third symmetry operation results.* This can be written symbolically

$$A \cdot B = C \tag{14}$$

where A, B, and C are the three symmetry operations. For example, the point group 4 can be represented as the operation $4 \cdot 4 = 1$. Note that this is symbolic representation and is not to be confused with ordinary algebra.

The symmetry that results when two rotation axes are combined can be determined by a construction suggested by *Euler*. Because of its relative complexity, *Euler's construction* is not given here; however, use is made of a relation that results from the analysis of one of its spherical triangles. This relation states that

$$\cos A = \frac{\cos \beta/2 \cos \gamma/2 + \cos \alpha/2}{\sin \beta/2 \sin \gamma/2}. \tag{15}$$

Here A is the angle between two rotation axes whose respective throws are γ and β, and α is the throw of the third rotation axis. Thus equation (15) can be used to determine what combinations of rotation axes are possible and at what angles the axes are inclined to each other. The actual determination can be carried out by systematically considering all possible combinations. For example, consider the combination of a 2-fold rotation with another 2-fold rotation to give a third 2-fold rotation, alternatively written $2 \cdot 2 = 2$. According to (15),

$$\begin{aligned}
\cos A &= \frac{\cos (180°/2) \cos (180°/2) + \cos (180°/2)}{\sin (180°/2) \sin (180°/2)} \\
&= \frac{0 + 0}{1} \\
&= 0 \quad (A = 90°).
\end{aligned} \tag{16}$$

Since the three rotation axes are alike, (16) states that three 2-fold axes can be combined at a point, provided that they are mutually orthogonal.

As a further example, consider $2 \cdot 2 = 3$. Here two interaxial angles must be determined, the angles between a 2-fold axis and a 3-fold axis and also the angle between the two 2-fold axes. According to (15),

$$\begin{aligned}
\cos A &= \frac{\cos (180°/2) \cos (120°/2) + \cos (180°/2)}{\sin (180°/2) \sin (120°/2)} \\
&= \frac{0 + 0}{\frac{3}{2}} \\
&= 0 \quad (A = 90°)
\end{aligned} \tag{17A}$$

and $\qquad \cos C = \dfrac{\cos\,(180°/2)\,\cos\,(180°/2)\,+\,\cos\,(120°/2)}{\sin\,(180°/2)\,\sin\,(180°/2)}$

$$= \frac{0 + \cos 60°}{1}$$

$$= \cos 60° \qquad (C = 60°). \tag{17B}$$

Similarly, the other possible axial combinations can be tested. It is left to the reader to prove (see the exercises at the end of this chapter) that only six combinations of proper rotation axes intersecting at a common point are possible. These possible combinations of three proper rotation axes at a point, 222, 32(2),† 422, 622, 23(3), 432, are shown in Fig. 27.

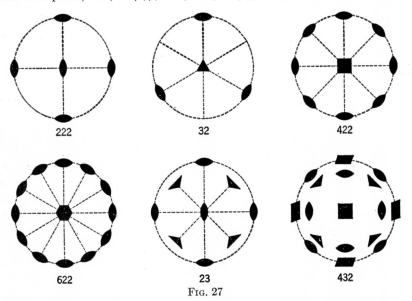

Fig. 27

All other conceivable combinations such as $6 \cdot 4 = 2$ cannot exist, as can be shown by direct substitution of appropriate values in equation (15).

Each of the five improper rotation axes also constitutes a point group. Accordingly, Fig. 28 shows the five point groups: $\bar{1}$, $\bar{2} = m$, $\bar{3}$, $\bar{4}$, and $\bar{6}$. Next, consider the combination of improper rotations with proper rotations. To begin, a mirror plane can be combined with a proper rotation axis by placing the mirror plane at right angles to the axis. This produces five point groups: $\dfrac{1}{m} = m = \bar{2}$, $\dfrac{2}{m}$, $\dfrac{3}{m} = \bar{6}$, $\dfrac{4}{m}$, and $\dfrac{6}{m}$. Of these, $\dfrac{1}{m}$ and $\dfrac{3}{m}$

† This point group is conventionally written 32 instead of 322. The reason for this is that the two 2-fold axes 60° apart are indistinguishable from the symmetry-equivalent 2-fold axes that result from the repetition of a single axis every 120° by rotation about the 3-fold axis. This case is different from the point group 422 where the 4 repeats each 2 at 90° intervals but the two different 2s are 45° apart.

have already been considered and are shown in Fig. 28. Hence only three new combinations come about as a result of combining a proper rotation axis with a perpendicular mirror plane, as shown in Fig. 29. It should be noted that in each of these point groups an even-fold axis is normal to a mirror plane. According to (14), a third symmetry operation results from the combination of any two so that the third symmetry element

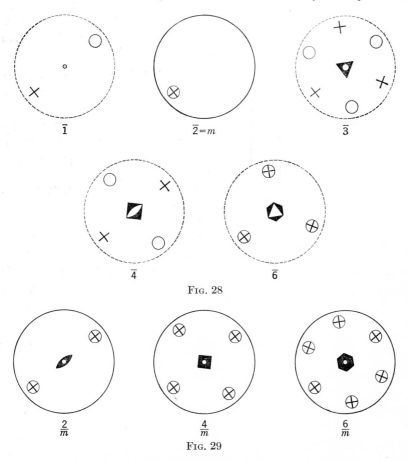

FIG. 28

FIG. 29

present in this case is an inversion center lying at the intersection of the even-fold axis and the orthogonal mirror. This is indicated in Fig. 29 by placing an open circle, the symbol for $\bar{1}$, at the center of the axial symbol.

A mirror plane can also be placed parallel to a proper rotation axis. In this case the third symmetry element produced is another mirror plane, also parallel to the rotation axis, and the angle between the two mirror planes is equal to one-half the throw of the rotation axis. This relation is best stated by changing the order of the above operations, namely, if two mirror planes intersect at an angle ψ a rotation axis having a throw of 2ψ arises at their intersection. A simple proof of this is shown in Fig. 30. Consider the two mirror planes intersecting at an angle ψ. The first one reflects a left-handed object l into a right-handed object r. The second one reflects r into l', and l into r'. That these two successive

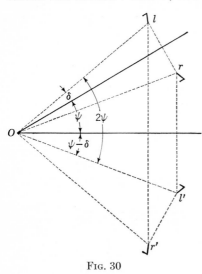

reflections are equal to a rotation about O by an amount 2ψ can be seen by adding the angles between the lines Ol and Ol' or between the lines Or and Or':

$$\delta + \psi + (\psi - \delta) = 2\psi. \quad (18)$$

Excluding the trivial combination $1m = m$ already discussed, four additional point groups are obtained by combining a rotation axis with a parallel reflection plane: $2mm$, $3m$,† $4mm$, $6mm$ (Fig. 31).

As might be expected, it is possible to combine both a parallel mirror plane and a perpendicular mirror plane with a proper rotation axis. Since these two mirror planes

Fig. 30

intersect each other at right angles, a 2-fold axis lies at their intersection, according to the theorem demonstrated in Fig. 30.

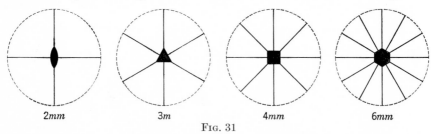

| 2mm | 3m | 4mm | 6mm |

Fig. 31

Consequently, the combination of two such planes with a rotation axis is equivalent to the addition of these planes to the point groups shown in Fig. 27. The resulting six point groups, $\dfrac{2}{m}\dfrac{2}{m}\dfrac{2}{m}$, $\dfrac{3}{m}m2$,‡ $\dfrac{4}{m}\dfrac{2}{m}\dfrac{2}{m}$, $\dfrac{6}{m}\dfrac{2}{m}\dfrac{2}{m}$,

† When a 3 is combined with a parallel m the angle between the mirror planes must be $120°/2 = 60°$. But this angle between the mirror planes also results by simply repeating a mirror plane every $120°$ as required by 3-fold rotation; hence, a new mirror plane is not produced as the symbol $3mm$ would indicate.

‡ The symbol is $\dfrac{3}{m}m2$, not $\dfrac{3}{m}\dfrac{2}{m}$, because the mirror plane parallel to the 3-fold axis is not perpendicular to any 2-fold axis.

$\dfrac{2}{m}\,\bar{3},\ \dfrac{4}{m}\,\bar{3}\,\dfrac{2}{m},$ are shown in Fig. 32. Note that all these point groups except

$\dfrac{3}{m}\,m2$ have an even-fold axis normal to a mirror plane and hence contain

an inversion center. This is the reason why in the last two point groups listed the 3-fold axes are rotoinversion axes.

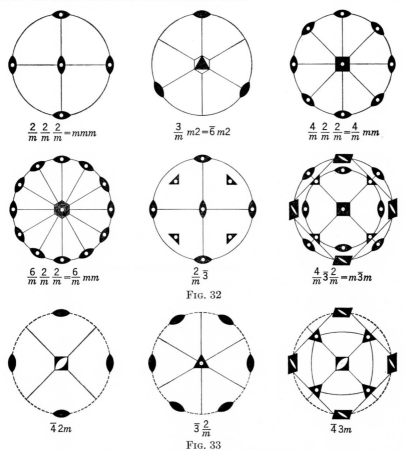

$$\frac{2}{m}\,\frac{2}{m}\,\frac{2}{m}=mmm \qquad \frac{3}{m}\,m2=\bar{6}\,m2 \qquad \frac{4}{m}\,\frac{2}{m}\,\frac{2}{m}=\frac{4}{m}\,mm$$

$$\frac{6}{m}\,\frac{2}{m}\,\frac{2}{m}=\frac{6}{m}\,mm \qquad \frac{2}{m}\,\bar{3} \qquad \frac{4}{m}\,\bar{3}\,\frac{2}{m}=m\bar{3}m$$

Fɪɢ. 32

$$\bar{4}\,2m \qquad\qquad \bar{3}\,\frac{2}{m} \qquad\qquad \bar{4}\,3m$$

Fɪɢ. 33

It remains to consider the possible combinations of the improper axes $\bar{3}$ and $\bar{4}$ with proper rotation axes. Three more point groups are obtained from such combinations, namely, $\bar{4}2m$, $\bar{3}\dfrac{2}{m}$ and $\bar{4}3m$, shown in Fig. 33. This brings the total number of point groups to thirty-two and completes the list of possibilities. The angles between all the symmetry elements are clearly seen in the illustrations except for the point groups containing four 3-fold axes. These interaxial angles are shown in Fig. 34 for the point group 432.

Categories of crystals. An examination of the thirty-two point groups just described suggests that they can be grouped into sets according to the highest-ranking rotation axis that they contain.   Such an axis,

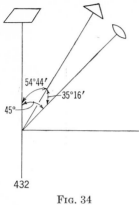

say a 6-fold rotation axis, is also the most prominent feature of the morphology of a crystal containing such an axis.   It is natural, therefore, that the early classifications of crystals were based on the more prominent features that different crystals shared.   The scheme finally adopted was to distribute the thirty-two point groups among the six *crystal systems* listed in Table 5.   The basis for assigning a crystal class to a particular crystal system is indicated in the column headed *minimal symmetry*.   For example, there are only three point groups that contain only three 2-fold axes, namely, *mmm*, *2mm*, 222.

Fig. 34

Accordingly, these three point groups are placed in the same system called the *orthorhombic system*.

Plane groups.   Having discovered the thirty-two point groups compatible with translation periodicity, it is logical to inquire next into the different ways that these point groups can be combined with one or more translations.   For obvious reasons, it is simpler to start with a consideration of the possible combinations with two noncollinear translations.   It

Table 5
Crystal systems and crystal classes

Crystal system	Minimal symmetry†	Crystal classes
Triclinic	1 (or $\bar{1}$)	$1, \bar{1}$
Monoclinic	2 (or $\bar{2}$)	$2, m, \dfrac{2}{m}$
Orthorhombic	222 (or $\overline{222}$)	$222, 2mm, mmm$
Tetragonal	4 (or $\bar{4}$)	$4, \bar{4}, \dfrac{4}{m}, 422, 4mm, \bar{4}2m, \dfrac{4}{m}\dfrac{2}{m}\dfrac{2}{m}$
Isometric	four 3s (or $\bar{3}$)	$23, 432, \dfrac{2}{m}\bar{3}, \bar{4}3m, \dfrac{4}{m}\bar{3}\dfrac{2}{m}$
Hexagonal	3 or 6 (or $\bar{3}$ or $\bar{6}$)	$3, \bar{3}, 32, 3m, \bar{3}\dfrac{2}{m}, 6, \bar{6},$ $622, 6mm, \bar{6}m2, \dfrac{6}{m}, \dfrac{6}{m}\dfrac{2}{m}\dfrac{2}{m}$

† The symmetry elements shown in this column are the least symmetry that a crystal can have and still belong to the corresponding crystal system.   In this sense, this column shows the diagnostic symmetry elements of each system.

has already been shown that two noncollinear translations define a plane lattice. Preliminary to forming the combinations, therefore, the different kinds of plane lattices are first discussed. Consider the general plane lattice shown in Fig. 35A. Since a primitive unit cell in this lattice has the shape of a parallelogram, this lattice is called a *parallelogram lattice*.

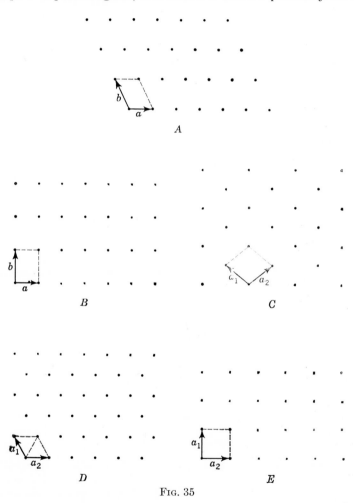

FIG. 35

Such a lattice can contain a 1-fold axis or a 2-fold axis normal to the lattice plane. It cannot accommodate other symmetry elements, however. For example, a *mirror-reflection line* (the two-dimensional equivalent of a mirror plane in three dimensions) requires that the lattice points lie on rows both parallel and perpendicular to the reflection line. This results in either a *rectangular lattice* or a *diamond lattice*, as shown in Fig. 35B

and C. A special case of the diamond lattice, wherein the angle between a_1 and a_2 is 120°, is called a 120° *rhombus lattice* or a *triangular lattice* since the two cell edges and the short cell diagonal enclose an equilateral triangle, as shown in Fig. 35D. The triangular lattice can accommodate either a 3-fold or a 6-fold axis. Finally, a *square lattice* (Fig. 35E) can accommodate a 4-fold axis, which requires that normal to the 4 there exist a set of four equivalent translations 90° apart.

When a rotation axis is combined with a translation at right angles to it, a new rotation axis results. This can be expressed symbolically:

$$A \cdot t = B. \tag{19}$$

To see what happens when a 2 is combined with an orthogonal translation, place a 2 at the lattice points of the parallelogram lattice of the

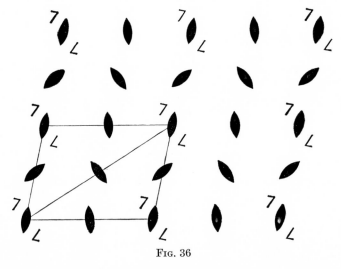

Fig. 36

two-dimensional lattice array shown in Fig. 36. Next, surround each translation equivalent 2, that is, each 2-fold axis connected by a lattice translation, with a pair of symmetry-related motifs (sevens in Fig. 36), constructing a lattice array thereby. It is now easy to see that new 2-fold axes "spring up" halfway between translation-equivalent 2-fold axes.

Similarly, the combination of a 3 with an orthogonal translation produces a new 3, and the combination of a 4 with an orthogonal translation produces a new 4. In the latter case note that a 4 also includes the operation of a 2; therefore, new 2-fold axes are also produced. The combinations of symmetry elements with plane lattices are called *plane groups*. The pure axial plane groups are illustrated in Fig. 37. The symbol p is used to denote a primitive plane lattice. A mirror-reflection line combines with an orthogonal translation to produce a new mirror line half-

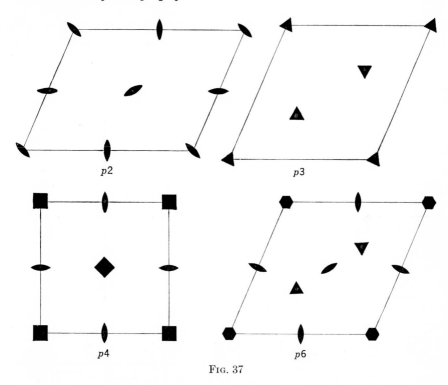

THE JOHN J. WRIGHT LIBRARY

Fig. 37

way between translation-equivalent mirror lines. Similarly, a *glide-reflection line* combines with an orthogonal translation to produce a new glide. (See Exercises 18 and 19.)

The combination of a mirror-reflection line with a diamond lattice is of special interest. As shown in Fig. 38, the lattice array corresponding to this symmetry contains, in addition to the parallel mirror lines, glide-reflection lines lying halfway between the mirror lines. The reason that these are glides and not mirrors is that the translations relating adjacent reflection lines are not orthogonal to these lines. It is, of course, possible to select a pair of translations in this lattice that are, respectively, orthogonal and parallel to the reflection lines. If this is done, however, a centered plane lattice denoted *c* is defined, as shown by the shaded unit cell in

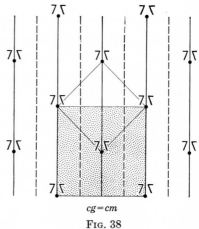

$cg = cm$

Fig. 38

Fig. 38. Since the unit cell edges in a centered lattice are not the shortest translations in that lattice, such a choice of reference axes introduces subtranslations in the lattice. It is not surprising, therefore, that centered lattices can contain symmetry elements having subtranslations also, that is, glide planes and screw axes.

Space lattices. The restrictions that are placed on a plane lattice by different symmetry elements have been shown above. Since a three-dimensional lattice can be thought of as a periodic stack of plane lattices, the possible space lattices can be deduced by considering the different ways of stacking each of the four primitive plane lattices consistent with the symmetries of the thirty-two point groups. An alternative procedure is first to deduce the uniquely different lattice types and then to observe what restrictions are placed on these lattices by the point groups. If the second procedure is followed, it can be shown that there are only five unique space-lattice types, listed in Table 6.

Table 6
Space-lattice types

Name	Location of nonorigin points	Symbol
Primitive	. . . .	P
Side-centered	Center of A face or (100) if A-centered	A
	Center of B face or (010) if B-centered	B
	Center of C face or (001) if C-centered	C
Face-centered	Centers of A, B, and C faces	F
Body-centered	Center of each cell	I
Rhombohedral	If primitive rhombohedron is referred to hexagonal cell, at $\frac{1}{3}\frac{2}{3}\frac{1}{3}$ and $\frac{2}{3}\frac{1}{3}\frac{2}{3}$ of that cell. (See Fig. 40.)	R

To see how these lattices are distributed among the six crystal systems, it is sufficient to consider the restrictions placed on each lattice in turn by the minimal symmetry of the crystal systems listed in Table 5. In the triclinic system, 1 or $\bar{1}$ places no restrictions on the space lattice. Hence, there is no advantage in selecting a nonprimitive lattice. The primitive triclinic or *general lattice* can therefore be described by a unit cell with $a \neq b \neq c$ and $\alpha \neq \beta \neq \gamma$.

In the monoclinic system, a 2-fold axis passing through each lattice point of a parallelogram lattice requires that successive plane lattices have their lattice points fall on 2-fold axes. Since $p2$ has four independent sets of 2-fold axes, the stacking sequence of two successive nets can go as shown in Fig. 39. (Open circles and dots are used to distinguish the two nets.) It is clear from this figure that the stacking in A gives a primitive lattice, the stacking in B a body-centered lattice, while C and D give side-centered lattices. Moreover, it is easy to show that the side-centered lat-

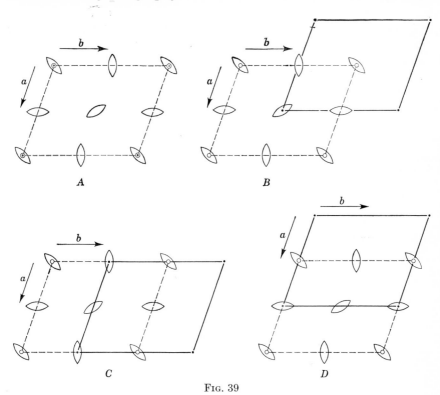

tices in *C* and *D* become body-centered if the diagonal of the parallelogram is chosen as one cell edge. Thus there are only two uniquely different lattices in the monoclinic system, namely, *P* and *I*. In each of these lattices, the presence of a 2-fold axis requires that the cell edge parallel to this axis be normal to the other two; therefore, the unit cell has $a \neq b \neq c$, $\alpha = \beta = 90° \neq \gamma$.

Similar reasoning leads to the conclusion that 222 in the orthorhombic system requires an orthogonal lattice whose unit cell can have unequal sides and that all the four lattice types are possible. It can also be shown that only two lattices can occur in the tetragonal system and three in the isometric or cubic system. The hexagonal system differs slightly from the others in that two different rotation axes, 3 or 6, are possible. In the case of a 6 it is easy to see from Fig. 37 that there are 6-fold axes only at the lattice points of the triangular lattice, and successive plane lattices, therefore, must superimpose to form a primitive space lattice. In the case of *p*3, however, there are three sets of 3-fold axes and, hence, three stacking sequences are possible, as shown in Fig. 40. Of these, *A* gives a primitive hexagonal lattice, and *B* and *C* give three-layer-high stacks which are identical, as can be seen by rotating either by 180° about a normal to the plane of the drawing. Figure 41 shows a perspective drawing of this stacking sequence. As can be seen in this figure, the primitive cell in the resulting lattice is a rhombohedron having three equal edges and three equal interaxial angles ($a_1 = a_2 = a_3$, $\alpha_1 = \alpha_2 = \alpha_3$). A more

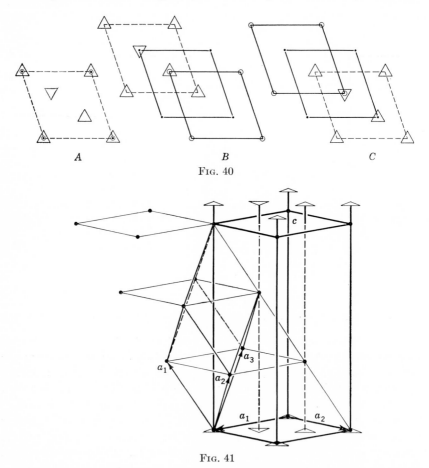

A   B   C

FIG. 40

FIG. 41

convenient hexagonal cell can be chosen, however, as shown by the heavy lines in Fig. 41. Such a cell contains two additional, equally spaced lattice points along the body diagonal of the cell. It is this uniqueness in the lattice that has led to a suggestion for the adoption of a *rhombohedral* subsystem of the hexagonal system, chiefly in the United States. An alternative subdivision, called the *trigonal* subsystem, includes all point groups containing a 3 (or $\bar{3}$) and is most popular in the United Kingdom. Because of the difficulties in allocating certain space groups, it is common practice nowadays to refer both cases to a hexagonal lattice and, hence, the subsystem designations should not be used.

The lattice types listed in Table 7 were first discovered in 1842 by Frankenheim, who incorrectly determined that fifteen lattices were possible. Bravais showed later that only fourteen were really unique, and Table 7

Table 7
Bravais lattices

Crystal system	Lattice types					Unit cell dimensions
	P	$A\ (B,C)$	F	I	R†	
Triclinic	X	...	...	...	...	$a \neq b \neq c$ $\alpha \neq \beta \neq \gamma$
Monoclinic	X	...	...	X	...	$a \neq b \neq c$ $\alpha = \beta = 90° \neq \gamma$
Orthorhombic	X	X	X	X	...	$a \neq b \neq c$ $\alpha = \beta = \gamma = 90°$
Tetragonal	X	...	...	X	...	$a = b \neq c$ $\alpha = \beta = \gamma = 90°$
Isometric	X	...	X	X	...	$a = b = c$ $\alpha = \beta = \gamma = 90°$
Hexagonal	X	...	...	...	X	$a = b \neq c$ $\alpha = \beta = 90°, \gamma = 120°$

† The symbol R denotes the rarely used primitive rhombohedral lattice shown in Fig. 41.

shows the distribution of the so-called *Bravais lattices* among the crystal systems. The unit cell dimensions listed in the last column of this table are minimal in the sense that chance equalities between magnitudes of normally unequal quantities are not excluded. The fourteen Bravais lattices are shown in Fig. 42.

Space groups. Having classified the point groups and lattice types of each system, it is possible to consider what combinations of symmetry elements with space lattices are possible. In considering such combinations, called *space groups*, it should be remembered that symmetry elements that exist in a space lattice can have translation components. Consequently, it is necessary to consider not only the thirty-two point groups but also the symmetry groups having identical angular relationships but containing screw axes in place of pure rotation axes and glide planes in place of pure reflection planes. If these *isogonal* symmetry groups are included, it turns out that there are 230 different ways to combine symmetry groups with lattices.

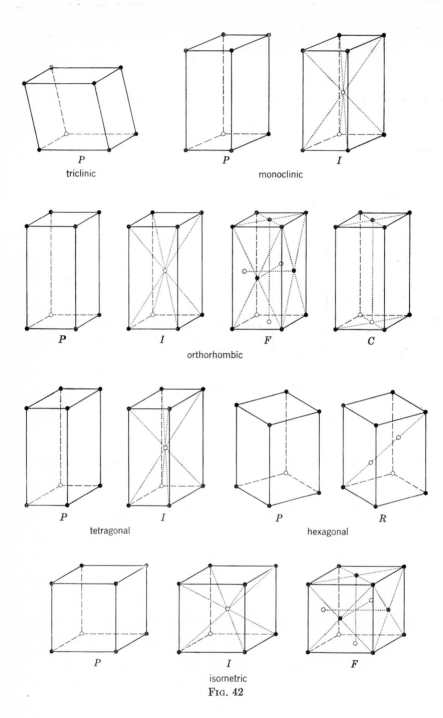

P
triclinic

P
monoclinic

I

P

I

F

C

orthorhombic

P

I

tetragonal

P

R

hexagonal

P

I

F

isometric

FIG. 42

Since the derivation of all the possible space groups is a lengthy undertaking, a few simple examples are given to illustrate the full symmetry that develops from the combination of symmetry elements with three noncoplanar translations. In the triclinic system, there are only two combinations possible, namely, $P1$ and $P\bar{1}$. In the monoclinic system, on the other hand, there are three point groups to consider and two lattice types. As an example, consider the possible combinations of the point group 2, the isogonal symmetry 2_1, and the two lattices P and I. Figure 43 shows a view along the c axis of the four possible combinations $P2$, $P2_1$, $I2$, and $I2_1$. Similarly to the procedure used in finding all the symmetry elements present in a plane group, motifs (circles in Fig. 43) are used to represent the operations of the symmetry elements and the translations. The actual height of the object above the plane of the drawing is indicated by the fraction placed within the circles in Fig. 43. It is easy to see that $I2$ and $I2_1$ are the same space group; only the origins are different. It is therefore concluded that three different space groups belong to the crystal class 2. Some additional examples are considered in the exercises at the end of this chapter.

The labels in Fig. 43 are the international symbols used to denote the appropriate space group. These symbols, also called Hermann-Mauguin symbols after their inventors, differ from an earlier notation proposed by Schoenflies. Since the Schoenflies notation may be encountered by the reader in other writings, both notations are tabulated in Appendix 4.

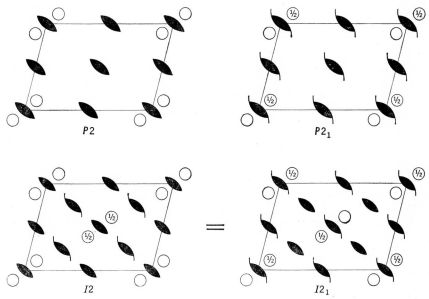

Fig. 43

The international space-group symbol is a shorthand notation describing the symmetry elements present, preceded by the appropriate lattice-type symbol. The description of the symmetry elements is not unlike that used in point-group notation. There is one important difference, however, in that in the space-group symbol the particular sequence of the symmetry elements listed describes their orientation in space relative to the three crystallographic axes. In the *triclinic system* this point is trivial; however, in all other systems it is not. Unfortunately, because of precedents arbitrarily arrived at, a consistent notational system for all crystal systems does not exist.

In the *monoclinic system* there is a choice between calling the unique axis c or b. In giving the complete space-group symbol, if the symmetry elements are listed in the sequence abc, the two symbols for $P2$ are, respectively, $P112$ and $P121$. These two possibilities are known as the *first setting* and *second setting*, respectively.

In the *orthorhombic system*, it is conventional to list the symmetry elements in the order abc.† This order has a very real importance, as can be seen in the space groups belonging to the crystal class $2mm$, which are properly presented with c as the unique axis, namely, $Pmm2$. The non-trivial nature of the need for consistency in this representation becomes apparent in the two space groups $Pmna$ and $Pnma$ whose full symbols are

$$P\frac{2}{m}\frac{2}{n}\frac{2_1}{a} \text{ and } P\frac{2_1}{n}\frac{2_1}{m}\frac{2_1}{a},$$ respectively.

In the *tetragonal system*, the c axis is the 4-fold axis. The sequence for listing the symmetry elements is c, a, [110], since the two crystallographic axes orthogonal to c are equivalent. For example, $P\bar{4}m2$ states that the unique (c) axis in a primitive tetragonal lattice has the symmetry $\bar{4}$, the two a axes each are parallel to m, and the [110] direction has the symmetry 2.

The above rule for listing the symmetry elements also applies to the *hexagonal system* since here again c is the unique axis and $a_1 = a_2$. The lattice symbol P denotes the primitive hexagonal lattice whereas R denotes the "centered" hexagonal lattice in which the primitive rhombohedral cell has been chosen as the unit cell.

In the *isometric system* all three crystallographic axes are equivalent, and the order of listing the symmetry elements is a, [111], [110]. Since [[111]] must have the symmetry 3 or $\bar{3}$, the appearance of a 3 in the second position serves to distinguish the isometric system from the hexagonal system.

Supergroups and subgroups. It is sometimes of interest to consider the symmetry that results from the addition of new symmetry to, or the

† Norman F. M. Henry and Kathleen Lonsdale, *International tables for x-ray crystallography* (The Kynoch Press, Birmingham, 1952).

suppression of existing symmetry in, a point group. If the addition of symmetry to an existing group produces a new group, this new group is said to be a *supergroup* of the existing group. Similarly, if the suppression of symmetry in a group produces a new group, then the new group is called a *subgroup* of the old group. For example, since the point group 1 has the lowest possible symmetry, it is the subgroup of each of the other thirty-one point groups. Conversely, the point groups $\frac{6}{m}$ *mm* and *m3m* can have no *supergroups* because it is not possible to obtain a new crystallographic point group by the addition of symmetry elements to either group. As an example of these relations, 1, 2, *m*, 2*mm*, and 4 are the subgroups of 4*mm*; and $\frac{4}{m}$ *mm* and *m3m* are its two supergroups.

Suggestions for supplementary reading

M. J. Buerger, *Elementary crystallography* (John Wiley & Sons, Inc., New York, 1956).
F. C. Phillips, *An introduction to crystallography* (Longmans, Green & Co., Ltd., London, 1949).

Exercises

1. Draw a plane lattice and indicate two kinds of double cells and one triple cell in that lattice.

2. Draw a pair of enantiomorphous objects about each lattice point in a plane lattice.

(*a*) Show that any primitive cell in that lattice contains only one pair of objects.
(*b*) Show that a triple cell contains three pairs of objects.

3. A possible cell in a lattice has $a = b = c$, $\alpha = \beta = \gamma = 90°$. Draw such a cube-shaped unit cell and indicate in it (001), (111), (101), (230).

4. Show, in a lattice based on the cube-shaped unit cell in Exercise 3, the directions [100], [1$\bar{2}$0], [$\bar{1}$00], [111].

5. Show that in a cube-shaped cell

(*a*) [111] is perpendicular to (111).
(*b*) [100] is perpendicular to (100).
(*c*) [122] is perpendicular to (122).

6. Show what relationships between the directions and the planes in Exercise 5 do not hold true for any other type of lattice. (For simplicity, consider a lattice based on a unit cell having $a = b \neq c$, $\alpha = \beta = \gamma = 90°$.)

7. In the cubic system, it is often of interest to determine the planes and directions containing the maximum number or density of lattice points. For example, in the body-centered cubic lattice, this would be ((110)) and [[110]]. Representing the combination of the densest direction within a densest plane by, say, (110) · [1$\bar{1}$0], list all such possible combinations for the face-centered cubic lattice and the body-centered cubic lattice.

8. Prove relation (5) for hexagonal axes and relation (6) for hexagonal indices.

9. List six planes lying in the zone of [110]. Repeat for [111].

10. By means of a sketch showing a view along the axis, indicate the symmetry of space about a 5-fold and 12-fold proper rotation axis.

11. By means of a sketch showing a view along the axis, indicate the symmetry of space about a 5-fold and 10-fold rotoreflection axis.

12. By means of a sketch showing a view along the axis, indicate the symmetry of space about a 5-fold and 9-fold rotoinversion axis.

13. Prepare a drawing showing the following screw axes: 8_3 and 8_5.

14. By means of sketches, compare an n glide with a d glide.

15. Using equation (15), derive all the point groups containing a 2-fold axis. Do this by systematically considering the combinations of a 2 with a 2 to give a 1, 2, 3, etc., followed by the combination of a 2 with a 3 to give a 1, 2, 3, etc.

16. Derive all the point groups containing a 3-fold axis, following the procedure outlined in Exercise 15.

17. Derive all the point groups containing a 4-fold axis, following the procedure outlined in Exercise 15.

18. Derive all the point groups containing a 6-fold axis, following the procedure outlined in Exercise 15.

19. Show that a reflection line combined with an orthogonal translation produces a new reflection line halfway between translation-equivalent reflection lines.

20. Show that a glide combined with a rectangular lattice produces a new glide halfway between translation-equivalent glides.

21. Draw the plane group cg, showing all the symmetry elements. Compare your drawing with the plane group cm shown in Fig. 37.

22. By means of simple sketches show that

(a) In the orthorhombic system it is possible to have a side-centered and a face-centered lattice but *not* a two-side-centered lattice.

(b) In the tetragonal system $C = P$ and $F = I$.

23. Derive the monoclinic space groups belonging to the crystal class m. Using the first setting, do this by considering the following possible combinations: Pm, Pa, Pn, Im, Ia, In.

24. Derive the orthorhombic space groups that result from the combinations of three orthogonal 2-fold axes (222, 222_1, 2_12_12, $2_12_12_1$) with

(a) A primitive lattice.

(b) A side-centered lattice.

(c) A face-centered lattice.

(d) A body-centered lattice.

25. What are the subgroups of $\bar{6}m2$ and mmm? What are the supergroups of 32 and $\dfrac{4}{m}$?

3

The structure of crystals

Up to this point, the discussion of crystal symmetry has been limited to an abstract discussion of symmetry elements and the rules that determine how they can combine with one or more translations. The way in which actual atom arrays occurring in crystals can conform to the resulting symmetry groups is considered in this chapter. To begin, it is necessary to find out how any point in a unit cell, that is, a possible atomic site, is repeated by the symmetry elements present in a crystal. Points that are equivalent to each other by virtue of the symmetry present are called *equipoints*. As described below, there can exist several sets of equipoints in a unit cell, each set containing a different number of symmetry-equivalent points. The number of equivalent points in a set is called the *rank* of the equipoint, and all the sets existing in one cell are called the *equipoints of a space group*.

The a priori knowledge of the equipoints of a space group is extremely valuable in determining the spatial arrangement of atoms in a crystal, or the so-called *crystal structure*. It is usually possible to determine the space group of a crystal from a study of its x-ray diffraction spectra. Similarly, it is a simple matter to determine the atomic contents of a unit cell. Since the atoms in a unit cell must be distributed among the equipoints of the cell, it is possible to utilize this knowledge in determining the crystal structure. Conversely, in the case of crystals whose structures are known, the relations between equipoints can be used to determine the environment or *coordination* of any atom. Because the properties of a crystal depend on the behavior of its constituent atoms, which, in turn, depends on the coordination of each atom in the crystal, this is an oft-recurring problem in the solid state.

In the final sections of this chapter, still another geometrical factor affecting the formation of crystal structures is considered, namely, the constraints imposed on a structure by the relative sizes of the atoms.

43

Because virtually all atoms in crystals can be represented quite accurately by spheres having specific radii, the spatial limitations imposed by their sizes can be deduced from the various possible ways of packing ordinary spheres. When spheres of like size are packed together so that the available space is occupied most economically, a so-called *closest packing* results. A similar model can be used to represent a crystal structure comprised of atoms having unequal sizes. Like atoms, usually the largest atoms present, constitute a closest packing in which the other kind (or kinds) of atoms are distributed among the available interstices or *voids*. Although it is not always advantageous to do so, the crystal structures of virtually all inorganic solids can be considered in these terms.

Equivalent positions in a unit cell

Plane groups. The several kinds of equipoints that exist in a unit cell are first described for a plane cell containing a 4-fold axis, that is, the plane group $p4$. Figure 1 shows a point having the general coordinates xy repeated by the symmetry of $p4$. It is usual to give the coordinates of a point in a unit cell in terms of fractions of the cell edges, thereby making them independent of actual cell dimensions. The value of the fraction x is the actual distance along the a axis, from the origin to the point, divided by the actual length of a. Similarly, the fraction y is the actual distance along the b axis divided by the length of b. Thus, one complete translation along a is $a/a = 1$, etc. Proceeding in a clockwise manner, the coordinates of the next point in Fig. 1 are the fraction y along the a axis and $1 - x = 1 + \bar{x} = \bar{x}$ along the b axis. Since it is customary to list the coordinate along a first and along b next, the coordinates of this point are $y\bar{x}$. The coordinates of the other equivalent points are also indicated in Fig. 1. Because there are four such points related by the symmetry of $p4$, the *rank* of the equipoint xy is 4 in this plane group. Since each of the coordinates of this equipoint, x and y, is variable between 0 and 1, this position in the cell is called a *general position*.

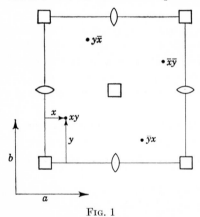

FIG. 1

Next, consider the pairs of points that are related by the 2-fold axes in $p4$ and let these points coalesce to single points on each 2, as indicated in Fig. 2 by the dashed lines. The coordinates of these equivalent points (the black dots in Fig. 2) are $\frac{1}{2}0$ and $0\frac{1}{2}$, and there are two such points in each cell. Finally, the points on the two different 4-fold axes, at 00 and $\frac{1}{2}\frac{1}{2}$, each have the rank 1. Since the x and y values of these equipoints are fixed, they are called *special positions*. Table 1 lists the various equipoints in $p4$ and their symmetry. Note, for example, that the equipoint 00 must have 4-fold symmetry since it occupies a 4-fold axis. Also note that the arithmetic product of the first two columns in Table 1 is a constant. This is so because a point lying on a symmetry axis is not repeated by that axis; hence its rank is decreased by the fold of the axis. This relationship holds true whether the axis is a proper or an improper axis.

Space groups. The equipoints of a space group can be determined in a similar manner. As a simple extension of the above example, con-

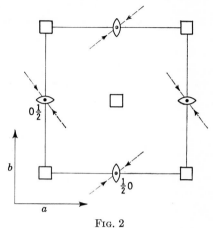

FIG. 2

sider the space group $P4$. The equipoints of this space group are obtained by adding the z coordinate to the equipoints of $p4$, as shown in Table 2. Since the symmetry of $P4$ does not affect z, this coordinate is not specified for any equipoint. Note that Table 2 contains an additional column headed *Wyckoff notation*. This notation was proposed in one of the first

Table 1
Equipoints of plane group $p4$

Rank of equipoint	Symmetry of location	Coordinates of equivalent points
1	4	00
1	4	$\frac{1}{2}\frac{1}{2}$
2	2	$0\frac{1}{2}, \frac{1}{2}0$
4	1	$xy, y\bar{x}, \bar{x}\bar{y}, \bar{y}x$

Table 2
Equipoints of space group $P4$

Rank of equipoint	Wyckoff notation	Symmetry of location	Coordinates of equivalent points
1	a	4	$00z$
1	b	4	$\frac{1}{2}\frac{1}{2}z$
2	c	2	$0\frac{1}{2}z, \frac{1}{2}0z$
4	d	1	$xyz, y\bar{x}z, \bar{x}\bar{y}z, \bar{y}xz$

published tabulations of such data, and it has become common practice to refer to a position in a unit cell by the rank and letter of the corresponding equipoint.

As a further illustration, consider the space group $P\bar{4}m2$ shown in Fig. 3. The arrows in the plane of this figure indicate the 2-fold axes along [[110]]; a two-sided arrowhead indicates a 2 and a single-sided arrowhead indicates a 2_1. The general position xyz is indicated in this drawing by a circle; a $+$ near the circle indicates that it lies above the plane of the drawing and a $-$ indicates that it lies an equal distance below the plane. Finally, a comma enclosed within a circle denotes an enantiomorphous

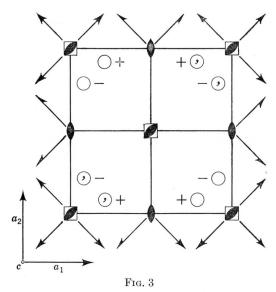

Fig. 3

relationship to a symmetry-related circle containing no comma. This notation is used here in order to acquaint the reader with the similar notation used in *International tables for x-ray crystallography*.

The equipoints of space group $P\bar{4}m2$ are listed in Table 3. The general position xyz is shown in Fig. 3. The special positions are obtained, for example, by "moving" pairs of points related by the two kinds of mirror planes intersecting at $00z$ and $\frac{1}{2}\frac{1}{2}z$, respectively, onto these mirror planes. This gives the special positions $4j$ and $4k$. Alternatively, pairs of points can coalesce onto the diagonal 2-fold axes to produce $4h$ and $4i$. Next, the points lying along the lines of intersection of the mirror planes can have the coordinates of the equipoints $2e$, $2f$, or $2g$. Note that these points occur in pairs differing only in whether the z coordinate is positive or negative. This is because of the 2-fold axes along [[110]] which intersect the c axis at $z = 0$ and $z = \frac{1}{2}$. (Compare these with equipoints $1a$

Table 3
Equipoints of space group $P\bar{4}m2$

Rank of equipoint	Wyckoff notation	Symmetry of location	Coordinates of equivalent points
1	a	$\bar{4}2m$	000
1	b	$\bar{4}2m$	$\frac{1}{2}\frac{1}{2}0$
1	c	$\bar{4}2m$	$00\frac{1}{2}$
1	d	$\bar{4}2m$	$\frac{1}{2}\frac{1}{2}\frac{1}{2}$
2	e	mm	$00z,\ 00\bar{z}$
2	f	mm	$\frac{1}{2}\frac{1}{2}z,\ \frac{1}{2}\frac{1}{2}\bar{z}$
2	g	mm	$0\frac{1}{2}z,\ \frac{1}{2}0\bar{z}$
4	h	2	$xx0,\ \bar{x}\bar{x}0,\ x\bar{x}0,\ \bar{x}x0$
4	i	2	$xx\frac{1}{2},\ \bar{x}\bar{x}\frac{1}{2},\ x\bar{x}\frac{1}{2},\ \bar{x}x\frac{1}{2}$
4	j	m	$x0z,\ \bar{x}0z,\ 0x\bar{z},\ 0\bar{x}\bar{z}$
4	k	m	$x\frac{1}{2}z,\ \bar{x}\frac{1}{2}z,\ \frac{1}{2}x\bar{z},\ \frac{1}{2}\bar{x}\bar{z}$
8	l	1	$xyz,\ \bar{x}\bar{y}z,\ \bar{x}yz,\ x\bar{y}z,$ $\bar{y}x\bar{z},\ y\bar{x}\bar{z},\ yx\bar{z},\ \bar{y}\bar{x}\bar{z}$

and $1b$ in $P4$.) Finally, if the points in $2e$, $2f$, and $2g$ are made to coalesce in pairs onto the positions $z = 0$ and $z = \frac{1}{2}$, the four special positions $1a$, $1b$, $1c$, and $1d$ result.

It is possible to make use of relations between equipoints to determine what the coordination of any atom in a crystal is in terms of the equipoints occupied by the other atoms. For example, suppose that a crystal structure whose space group is $P\bar{4}m2$ has an A atom in equipoint $1d$ surrounded by two B atoms in $2f$ and four B atoms in $4i$. The resulting 6-fold coordination of the A atom is said to be *octahedral* because the polyhedron formed by connecting the centers of the six B atoms surrounding it is an octahedron, as shown in Fig. 4. The center of the A atom is shown at the body center of the unit cell, $\frac{1}{2}\ \frac{1}{2}\ \frac{1}{2}$, and the six B atoms are grouped around it according to the equipoint listing in Table 3. It is easy to see in this figure that the interatomic distances between the central A atom and the two B atoms in $2f$ are equal to $(\frac{1}{2} - z)c$. Similarly, the four B atoms lying at the corners of the square in the $xy\frac{1}{2}$ plane are each equidistant from the central A atom. This interatomic distance is

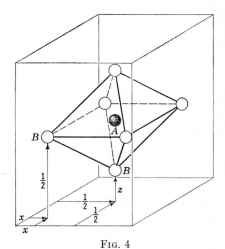

Fig. 4

given by the vector sum of $(\frac{1}{2} - x)\mathbf{a} + (\frac{1}{2} - x)\mathbf{b}$ or, since $a = b$ in the tetragonal system, the interatomic distance is simply $\sqrt{2(\frac{1}{2} - x)^2}\, a$.

The interatomic distances can be determined directly from the equipoints without recourse to a model of the actual structure. This is particularly easy if the reference or crystal axes are mutually orthogonal. Using the above example, convert the coordinates of each equipoint to absolute dimensions by multiplying x by $\mathbf{a}$, y by $\mathbf{b}$, etc. (If an equipoint set has a rank higher than 1, the use of any one of its equivalent points produces the same final result.) The absolute coordinates of the three atoms of interest are as follows:

Absolute coordinates of A atom in $1d$ are $\frac{1}{2}\mathbf{a}$, $\frac{1}{2}\mathbf{b}$, $\frac{1}{2}\mathbf{c}$.
Absolute coordinates of B atom in $2f$ are $\frac{1}{2}\mathbf{a}$, $\frac{1}{2}\mathbf{b}$, $z\mathbf{c}$.   (1)
Absolute coordinates of B atom in $4i$ are $x\mathbf{a}$, $x\mathbf{b}$, $\frac{1}{2}\mathbf{c}$.

The interatomic distances between any two atoms is simply the vector difference between their absolute coordinates. For example, the interatomic distance between the A atom and the B atom in $2f$ is

$$(\tfrac{1}{2}\mathbf{a} + \tfrac{1}{2}\mathbf{b} + \tfrac{1}{2}\mathbf{c}) - (\tfrac{1}{2}\mathbf{a} + \tfrac{1}{2}\mathbf{b} + z\mathbf{c}) = (\tfrac{1}{2} - z)\mathbf{c}. \qquad (2)$$

Similarly, the other $A - B$ distance is

$$(\tfrac{1}{2}\mathbf{a} + \tfrac{1}{2}\mathbf{b} + \tfrac{1}{2}\mathbf{c}) - (x\mathbf{a} + x\mathbf{b} + \tfrac{1}{2}\mathbf{c}) = (\tfrac{1}{2} - x)\mathbf{a} + (\tfrac{1}{2} - x)\mathbf{b} \qquad (3)$$

in full agreement with the result derived earlier from Fig. 4. In carrying out such calculations, it should be borne in mind that the operations in equations (2) and (3) are vector operations. Thus, if the crystallographic axes are not mutually orthogonal, the angular relations between the vectors must be kept in mind when the interatomic distances are computed. It is usually helpful in such cases first to make an accurate sketch or model of the structure. (See Exercise 4 at the end of this chapter.)

Determination of crystal structures

Historical background. Following Röntgen's discovery of x-rays in 1895, Laue noted in 1912 that these x-rays were believed to have wavelengths of the order of 10^{-8} cm and that crystals were believed to consist of periodic arrays of atoms having similar dimensions. Therefore he concluded that crystals could serve as gratings for the diffraction of x-rays. This theory was substantiated that same year by the experiments of two of his colleagues, Friedrich and Knipping. When the results became known in Cambridge, England, a meeting of minds occurred that led to a most revolutionary discovery in physical science. W. H. Bragg and his son W. L. Bragg were studying the optical properties of x-rays when they learned of the experiments of Friedrich and Knipping. Their subsequent researches along the same line became known to W. Barlow, who had proposed in the 1890s that crystals consisted of atoms packed like spheres in closest possible packing. In collaboration with Professor Pope at Cambridge, he suggested that sylvite, KCl, and halite, NaCl, had structures based on a face-centered cubic packing of spheres. Pope prevailed on the Braggs to test their theories, with the result that the younger Bragg demonstrated that the observed x-ray diffraction spectra were indeed in agreement with the postulated structures. This discovery pointed the way to the determination of atomic arrangements in a large number of solids, revolutionizing thereby the fields of chemistry, metallurgy, mineralogy, solid-state physics, and related sciences. The full repercussions of this discovery cannot be appraised as yet.

Following De Broglie's postulate in 1924 that electrons also behaved like waves, two American scientists, Davisson and Germer, showed in 1927 that electrons similarly can be diffracted by crystals. For some time following these experiments, electron diffraction fell by the wayside as x-ray diffraction was making tremendous strides in developing successively more powerful tools for determining increasingly more complex structures. Recently, Pinsker, in Russia, and subsequently Cowley, in Australia, have led a revival in the application of electron diffraction to crystal-structure analysis. Special problems arise when the less penetrating electrons are used. It turns out, however, that electron diffraction is particularly useful in certain cases where x-ray diffraction methods fail.

With the further evolution of nuclear physics, particularly following the construction of nuclear reactors, neutrons, deuterons, and α-rays have been diffracted from crystals. Of these different nuclear particles, neutrons have been shown to be particularly useful in crystal-structure analysis. Unlike x-rays and electrons, neutrons interact with atomic nuclei and are sensitive to their magnetic properties. Consequently, neutron diffraction can be used in the elucidation of many structures whose detailed atomic arrangements do not affect their x-ray diffraction spectra in the same way.

Elementary diffraction theory. Although the details of the diffraction of x-rays, electrons, and neutrons differ, the fundamental principles of diffraction are the same. In each case, it is the periodicity of the atomic arrays in crystals that makes diffraction possible. Consider the diffraction of radiation, say x-rays, by the atomic array shown in Fig. 5. A more convenient representation of this array is to consider it as made up of a stack of parallel planes passing through the centers of the atoms. An edge view of these planes is shown in Fig. 6.

When a wave front of x-rays impinges on a crystal, each atom scatters the x-rays in all directions. Certain directions of scattering are of particular interest.   Consider the incoming rays *OE* and *O'A* inclined at the angle θ to the planes (*hkl*).   Observe that the scattered rays *AP* and *EP'*

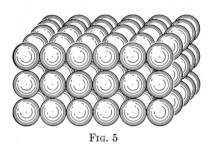

also form the angle θ with (*hkl*). Since the total pathlengths of the rays *O'AP* and *OEP'* are the same, these rays are said to scatter *in phase* with each other; that is, the waves of the individual rays arriving at *PP'* again form a common wave front.   This is the condition for scattering in phase by one plane in a crystal.

Fig. 5

Next, consider the incoming ray *O'C* and the scattered ray *CP''*.   The total pathlength *O'CP''* is greater than that of rays *O'AP* and *OEP'* by an amount

$$\Delta = BCD$$
$$= 2BC. \tag{4}$$

Since

$$BC = d \sin \theta, \tag{5}$$

the path difference is

$$\Delta = 2BC$$
$$= 2d \sin \theta. \tag{6}$$

If *O'CP''* is to arrive at *PP'P''* in phase with rays *O'AP* and *OEP'*, that is, if the two planes are to scatter in phase, then the path difference Δ must

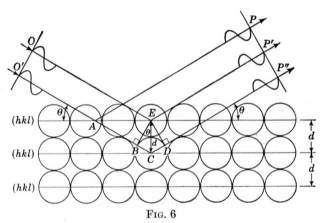

Fig. 6

equal an integral number of wavelengths, $n\lambda$, where $n = 0, 1, 2, 3, \ldots$. Thus the condition for in-phase diffraction by a set of parallel crystal planes is

$$n\lambda = 2d \sin \theta. \tag{7}$$

The meaning of (7) is that the diffraction intensities can build up only at certain values of θ, corresponding to a specific value of λ and d. This is so because the wavelets scattered from various points in the crystal have a common wave front only at these angles. Consequently, the amplitudes of all the individual wavelets add up to give a resultant wave having the maximum amplitude possible, as shown in Fig. 7A. On the other hand, at other scattering angles, the wavelets emanating from different parts of the crystal are not in phase with each other. When the amplitudes of the wavelets are summed at these angles, some of the amplitudes are positive while others are negative, as shown in Fig. 7B. The

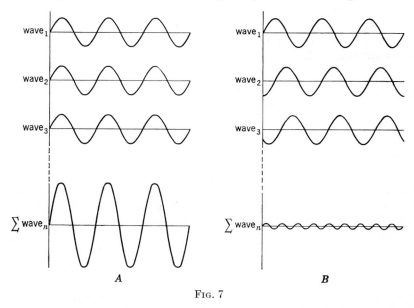

Fig. 7

resultant wave, therefore, has an amplitude equal to zero if a sufficiently large number of wavelets are considered. As can be seen in Fig. 6, the diffraction of x-rays by a crystal can be treated as the reflection of x-rays by families of parallel planes in that crystal. (Note that θ is the complement of the usual angle of incidence i.) This viewpoint was first proposed by W. L. Bragg, and relation (7) is accordingly known as the *Bragg law*.

Recasting (7) to solve for θ,

$$\theta = \sin^{-1} \frac{n\lambda}{2d}, \tag{8}$$

it is seen that rays diffracted by a crystal are given off in different directions corresponding to the different values of the interplanar spacing d. It is possible to reverse this statement and say that from a knowledge of the experimentally observed diffraction angles it is possible to determine the interplanar spacings of a crystal.   From a list of such spacings it is then possible to deduce the lattice of a crystal.   Thus one piece of information that can be obtained from any diffraction experiment employing monochromatic radiation is the unit cell size and shape.

To see what influence the atomic arrangement in the crystal has on the observed diffracted beams, consider Fig. 8.   This figure shows a crystal structure composed of two mutually displaced lattice arrays of atoms. At an angle θ satisfying equation (8) for both arrays, the atoms in each array scatter radiation in phase with other atoms in the same array.   But the total pathlength is longer for rays scattered by one array than for the other.   Consequently each array contributes to the resultant wave, scattered by the whole crystal, waves that are not quite in phase with each other.   This has the effect of reducing the intensity of the diffracted beam from what it would be if all the atoms in the crystal structure scattered in phase.

It is possible to describe this phenomenon analytically.   The x-ray scattering power of an atom is directly proportional to the number of electrons composing it and can be expressed by a *scattering factor f.*   (The scattering power of an atom decreases as θ increases because of the phasal relationship between wavelets emanating from different points in the same atom.)   Since the entire crystal structure can be represented by the atomic array within one unit cell of the lattice, the contribution from atoms in one unit cell only need be considered.   In order to determine the combined scattering power of all the atoms in a unit cell, it is necessary to relate the differences between the pathlengths of x-rays scattered

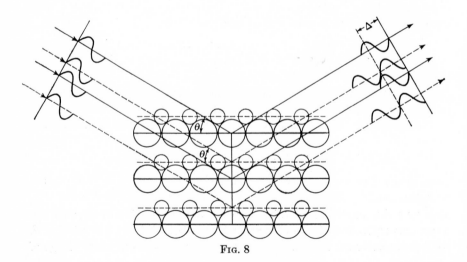

FIG. 8

by each atom. This is done most conveniently by a geometrical factor which is a function of the position of each atom in the cell, that is, the actual distribution of atoms among the equipoints. When the amplitudes of the wavelets scattered by each atom in the unit cell are added, one obtains the so-called *structure factor*

$$F_{hkl} = f_1 e^{2\pi i(hx_1+ky_1+lz_1)} + \cdots + f_N e^{2\pi i(hx_N+ky_N+lz_N)}$$
$$= \sum_{n=1}^{N} f_n e^{2\pi i(hx_n+ky_n+lz_n)} \tag{9}$$

where N is the total number of atoms contained in a unit cell. The exponential term expresses the relative phase of the radiation scattered by each atom n as a function of its position in the unit cell $x_n y_n z_n$. Since a set of planes (hkl) reflects monochromatic x-rays only at a specific angle, according to equation (7) or (8), the amplitude of the reflected x-ray beam can be calculated for each reflection by substituting the appropriate hkl values in equation (9).

In an actual x-ray diffraction experiment one measures the intensities rather than the amplitudes of the reflected beam. The intensity is directly proportional to the square of the amplitude

$$I_{hkl} \sim F_{hkl}^2 \tag{10}$$

so that it appears that it is possible to determine the positions of the atoms in a unit cell, that is, the crystal structure, directly from the observed intensity values.

Determination of unit cell contents. Having determined the lattice of a crystal from a diffraction experiment, it is possible to determine the volume V of the unit cell in that lattice. The density of the crystal is also the density of the unit cell which is

$$\text{Density of cell} = \frac{\text{mass of cell}}{\text{volume of cell}}. \tag{11}$$

The mass of the cell consists of the mass of n chemical formula weights, or molecules, each having the mass M, so that (11) can be written

$$\text{Density of cell} = D = \frac{nM}{V}. \tag{12}$$

Usually the chemical composition of the crystal is known so that M can be determined by adding the masses of the individual atoms in the formula. The usual list of atomic weights found in chemical tables is based on oxygen equal to 16 atomic mass units (AMU). To convert an atomic weight A, expressed in AMU, to grams, it must be divided by Avogadro's number (6.023×10^{23} molecules/g mole) or multiplied by its reciprocal, 1.660×10^{-24} g/AMU. Putting in all units, equation (12) becomes

$$D \; (\text{g/cm}^3) = \frac{nA \; (\text{AMU}) \times 1.660 \times 10^{-24} \; (\text{g/AMU})}{V \; (\text{cm}^3)}. \tag{13}$$

The density of most crystals is known or can be readily determined by flotation in liquids of known density or by other standard methods. Also the atomic weights A are known. If the volume V of the cell has been determined, everything in (13) is known except n, the number of formula weights in a unit cell. This number can be readily calculated, therefore, by simply rearranging the terms in (13). In doing this, note that the unit cell volume is usually measured in Ångstroms cubed ($1 \; \text{Å} = 10^{-8}$ cm), so that

$$n = \frac{D \; (\text{g/cm}^3) \times V \; (\text{Å}^3) \times 10^{-24} \; (\text{cm}^3/\text{Å}^3)}{A \; (\text{AMU}) \times 1.660 \times 10^{-24} \; (\text{g/AMU})}. \tag{14}$$

According to the concepts of geometrical crystallography, the number of formula weights in a unit cell must be an integer. Usually n differs from an integer by a few per cent because of errors in the measured value of the density. The integer value of n determined by (14) must, of course, be compatible with the ranks of the equipoints of the corresponding space group, as discussed below.

Determination of atomic arrangement. In addition to being able to determine the lattice of a crystal, diffraction experiments also disclose the symmetry of the crystal. It is possible, therefore, to determine the space group of the crystal.[†] Knowing the number of formula weights contained by a unit cell and the space group of the crystal, it is possible to obtain a preliminary picture of the distribution of the atoms among the equipoints of the space group.

For example, assume that the space group of a crystal is $P4$ and that it contains two molecules in a unit cell. By consulting Table 2 it can be seen that the two molecules can occupy the special position $2c$ or they can occupy special positions $1a$ and $1b$. It is obvious that they cannot have the general coordinates of $4d$ because the symmetry would require that there be four identical molecules in each cell. Such reasoning, supplemented by additional knowledge of chemical or physical properties, is frequently sufficient to determine simple crystal structures. For instance, in the above example, if the configuration and symmetry of the two molecules are known from stereochemical reasoning, then equipoints $2c$ or $1a$

[†] In practice, a direct determination of the space group is not always possible because the nature of x-ray diffraction experiments is such that a center of symmetry is added to whatever symmetry the crystal may possess. In order to distinguish the centrosymmetric and noncentric space groups, it is usually necessary to determine whether a structure is centrosymmetric or not by some other means.

and 1*b* can be eliminated, depending on whether the known symmetry of the molecule is 2-fold or 4-fold.

As a further example, assume that the space group is $P\bar{4}m2$ and that the unit cell contains one formula weight, $A(BC_4)_2$. It can be seen from Table 3 that the A atom can occupy any one of the four special positions 1*a*, 1*b*, 1*c*, or 1*d*, but no others. It should be noted that this choice is arbitrary in that these four positions are simply alternative choices for the origin of coordinates in the unit cell. For simplicity, therefore, the A atom can be placed in 1*a* at 000. This choice, however, then fixes the relative positions of the B and C atoms. The B atoms can occupy any of the positions of rank 2 or any pair of unoccupied positions of rank 1. The C atoms, in turn, can occupy the positions 8*l*, or any pair of positions of rank 4, or any position of rank 4 and any pair of unoccupied positions of rank 2, etc.

It can be seen, even in the above relatively simple example, that a choice must be made between a large number of permutations. Moreover, to determine the actual crystal structure, the unspecified values of the xyz coordinates must be determined. Although it may appear from equations (9) and (10) that this is a straightforward procedure, in practice this is not normally the case. The reason for this is that, in measuring the intensity of a reflection, the magnitude, $|F_{hkl}|^2$, is determined but not the phase of the reflection relative to the incident beam. Consequently, it is not possible to combine the intensities of several reflections by a simple procedure in order to deduce the atomic arrangement. The problem can be solved by trial-and-error procedures, based on a knowledge of the atomic distribution among the available equipoints, if the number of atoms in the unit cell is not very large. For more complicated structures, however, more elaborate procedures are required. This is known as the *phase problem* in crystallography, and a whole new science of crystal-structure analysis has evolved in the twentieth century to cope with it.

Spheres in closest packings

What a closest packing is. A *close packing* is a way of arranging equidimensional objects in space so that the available space is filled very efficiently. Such an arrangement is achieved when each object is in actual contact with the maximum number of like objects. A honeycomb is an example of a close packing found in nature. Unwittingly, bees form hexagonal cells to store their honey in order to utilize space most efficiently. Similarly, squirrels mound nuts in close packing for the same reason. As man's understanding of the structure of matter matured, therefore, it was natural for him to assume that the spherical atoms believed to comprise solids are arranged in close packings also.

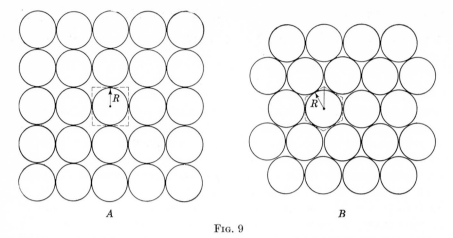

A   B

F<small>IG</small>. 9

A *closest packing of like spheres*† is that arrangement of spheres which permits each sphere to form intimate contact with the largest number of its neighbors, occupying the available space most efficiently thereby. For spheres of equal size, this means that each sphere has six nearest neighbors in a *closest-packed layer* and twelve nearest neighbors in a three-dimensional *closest packing*. To see this, consider the two close-packed layers of spheres shown in Fig. 9. Figure 9*A* shows a layer of spheres arranged on the points of a square lattice. In two dimensions, the spheres become circles. The area "belonging" to each circle is a square whose area is $4R^2$. The area of the circle, of course, is πR^2. Hence, the efficiency with which the available space is occupied is given by the ratio of these two areas,

$$\frac{\text{Area of circle}}{\text{Area of square}} = \frac{\pi R^2}{4R^2} = \frac{\pi}{4}$$
$$\text{Efficiency} = 78.5 \text{ per cent.} \tag{15}$$

Figure 9*B* shows a layer of spheres arranged on the points of a triangular lattice. The area associated with each circle is a hexagon comprised of twelve right triangles, each having an area of

$$(\tfrac{1}{2}R)\left[\left(\frac{1}{\sqrt{3}}\right)R\right] = \left(\frac{1}{2\sqrt{3}}\right)R^2.$$

The area of the hexagon is equal to twelve times the area of one triangle or $2\sqrt{3}\,R^2$. The efficiency with which the available space in this layer is

---

† In the past, the terms *closest packing, close packing,* and *close-packed* have been used interchangeably. In order to distinguish close-packed arrangements of like spheres satisfying the condition of closest possible packing, the terms *closest packing,* for a three-dimensional array, and *closest-packed layer,* for a two-dimensional array, are adopted in this book.

utilized is given by

$$\frac{\text{Area of circle}}{\text{Area of hexagon}} = \frac{\pi R^2}{2\sqrt{3}\,R^2} = \frac{\pi}{2\sqrt{3}}$$
$$\text{Efficiency} = 90.7 \text{ per cent.} \tag{16}$$

It should be obvious that a more efficient occupation of space in two dimensions is not possible, since more than six circles cannot be placed in contact with one circle of the same size. It is concluded, therefore, that the arrangement of spheres shown in Fig. 9B is the only closest packing possible in two dimensions. Since the symmetry of this layer is $6mm$, such a layer is called a *hexagonal closest-packed* layer.

The number of closest packings possible in three dimensions is infinite. The various closest packings of spheres of equal size differ in the way that the hexagonal closest-packed layers comprising them are arranged. The different closest packings have one thing in common, however; each sphere in a closest packing is in intimate contact with twelve other spheres. Similarly to the two-dimensional case described above, it is not possible to place more than twelve spheres about any one sphere and still have all spheres touch the central one. It is, of course, possible to place less than twelve spheres around a single sphere. Such arrangements are not closest packings, however. The proof that a closest packing is the most efficient way to utilize space in three dimensions is left to the reader. (See Exercises 10, 11, and 12 at the end of this chapter.)

It has been shown above that the only closest packing possible in two dimensions is the hexagonal closest-packed layer. This layer has several interesting properties.

1. Each sphere is surrounded by six spheres.
2. Each sphere is surrounded by six voids.
3. Each void is surrounded by three spheres.
4. The symmetry of the layer about each sphere is $6mm$.
5. The symmetry of the layer about each void is $3m$.

The significance of the first three properties is that, on an average, $6 \times \frac{1}{3} = 2$ voids belong to each sphere. This statement is illustrated in Fig. 10A, which shows that the hexagonal unit cell in this layer contains one sphere and two voids. These two triangular voids differ in that one triangular void has its apex pointing up and the other one has its apex pointing down. To distinguish the two kinds of voids, they are labeled B and C, respectively, in Fig. 10B and in Fig. 11.

It is readily seen in Fig. 11 that, if the spheres in a hexagonal closest-packed layer are all moved from their original sites A to new sites B, another hexagonal closest-packed layer results. Similarly, if all the C sites are occupied by equal spheres, a hexagonal closest-packed layer is

again obtained.   It should also be obvious that, in the stacking of layers
to form a closest packing, a hexagonal closest-packed layer can occupy
only the sites A or B or C.

The above discussion has a very real importance when the stacking of
hexagonal closest-packed layers above each other is considered.   If a
layer is named A, B, or C, accordingly as the spheres in that layer occupy

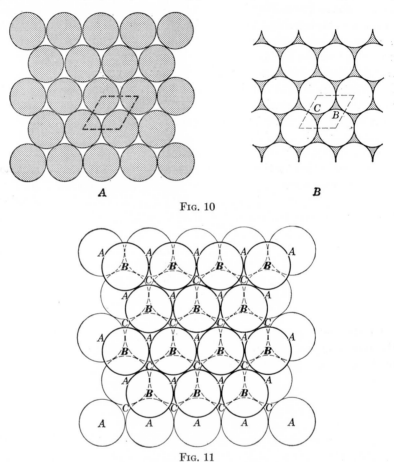

A   B

Fig. 10

Fig. 11

A, B, or C sites, then a twofold choice exists in placing one hexagonal
closest-packed layer above another.   Let the first layer be an A layer.
The next layer can be either a B layer or a C layer.   Say that it is a B
layer.   The next layer above can now be either an A layer or a C layer,
and so forth.   From this discussion it follows that the stacking sequence
of hexagonal closest-packed layers can be designated by representing the
layers in a sequence by the letters A, B, C.

The symmetry of a single layer is $6mm$. The symmetry of two super-imposed layers is lower because the spheres of one layer lie above the voids of the other. The lowest possible symmetry for any sequence of layers, however, is $3m$, the symmetry of a void. (Note that $3m$ is a subgroup of $6mm$.) It follows from the above that the lowest symmetry that a three-dimensional closest packing can have is uniquely described by the space group $P3m$. In fact, this is the space group of a closest packing comprised of a completely arbitrary periodic stacking sequence of hexagonal closest-packed layers, provided only that no two identical layers are adjacent. If the arbitrariness in stacking successive layers is limited by requiring a finite translation period normal to the layers, then the symmetry of the closest packing may be higher. In all cases, however, this symmetry must be a supergroup of $P3m$, with the additional condition that the maximum number of mirrors normal to the layers not exceed the three vertical mirror planes in $P3m$. Thus, $P6mm, P\dfrac{6}{m}mm$, $P\bar{4}3m$, and other supergroups are excluded. In fact, the only space groups to which closest packings can belong are as follows:

$$
\begin{array}{ll}
P3m & P\dfrac{3}{m}m2 \\[2mm]
R3m & P6_3mc \\[2mm]
P\bar{3}m & P\dfrac{6_3}{m}mc \\[2mm]
R\bar{3}m & Fm3m
\end{array}
\tag{17}
$$

Of the eight possible space groups in (17), the space group $Fm3m$ is the only one that is not hexagonal. Actually, there is only one closest packing that belongs to this space group, the so-called *cubic closest packing* consisting of three different layers stacked in the sequence $...ABCABC...$ shown in Fig. 12. The other seven space groups are represented by an innumerable number of closest packings. Of these, $P\dfrac{6_3}{m}mc$ is of interest because it contains the simple two-layer sequence $...ABAB...$ or the so-called *hexagonal closest packing* shown in Fig. 13. The way that a stacking of hexagonal closest-packed layers in the sequence $...ABC...$ must be reoriented to show the cubic symmetry $Fm3m$ is indicated by the sequence of illustrations in Fig. 14. Figure $14A$ shows three layers in such a stack with the stacking direction vertical. Figure $14B$ shows the stack tipped over, and Fig. $14C$ shows the same view with several spheres added to layers B and C. Finally, Fig. $14D$ shows the face-centered cubic cell that results if the four uppermost spheres in Fig. $14C$ are deleted from the illustration.

Classification of closest packings. In addition to differences in
their space groups, closest packings are distinguished by the number of
hexagonal closest-packed layers required to complete the stacking
sequence. This number of layers, n, is called the *identity period* of a

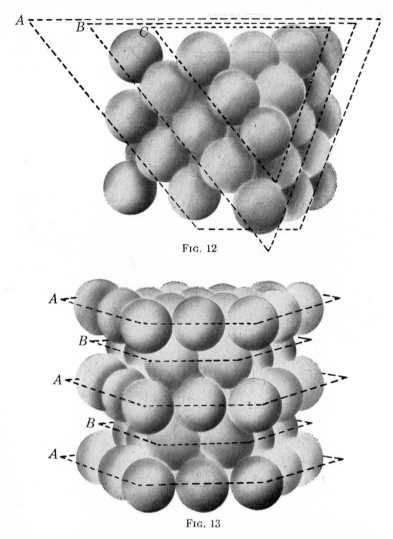

Fig. 12

Fig. 13

closest packing and can be used as a basis for classification. Thus, the
smallest value that n can have in a closest packing is 2, which is the
identity period of the hexagonal closest packing. Similarly, the cubic
closest packing is the only one possible for a stacking period $n = 3$.
Next, ...$ABAC$... is the only closest packing possible when $n = 4$ and is

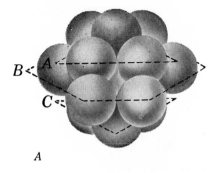

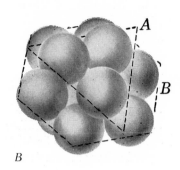

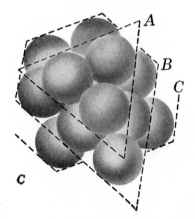

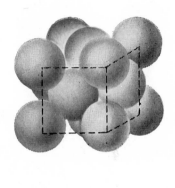

FIG. 14

sometimes called the topaz closest packing because it occurs in the mineral topaz. It can be shown that, when $n = 5$, there is only one closest packing possible, namely, $...ABCAB...$, but when $n = 6$, there are two possible closest packings, namely, $...ABCACB...$ and $...ABABAC...$, and so forth. Ellipses (three successive dots) are used to indicate that the sequence of letters, or *stacking formula*, is periodically repeated. For example, $...AB... = ...ABAB... = ...ABABAB...$, etc. It follows from the above discussion that, as the identity period becomes longer, that is, as n increases, an ever larger number of closest packings can occur for each value of n.

In discussing the symmetries of individual closest packings having a relatively large identity period, it is convenient to use an alternative method of designating these layers, suggested by Pauling. Instead of designating a layer by *A*, *B*, or *C*, let *h* represent a layer surrounded by two identical layers (for instance, any layer in a hexagonal closest packing) and *c* a layer surrounded by two different layers (for instance, any layer in a cubic closest packing). In terms of this nomenclature, the two-layer hexagonal closest packing ...*AB*... becomes ...*hh*.... Similarly, the three-layer cubic closest packing ...*ABC*... becomes ...*ccc*..., and the four-layer closest packing ...*ABAC*... becomes ...*chch*.... In extending the stacking formula it is important to remember that the first letter on the left of a sequence becomes the first letter in the continuation. For example, ...*hchc*... = ...*hchchc*... but

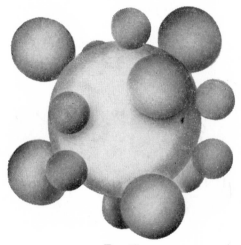

Fig. 15

...*hchch*... = *hchchhchch*.... Note, therefore, that a sequence of letters in a stacking formula cannot be terminated arbitrarily but must end with the last letter of a periodic sequence.

The designation of different hexagonal closest-packed layers by the letters *A*, *B*, or *C* is quite arbitrary. The letters *h* and *c* cannot be assigned arbitrarily, however, because they denote not only a specific layer but also the relative orientations of the two layers adjacent to it. Consequently, the environments of a sphere in an *h* layer and in a *c* layer are different. If the voids surrounding a sphere are represented by smaller spheres whose volumes equal the volumes of the voids, then the environment of a sphere in an *h* layer is as shown in Fig. 15, and of a sphere in a *c* layer as shown in Fig. 16.

The stacking formula of a closest packing consists of the proper sequence of the letters *h* and *c*. Compared with the *ABC* nomenclature, it has the disadvantage that the identity period is not immediately obvious. For example, in the simple hexagonal closest packing $\ldots hh \ldots$ or the cubic closest packing $\ldots ccc \ldots$ the true identity period is not the same as the period of the letters themselves. It is, of course, possible to return to the ABC designation and obtain the period directly. Consider the stacking formula

$$\ldots hcchcc \ldots . \tag{18}$$

In order to convert (18) to the ABC designation, let the first layer be a C layer. The next layer can be either an A or a B layer. Let it be an A layer. Then, since this A layer is a c-type layer, the layer following it

Fig. 16

must be different from the layer preceding it; that is, the next layer must be a B layer. Similarly, this B layer is a c-type layer which requires that the next layer must be a C layer. This C layer, however, is an h-type layer which requires that two identical layers be adjacent to it. Since it was preceded by a B layer, it must be followed by a B layer. The last two layers in (18) are c-type and require different layers surrounding them. The systematic conversion of (18) to the ABC designation, therefore, follows the scheme

$$
\begin{aligned}
&\ldots hcchcc \ldots \\
&\ldots C \\
&\ldots CA \\
&\ldots CAB \\
&\ldots CABC \\
&\ldots CABCB \\
&\ldots CABCBA \ldots
\end{aligned}
\tag{19}
$$

from which it can be seen that the correct identity period consists of six layers, whereas the minimum period of letters in the stacking formula (18) is three.

Voids in closest packings

Significance of voids. Although the possible varieties of closest packings are infinite, a very small number actually occur in nature. In fact, most actual closest packings encountered are either the hexagonal closest packing or the cubic closest packing of metals. Similarly, a large part of all known inorganic compounds have structures that are either slightly distorted closest packings or are related to closest packings in another way. Frequently, one kind of atoms present in a crystal are in a closest packing while the other atoms present occupy the voids between the closest-packed atoms. For example, many oxides consist of oxygen atoms arranged in a hexagonal or cubic closest packing with the smaller metal atoms distributed among the voids. Another familiar example is found in steels whose many practical properties depend entirely on the way small numbers of "foreign" atoms are distributed in the voids of a body-centered cubic packing of iron atoms. These and many other examples of related structures are further discussed in later chapters.

The voids between atoms in closest packings are of interest for other reasons also. For example, many of the properties of matter are profoundly influenced not only by the structural arrangement of the atoms but also by imperfections occurring in their arrangement. A very important kind of imperfection is the so-called *interstitial atom*. An interstitial atom may be an impurity, either intentionally or accidentally added to the normal complement of atoms, or it may be an atom that has been accidentally displaced from its correct position in the structure to an interstitial position. Recently developed techniques, such as paramagnetic resonance, for example, are capable of detecting and characterizing these interstitial atoms very precisely. The interpretation of these measurements, however, relies on knowing what the environments of the interstitial atoms are. Whether one thinks of the distribution of metal atoms among the voids in a closest packing or of the interstitial atoms occasionally found in such voids, it should be recognized that not all the voids can be occupied. In most inorganic structures based on closest packings only certain voids related by symmetry are occupied. In this chapter the different kinds of voids that occur in closest packings are described in detail. Voids differing from these are possible in other kinds of close-packed structures, and the discussion given below should be useful in analyzing such other voids also.

Classification of voids. There are two kinds of voids that occur in all closest packings. If the triangular void in a closest-packed layer has a sphere directly over it, there results a void with four spheres around it, as shown in Fig. 17*A*. The four spheres are arranged on the corners of a tetrahedron (Fig. 17*B*), and such a void is called a *tetrahedral void*. On the other hand, if a triangular void pointing up in one closest-packed layer is covered by a triangular void pointing down in an adjacent layer,

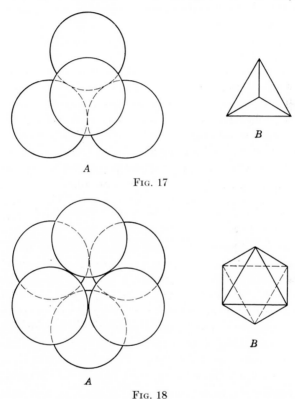

FIG. 17

FIG. 18

then a void surrounded by six spheres results (Fig. 18*A*). These six spheres are arranged on the corners of an octahedron (Fig. 18*B*), and such a void is called an *octahedral void*. It can be shown, by examining Fig. 11 carefully, that these are the only kinds of voids that can occur in a closest packing despite the fact that the number of different closest packings possible is infinite.

The number of voids surrounding any sphere in a closest packing is readily determined. A sphere in a hexagonal closest-packed layer *A* is surrounded by six triangular voids of two kinds, *B* and *C*. When the next closest-packed layer above is added, say that it is a B layer, then the three B voids become tetrahedral voids and the three C voids become octahedral voids. If the added layer is a C layer, the C voids become tetrahedral voids and the B voids become octahedral voids. Similarly, the closest-packed layer below the A layer gives rise to three tetrahedral and three octahedral voids. Furthermore, the particular sphere in layer A being considered itself covers a triangular void in the closest-packed layer above and in the layer below the sphere. Thus, two more tetrahedral voids surround the sphere. This results in $2 \times 3 = 6$ octahedral voids and $2 \times 3 + 1 + 1 = 8$ tetrahedral voids surrounding the sphere. Since the total number of spheres and voids in a closest packing is very large, it is possible to determine only the average number of voids of each kind belonging to a sphere. Each octahedral void is surrounded by six spheres and each sphere is surrounded by six octahedral voids. The number of octahedral voids belonging to one sphere is given by the ratio

$$\frac{\text{Number of octahedral voids around sphere}}{\text{Number of spheres around void}} = \frac{6}{6} = 1. \qquad (20)$$

Each tetrahedral void is surrounded by four spheres and each sphere is surrounded by eight voids. The number of tetrahedral voids belonging to one sphere is given by the ratio

$$\frac{\text{Number of tetrahedral voids around sphere}}{\text{Number of spheres around void}} = \frac{8}{4} = 2. \qquad (21)$$

The number of octahedral voids in a closest packing, therefore, is equal to the number of spheres. Similarly, the number of tetrahedral voids in a closest packing is twice the number of spheres, or twice the number of octahedral voids present.

Coordination of voids. The voids in a closest packing can be described in terms of the spheres that are arranged about each void. The number of spheres surrounding a void is called the *coordination number* of that void. If the void is also represented by a sphere, then the collection of spheres coordinating the sphere representing the void is called a *coordination polyhedron*. Accordingly, a tetrahedral void has a

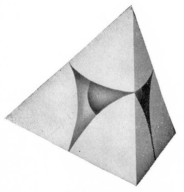

Fig. 19

coordination number of 4. The resulting coordination polyhedron is the tetrahedron shown in Fig. 19. Only those parts of the four spheres that belong to a tetrahedral void are shown in Fig. 19. As can be seen in this figure, one-eighth of the volume of four spheres, or one-half of a sphere, belongs to a tetrahedral void.

The tetrahedron in Fig. 19 can be used to determine the radius of the sphere representing the tetrahedral void. Figure 20A shows the tetrahedron inscribed inside a cube. The shaded diagonal plane of the cube in Fig. 20A is shown enlarged in Fig. 20B. It is easy to see in this figure

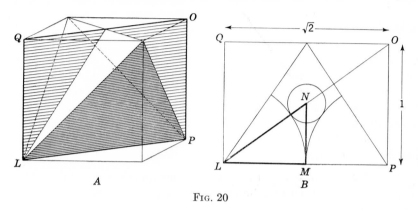

FIG. 20

that the right triangle *LMN* is similar to the right triangle *LPO*. It follows, therefore, that

$$\frac{LM}{LN} = \frac{LP}{LO} = \sqrt{\frac{2}{3}}. \tag{22}$$

Let r be the radius of the sphere representing the void and R the radius of the spheres in a closest packing. Then,

$$\frac{LM}{LN} = \frac{R}{R + r} = \sqrt{\frac{2}{3}}. \tag{23}$$

The radius of the sphere representing the tetrahedral void is obtained by rearranging the terms in (23).

$$r = \frac{\sqrt{3} - \sqrt{2}}{\sqrt{2}} R$$

$$= 0.225R. \tag{24}$$

An octahedral void is surrounded by six spheres, and its coordination number, therefore, is 6. If the octahedral void is represented by a sphere, the resulting polyhedron is an octahedron, as shown in Fig. 21. As before, only that part of each coordinating sphere that belongs to the octahedral void is shown in Fig. 21A. Since six spheres, each contributing one-sixth of its volume, coordinate the octahedral void, one sphere in a closest packing belongs to the octahedral void. This octahedron can be

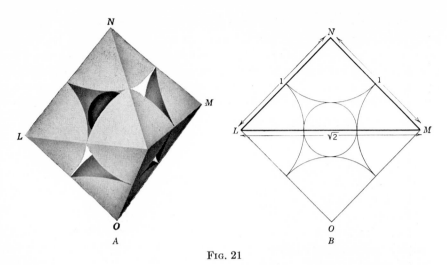

Fig. 21

used to determine the radius of the sphere representing an octahedral void. Consider the plane passing through four coordinating spheres and the central sphere representing the void. This cross section of the octahedron is the square shown in Fig. 21*B*. In the isosceles right triangle *LMN*

$$\frac{LM}{LN} = \frac{\sqrt{2}}{1}. \tag{25}$$

Letting r be the radius of the sphere representing the octahedral void and R the radius of the spheres in a closest packing, it follows from (25) that

$$\frac{2R + 2r}{2R} = \sqrt{2} \tag{26}$$

or

$$r = \sqrt{2}\,R - R$$
$$= 0.414R. \tag{27}$$

Body-centered cubic packings

The body-centered cubic structure shown in Fig. 22 is one of the commonest examples of a close-packed structure that is *not* a closest packing (see Exercise 10). It is of interest, therefore, to consider the voids that occur in this structure. There are essentially only two kinds of voids present in this type of packing also. One of these occurs at the centers of the cube faces and is coordinated by four atoms at the corners of the face and two atoms at the body centers of the two cubes sharing the face. Figure 23 shows a view of the irregular octahedron thus formed. The void is represented in this figure by a sphere of commensurate size but the coordination spheres representing part of the body-centered cubic structure are purposely reduced in size. As can be seen in Fig. 23, the coordination polyhedron of this void is a slightly compressed octahedron. It is easy to show (Exercise 16) that the maximum radius of a sphere that can fit into this void is $0.154R$, where R is the radius of the coordinating spheres. Since there are six such spheres coordinating each void and 18 voids coordinating each sphere, the ratio of spheres to voids is $1:3$.

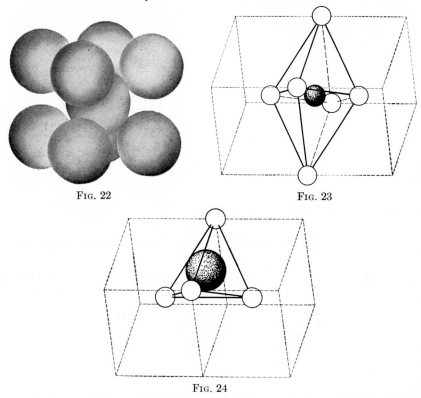

FIG. 22   FIG. 23

FIG. 24

The second type of void occurs not at the cube edges, as might be guessed, but rather in the tetrahedrally coordinated position shown in Fig. 24. It can be shown (Exercise 17) that the largest sphere that can fit into this void has a radius of $0.291R$. There are 24 such voids surrounding each sphere and four spheres around each void so that the ratio of spheres to voids is $1:6$. Note that the tetrahedral voids in a body-centered cubic structure are irregular tetrahedra and are larger than the irregular octahedral voids. Nevertheless, the irregular tetrahedral voids are smaller than the regular octahedral voids in closest packings. This factor accounts for the different kinds of interstitial atoms that can be accommodated in these two types of structures.

Representation of closest packings

As might be expected from the above discussion, a closest packing can be represented by the packing of coordination polyhedra of voids instead of by the packing of the spheres themselves. In fact, such a representation may have certain advantages. For example, to display properly the cubic symmetry, the correct orientation of a cubic closest packing may not be immediately obvious. On the other hand, the correct packing of octahedra and tetrahedra, each of which visibly displays cubic symmetry, simplifies the visualization considerably. This is so because the two different kinds of polyhedra form interpenetrating layers along the 4-fold axis, whereas the spheres first must be packed along a 3-fold axis and then reoriented according to the scheme shown in Fig. 14.

The sequence of polyhedral layers in a cubic closest packing is shown in an exploded view in Fig. 25. For convenience in visualization, this view shows successive layers normal to [100], not [111], which is the actual stacking direction of the closest-packed layers. The layers of tetrahedra lie within one-half of the interpenetrating octahedral layers above and below. When the layers are collapsed, only the octahedra can be seen. Figure 26 shows such a representation of the cubic closest packing. For comparison purposes, an exploded view of a hexagonal closest packing

FIG. 25

is shown in Fig. 27. There are two tetrahedral layers that fit inside two adjacent octahedral layers; the two similar layers in each case are related by a mirror plane lying between the layers.

FIG. 26

FIG. 27

The representation of closest packings by coordination polyhedra is also physically more meaningful. As stated earlier in this chapter, many inorganic compounds have structures in which the nonmetal atoms are arranged in closest packings and the metal atoms occupy specific voids. The coordination polyhedra of the metal atoms can be used, in a manner analogous to the packing schemes shown above, to represent the structure of the compound. This kind of representation was first employed by Pauling, who showed that definite rules governed the packing of such polyhedra. These rules are called Pauling's rules and are discussed in the next chapter.

Suggestions for supplementary reading

N. V. Belov, Struktura ionnich kristallov i metallitcheskich faz (in Russian), *Akad. Nauk S.S.S.R.*, 1947.

Sir Lawrence Bragg, *The crystalline state*, vol. 1, *A general survey* (G. Bell & Sons, Ltd., London, 1949).

M. J. Buerger, *Elementary crystallography* (John Wiley & Sons, Inc., New York, 1956).

C. W. Bunn, *Chemical crystallography* (Oxford University Press, London, 1945).

Linus Pauling, *The nature of the chemical bond*, 2d ed. (Cornell University Press, Ithaca, N.Y., 1948).

Exercises

1. Derive the equipoints of the following plane groups:

(a) $p2$ and $p6$.
(b) pmm and pgg.
(c) cg and $p4m$.

2. Derive the equipoints of the following space groups:

(a) $P\bar{3}m1$.
(b) $P\bar{3}1m$.
(c) $P4bm$.

3. Using the absolute coordinates of the example structure given in (1) in the text, calculate the two different kinds of interatomic distances that exist between the B atoms in this structure. What would the relative lengths of a, b, and c have to be if the $B - B$ distances are to be equal? Is this compatible with space group $P\bar{4}m2$? Qualify your answer.

4. Calculate the interatomic distances between zinc atoms in a crystal of zinc. The crystal structure of zinc is a slightly distorted hexagonal closest packing with $c = 4.945$ Å and $a = 2.664$ Å. (There are two atoms in the hexagonal unit cell at 000 and $\frac{1}{3} \frac{2}{3} \frac{1}{2}$.)

5. Making use of the Bragg law, determine the angles at which the (111), (200), and (220) planes of a nickel crystal will diffract x-rays of wavelength $\lambda = 1.54$ Å. Nickel has a face-centered cubic lattice with $a = 3.52$ Å.

6. Calculate the structure factors for reflections from the (100), (110), (111), (200), and (311) planes of a cubic crystal, assuming that one atom occupies each lattice point of

(a) A primitive cubic cell.
(b) A body-centered cubic cell.
(c) A face-centered cubic cell.

As can be seen, certain reflections are zero in (b) and (c). These so-called *systematic absences* serve as an indication of the lattice type and aid in the determination of the space group of a crystal.

7. The density of $SrCl \cdot 6H_2O$ is 1.93 g/cm³. $SrCl \cdot 6H_2O$ is hexagonal, $a = 7.91$ Å, $c = 4.07$ Å. How many formula weights does one unit cell contain?

8. Carbon crystallizes in two modifications, as diamond (isometric, $a = 3.568$ Å) and graphite (hexagonal, $a = 2.461$ Å, $c = 6.701$ Å). If the density of diamond is 3.51 g/cm³ and of graphite 2.25 g/cm³, how many atoms of carbon does each of the two kinds of cells contain?

9. Cuprite, Cu_2O, is isometric, $a = 4.26$ Å, and its density is 6.0 g/cm³. The symmetry determined from x-ray diffraction studies is consistent with the following possible space groups: $Pn3$, $P4_23$, $Pn3m$.

(a) How many formula weights does one unit cell of Cu_2O contain?
(b) Determine the correct space group and, hence, the structure of Cu_2O by attempting to distribute the atoms among the equipoints of each of the possible space groups. (Look up the equipoints of each space group in the *International tables for x-ray crystallography.*)

10. Compute the packing efficiency of spheres of the same size arranged on the points of a simple cubic lattice, a body-centered cubic lattice, and a face-centered cubic lattice.

11. Compute the packing efficiency of spheres of the same size arranged on the points of a simple hexagonal lattice and a rhombohedral lattice. Compare these efficiencies with that of a hexagonal closest packing.

12. How does the packing efficiency of spheres of the same size in a hexagonal closest packing compare with that of a cubic closest packing? A four-layer closest packing?

13. Determine the identity period n from the following stacking formulas

(a) ...hcchhccc...
(b) ...hc...
(c) ...hhcc...

by converting these formulas to the ABC designation.

14. Using a procedure similar to that outlined by the relations (22) to (24), determine the maximum radius that a sphere representing an 8-fold coordinated void can have. (*Hint:* Use a cube as the coordination polyhedron.)

15. Using a procedure similar to Exercise 14, determine the maximum radius of a sphere at the center of a coordination polyhedron having the shape of a trigonal prism.

16. Show that the maximum radius that a sphere located at $\frac{1}{2} \frac{1}{2} 0$ in a body-centered cube can have is $0.154R$, where R is the radius of the spheres in the body-centered cubic packing.

17. Show that the maximum radius that a sphere representing a void inside the irregular tetrahedron in a body-centered cubic packing can have is $0.291R$, where R is the radius of the spheres in the body-centered cubic packing.

18. What are the coordinates xyz of a tetrahedral void in a cubic closest packing and a body-centered cubic packing? What are the equipoint ranks of these positions?

19. What are the coordinates xyz of an octahedral void in the two kinds of closest packings? What are their equipoint ranks?

4

Atomic packings in crystals

Atomic theory

Early discoveries. Men have speculated about the structure of matter for thousands of years, yet modern concepts did not start to develop until the beginning of the nineteenth century. In the years 1803 to 1809 Dalton argued that matter was comprised of a large number of very small particles, called atoms, which were held together by mutually attractive forces. He next showed empirically that the proportions in which elements combined to form compounds could be expressed by ratios of small whole numbers. In 1833, Faraday discovered that a dissolved compound can be dissociated by passing an electric current through the solution. He further observed that the material deposited at the two electrodes has masses that are proportional to the combining weights of the dissolved compound. If different solutions are used, certain elements always collect at the positive electrode, whereas others always collect at the negative electrode. This suggests that the atoms are electrically charged and can be classified into positive or negative *ions* accordingly as their electrical charge is positive or negative. Following the convention for designating electric currents, the positive ions are attracted by the negative electrode, or cathode, and are called *cations;* the negative ions are attracted by the positive electrode, or anode, and are called *anions.*

J. J. Thomson's discovery of negatively charged electrons, around 1897, suggested that the electrical charges in atoms are due to the coexistence of positively and negatively charged particles in their makeup. Although the detailed structure of an atom is not fully understood as yet, Sir Ernest Rutherford showed as early as 1911 that the structure of an atom consisted of a positively charged nucleus, having very nearly the mass of the entire atom, surrounded by negatively charged electrons each having a mass approximately equal to $\frac{1}{2000}$ of the mass of the lightest atom, hydrogen. Rutherford pictured the nucleus at the center of a miniature solar system, with the electrons traveling around it as planets travel around the sun.

Concurrently, a wealth of spectroscopic data was accumulating that clearly showed that the radiation emanating from specific atoms always has the same specific energy. Now, according to the laws of classical electrodynamics, an electron in an atom can radiate energy only while its velocity is changing. Since there is no reason, according to classical mechanics, why such a velocity change should not be continuous, it was not possible to reconcile experimental observations of only a limited number of energy values with classical theory. A way out of this dilemma was suggested by Niels Bohr, who in 1913 postulated two conditions concerning the structure of an atom:

1. For each atom, a discrete set of *energy states* exists in which the electrons can move without radiating energy. These states can be identified by a set of integers, the so-called quantum numbers. Although the motion of the electrons is supposed to obey the laws of classical mechanics, the absence of radiation contravenes the laws of classical electrodynamics.

2. Under suitable conditions, an electron can pass from one such state to another. Since the energy of each state is different, such a transition requires that the atom either absorb or emit energy in order to satisfy the fundamental law of conservation of energy.

According to the first condition, the energy states have discrete values; that is, they are *quantized*. Consequently, the energy that is absorbed or emitted must be quantized also. If the frequency of the emitted radiation is designed ν, then according to Planck's radiation law this energy is $h\nu$, where h is Planck's constant and is equal to 6.63×10^{-27} erg-sec. This condition can be written

$$h\nu = E_2 - E_1 \tag{1}$$

where E_2 is the energy of the new state and E_1 is the energy of the previous state of the electron.

Bohr's first condition expresses the restriction of the energy values or *energy states* that an atom can have. Although his calculations have been supplanted by more recent, but more intricate, calculations based on so-called *quantum mechanics* described in Chapter 9, they are so simple that it is worth considering them here. The electron's orbit can be represented by a thin cylindrical ring having the mass of the electron m. If the ring's radius is r then its moment of inertia is $I = mr^2$ and the angular momentum is $I\omega = mr^2\omega$. Quantitatively, Bohr found that an electron can travel in any orbit provided that the electron's angular momentum is equal to an integral multiple of $h/2\pi$.

$$I\omega = mr^2\omega = \frac{nh}{2\pi} \qquad n = 1, 2, 3, \ldots \qquad (2)$$

It follows from (2) that the angular velocity ω is given by

$$\omega = \frac{nh}{2\pi mr^2}. \qquad (3)$$

The electron is maintained in its orbit of radius r by a balance between the electrostatic attractive force of the nucleus Ze^2/r^2 (Ze is the nuclear charge, $-e$ is the electronic charge, and r their separation) and the centrifugal force $m\omega^2 r$. This requires that

$$m\omega^2 r = \frac{Ze^2}{r^2} \qquad (4)$$

from which it follows that

$$\omega = \left(\frac{Ze^2}{mr^3}\right)^{\frac{1}{2}}. \qquad (5)$$

By equating the squares of equations (3) and (5),

$$\omega^2 = \frac{n^2 h^2}{4\pi^2 m^2 r^4} = \frac{Ze^2}{mr^3}$$

and it is possible to determine the radius of the nth orbit:

$$r_n = \frac{n^2 h^2}{4\pi^2 m Z e^2}. \qquad (6)$$

Similarly, it is possible to calculate the energy corresponding to the nth orbit. The potential energy V for an electrostatic force field is

$$V = -\frac{Ze^2}{r}$$
$$= -\frac{4\pi^2 m Z^2 e^4}{n^2 h^2}, \qquad (7)$$

assuming that V goes to zero when the electron is at infinity. The kinetic energy is

$$KE = \tfrac{1}{2}mv^2$$
$$= \tfrac{1}{2}m\omega^2 r^2$$
$$= \frac{2\pi^2 m Z^2 e^4}{n^2 h^2}. \qquad (8)$$

Finally, the total energy of an electron in the nth orbit is

$$E_n = V + \text{KE}$$
$$= - \frac{2\pi^2 mZ^2 e^4}{n^2 h^2}. \tag{9}$$

Spherical atoms. According to modern theories discussed in Chapter 9, there is an inherent uncertainty about the whereabouts of a specific electron. It is nevertheless possible to give a statistically accurate picture of the structure of an atom. The nucleus of an atom is a small positively charged sphere whose diameter is of the order of magnitude of 10^{-13} cm and whose mass is of the order of magnitude of 10^{-24} g. The charge of the nucleus is Z times the charge of one electron, $e = 4.80 \times 10^{-10}$ esu, and Z is the atomic number used to classify the elements.† In an electrically neutral atom, therefore, Z electrons surround the nucleus. Although, as already noted, the exact location of an electron cannot be specified, their most probable locations form concentric spherical shells having the nucleus at their common center. The shells are frequently designated by the letters K, L, M, N, etc., in order of increasing radius. According to the Bohr postulates, the energies of the electrons occupying different shells differ by discrete amounts. According to quantum mechanics, developed later, only a specified number of electrons can populate any given shell.

The above arrangement is only slightly affected if the atom is not electrically neutral. For example, an atom can lose one or more electrons, becoming positively charged. The electrons that are most easily removed lie in the outermost shell of the atom. Such electrons are called outer electrons or, more usually, *valence electrons.* The energy required to remove one valence electron from a neutral atom is called its *first ionization potential;* the energy required to remove the second valence electron is called the *second ionization potential,* and so on. The resulting positive ion has a higher energy than the neutral atom and is said to have a valence of $+1, +2$, etc.

On the other hand, one or more electrons can attach themselves to an atom. In this case the atom becomes negatively charged, and the resulting ion is said to have a valence of $-1, -2$, etc. Whereas most positive ions are stable, unless brought in the vicinity of other electrons with the aid of which they can neutralize their electrical charge, most negative

---

† The chemical properties of an element depend on its atomic number, not on its weight. It is possible that nuclei having the same atomic number differ in their atomic weights. Such atoms are called *isotopes* and with few exceptions, notably hydrogen, have very similar properties. Although many isotopes occur in nature, their similarity to the regular elements allows one to disregard them in most discussions of the structure of solids.

ions are unstable, the negatively charged ion tending to repel the negatively charged electron. There are some exceptions to this, however,
notably the halogens, oxygen, and sulfur. These elements actually lose
energy on becoming negatively charged. The energy difference between
the energy state of a neutral atom and the energy state of a negative ion
is called *electron affinity* and is used as a measure of the *electronegativity*
of an atom. Similarly, the ease with which an atom gives up its valence
electrons determines how *electropositive* it is.

The loss or gain of one or more electrons does not greatly affect the
spherical shape of an atom. To be sure, if an atom loses electrons, the
positively charged nucleus tends to draw in the remaining electrons more

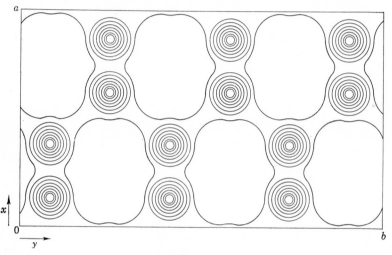

Fig. 1

tightly. Conversely, if an atom adds on electrons, the repulsive forces
tend to push the outer electrons farther away. This, however, generally
affects the size and not the shape of an atom. Experimental proof that
atoms are nearly spherical is given by the results of x-ray diffraction
investigations of crystal structures. Because x-rays are scattered by
the electrons in each atom, it is possible to synthesize a picture of the
electron distribution or *electron density* directly from the experimentally
determined intensities, after their relative phases have been determined.
Such a synthesis is shown in Fig. 1, which is a plot of the electron density
of cubanite, Cu_2FeS_3, projected on the xy plane. The contours in Fig. 1
join points having the same electron-density values. Such structure
studies are obviously useful in determining the *effective radii* of the spherical atoms. These radii are deduced from distances separating two atoms
and may vary from structure to structure according to the variation in
the coordination number of the atoms and other factors discussed below.

Atomic radii. When two oppositely charged ions are brought together they are at first attracted by electrostatic or Coulomb attraction. As the atoms come closer, however, their respective electrons, being negatively charged, repel each other. At some interatomic distance, therefore, one can expect an equilibrium to occur between the forces attracting the two ions and the forces repelling them. When more atoms are added other considerations enter. Since the ions are spherical, the distribution of their charge is spherically symmetrical also. As more ions are added, therefore, an ion tends to neutralize its charge by surrounding itself with the maximum number of oppositely charged ions possible. The surrounding atoms, however, have the same charge and tend to repel each other. Again, an equilibrium between opposing forces must occur when the different ions are separated by distances at which the attractive and repulsive forces just cancel. It follows from the above discussion that the effective size of an ion will depend on the number and kinds of atoms surrounding it.

It has been assumed above that the structure of matter consists of oppositely charged ions held together by electrostatic forces. Actually this is true of compounds composed of atoms that are strongly electronegative and electropositive. It is possible, however, to form compounds from other kinds of atoms also. The cohesion of these compounds is not based on simple electrostatic forces alone, however, and their detailed discussion is postponed until later. Those compounds whose atoms are joined primarily by electrostatic forces are said to be *ionic* in character.

The methods of x-ray diffraction, and more recently electron and neutron diffraction, are capable of disclosing the actual positions of atoms in crystals. The interatomic distances in such crystals can, therefore, be determined with fairly high precision. On the other hand, the assignation of specific radii to each of the atoms is more difficult. The procedure usually used consists of first determining the radius of a particular atom and then using this radius to deduce the radii of adjoining atoms. Several procedures have been employed for deducing the radius of the first kind of atom. Bragg started by halving the 0-0 distance in silicates. Similarly, Landé assumed that the halogen atoms in lithium halides were in contact with each other and deduced their radii by halving the interhalogen separations. Using still another procedure, Wasastjerna divided the interionic distances in alkaline-earth halides according to their respective molar refractivities. The radii thus deduced are fairly accurate for the atoms within a single compound. When use is made of an atomic radius determined in one compound to deduce the radii of different atoms in other compounds, certain difficulties occur. The size of an atom is affected by its coordination number. It is also affected by the type of forces existing between the atoms, and these forces may differ in unlike compounds or even different structural arrangements of the same compound. It is important, therefore, to realize that absolute values of atomic radii are only approximately known. Furthermore, the same atom can have several different radii according to its coordination number and the type of compound in which it occurs. Tables of atomic radii are given in Appendix 3.

Pauling has proposed a set of ionic radii that can be used, after making simple corrections, to yield interatomic distances directly by addition. These radii are based on semi-empirical calculations using experimental values of interionic distances in NaF, KCl, RbBr, CsI, and Li_2O. The radii of the cations, Li^{+1}, Na^{+1}, K^{+1}, Rb^{+1}, and Cs^{+1}, are first deduced by assuming that the anion-cation packing is such that all the ions are in contact with each other. The radius of an atom, r, depends on the most probable distance for the outer, valence, electrons and is given by

$$r \sim \frac{1}{Z_{eff}} \tag{10}$$

where Z_{eff} is the *effective* charge of the nucleus. This effective nuclear charge is equal to the actual charge Ze minus the screening effect Se of the electrons in the inner shells. Equation (10) can, therefore, be written

$$r = \frac{k}{Z - S} \tag{11}$$

where k is a constant determined by the number of valence electrons present. Pauling determined the value of S for the five ions listed above and used equation (11) to calculate the radii of other ions having the same inner electron structure. These radii, therefore, are referred to an ion having unit valence and are called *univalent radii*. To convert these radii to *crystal radii* whose sums yield interatomic distances directly, it is necessary to multiply them by a readily determinable factor which depends on the particular crystal structure and its physical properties. It should be remembered that this procedure can be used only for ions having identical inner electron structures. Such ions are said to form an *isoelectronic* series.

More recently, Ahrens has shown that ionic radii are related to their ionization potentials. This is not surprising because an ionization potential is related to the force binding a valence electron to the nucleus. Since this force is affected by the screening constant S, it follows that ionization potentials can be used similarly to the procedures described above to determine ionic radii. In fact, Ahrens has shown that it is possible to deduce ionic radii hitherto unknown by such a procedure.

Rules governing the packing of atoms

Effect of the radius ratio. Having established above that atoms have spherical shapes, it is natural to apply the rules governing the packing of spheres to the packing of spherical atoms. According to the discussion in Chapter 3, the coordination number of an atom, frequently abbreviated to CN, depends on the relation of its size to that of the coordinating atoms. This statement can equally well be inverted: *The size of the central atom is limited by the size and number of the coordinating atoms.* The ratio of the size of the central atom to the size of the coordinating atoms can be expressed by the ratio of their respective radii. This is the so-called *radius ratio.*

The coordination numbers of cations most frequently encountered in actual structures are 3, 4, 6, 8, and 12. Of these, 4 and 6 are most common in structures having anions in closest packing, and either 4, 6, or 8 occurs in almost all close-packed structures. Three is the coordination number of atoms forming planar complexes, and 12 is the coordination number of like atoms in closest packings. With the exception of CN = 3, the radius ratios for these

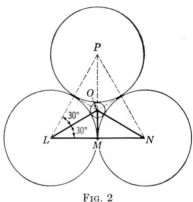

Fig. 2

coordination numbers have already been derived in Chapter 3. The 3-fold coordination of an atom is shown in Fig. 2. Let r be the radius of the central sphere and R the radius of the coordinating spheres. From the construction in Fig. 2,

$$\frac{LM}{LO} = \frac{R}{R + r} = \cos 30°. \tag{12}$$

Rearranging the terms in (12),

$$r = \frac{R}{\cos 30°} - R$$
$$= 0.155R. \tag{13}$$

The coordination number of an atom obviously imposes a limitation on the radius ratio. Conversely, the relative sizes of atoms present in a crystal impose limitations on the coordinations that they can have in real structures. Consequently, it is possible to determine the limiting conditions under which a given coordination number is possible. For example, consider the compound AB composed of equal amounts of A

atoms and B atoms whose sizes are given by r_A and r_B, respectively. Since the number of each type of atom present is the same, the coordinations that the two kinds of atoms can have must be the same also, namely, 1:1, 2:2, 3:3, 4:4, etc. The coordinations 1:1 and 2:2 impose no limitations since the atoms can have any relative size whatever and still have 1-fold or 2-fold coordination. The case 3:3 is no longer trivial, however. According to equation (13), r_A/r_B must be at least 0.155 if the A atom is to touch the three B atoms coordinating it. Similarly, $r_B/r_A \geq 0.155$ if atom B is to touch the three A atoms coordinating it. Thus the value that the radius ratio can have lies in the range 0.155 to 1/0.155. Identical arguments apply to the other coordination numbers

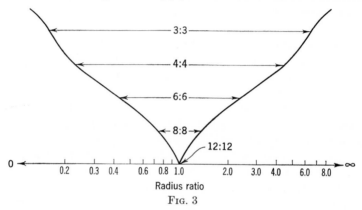

FIG. 3

also. The permissible ranges of the radius ratio in AB compounds for coordination numbers most frequently encountered are given in Table 1. A graphical representation of these ranges is given in Fig. 3.

The possible coordination numbers are directly related to the chemical formula of the compound. Consider a compound composed of only two

Table 1

Radius-ratio limits in AB compounds for different coordination numbers

Coordination number	A's requirements from A's point of view (r_A/r_B)	B's requirements from B's point of view (r_B/r_A)	B's requirements from A's point of view (r_A/r_B)	Radius-ratio limits
1:1	0–∞	0–∞	∞–0	0–∞–0
2:2	0–∞	0–∞	∞–0	0–∞–0
3:3	0.155–∞	0.155–∞	∞–0.155	0.155–1/0.155
4:4	0.225–∞	0.225–∞	∞–0.225	0.225–1/0.225
6:6	0.414–∞	0.414–∞	∞–0.414	0.414–1/0.414
8:8	0.732–∞	0.732–∞	∞–0.732	0.732–1/0.732
12:12	1.0	1.0	1.0	1.0

kinds of atoms, A and B. Let A be surrounded by a atoms B, and let B be surrounded by b atoms A. Then, for every atom A in this compound there must be a atoms B. Similarly, for every B atom present, there must be b atoms A. The chemical composition, therefore, is $A_b B_a$. This is an example of the *rule for ratios of coordination numbers*.

$$\frac{\text{CN of } A}{\text{CN of } B} = \frac{a}{b}. \tag{14}$$

According to this rule, the coordinations possible for AB_2 compounds are $2:1, 4:2, 6:3, \ldots$, and for $A_2 B_3$ compounds $3:2, 6:4, \ldots$, and so on.

Pauling's rules. The above described relations between ionic sizes and the coordination numbers of ions are actually found to hold in structures of many compounds occurring in nature. Thus certain cation-anion combinations always form similar arrangements which persist with little change from one compound to another. It is meaningful, therefore, to think of many such compounds as being composed of coordination polyhedra of anions surrounding a cation at their center. For example, the largest single group of naturally occurring compounds, namely, silicates, have structures that are based on packing arrangements of SiO_4 tetrahedra, as described in Chapter 15. Based on the observation of such packing arrangements, Pauling postulated a set of rules that determine the nature of possible arrangements. Although these rules apply strictly only to ionic compounds, to a large extent they are applicable to other compounds also with very little modification. Notable exceptions are pure metals and organic compounds. *Pauling's rules are as follows:*

Rule 1. A coordination polyhedron of anions is formed about each cation. The cation-anion distance is determined by the sum of the respective radii, and the coordination number is determined by the radius ratio.

Rule 2. In a stable structure, the total strength of the valency bonds that reach an anion in a coordination polyhedron, from all neighboring cations, is equal to the total charge of the anion.

Rule 3. The polyhedra in a structure tend not to share edges, and in particular not faces, common to two polyhedra. If edges are shared, the shared edges are shortened.

Rule 4. Since sharing of polyhedron elements decreases the stability of a structure, cations with high valency and small coordination numbers tend not to share polyhedron elements with each other.

Rule 5. The number of essentially different kinds of atoms in a structure tends to be small. This is the so-called rule of parsimony.

Applications of Pauling's rules to actual structures. The meaning of the above rules can be best understood by considering their application to ionic structures. In fact, it is possible to gauge the ionic nature of a structure by the extent to which Pauling's rules are satisfied. Rule 1 is simply a concise statement of the radius-ratio effect already discussed. Rule 2 can be paraphrased as follows: In a stable structure, local charge neutrality must be maintained. Thus, if an anion forms a common corner for two or more polyhedra, the sum of the electrostatic bonds connecting it to the surrounding cations must be equal to the charge of the anion.

Let z be the valence and ze the charge of a cation in a polyhedron. Then, the *electrostatic bond* that it forms with each anion in its coordination polyhedron is

$$Se = \frac{ze}{CN} \tag{15}$$

where S is defined as the *strength of the electrostatic bond*,

$$S = \frac{z}{CN}. \tag{16}$$

Now, if an anion is surrounded by j cations and if the strength of the bond joining it to the ith cation is S_i, then the sum of the strengths of the bonds reaching it is

$$\zeta = \sum_{i=1}^{j} S_i. \tag{17}$$

In order to preserve charge neutrality, $-\zeta e$ must be equal to the electric charge of the anion.

As an illustration, consider the compound $MgAl_2O_4$. Each magnesium atom has $z = +2$ and is tetrahedrally coordinated by four oxygen atoms.

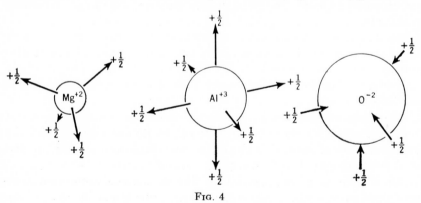

Fɪɢ. 4

According to equation (16) it forms four electrostatic bonds of strength

$$S_{Mg} = \frac{+2}{4} = +\frac{1}{2}. \tag{18}$$

Each aluminum atom, $z = +3$, is octahedrally coordinated. The strength of each of the six bonds it forms is

$$S_{Al} = \frac{+3}{6} = +\frac{1}{2}. \tag{19}$$

Since each oxygen ion, $z = -2$, receives four bonds like (18) or (19),

$$\zeta = \tfrac{1}{2} + \tfrac{1}{2} + \tfrac{1}{2} + \tfrac{1}{2} = +2 \tag{20}$$

and charge neutrality is preserved. This analysis is diagrammatically represented in Fig. 4.

Rules 3 and 4 can be considered jointly. The reason that cations tend not to share polyhedron elements can be seen in Fig. 5, which shows two

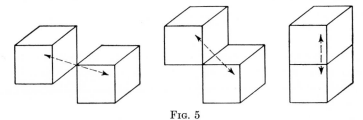

Fɪɢ. 5

units cubes sharing a corner, an edge, and a face. The distance separating the two positively charged cations at the centers of the cubes successively decreases from $\sqrt{3}$ to $\sqrt{2}$ to 1. Since the two positively charged cations repel each other, they naturally tend to be as far apart as possible. The higher the charge on the cation and the smaller its coordination number, the greater this tendency becomes. Generally, tetrahedra can share only corners; octahedra can share corners and edges; and cubes can share corners, edges, and faces, although the number of structures in which cubes share faces is small, because the cubic coordination is not very stable in itself. The sharing of corners by tetrahedra and edges by octahedra has already been encountered in Figs. 24, 25, and 26 of Chapter 3.

It logically follows from the above that, if an edge is shared, the mutual repulsion of the two cations will shorten the shared edge. This is diagrammatically illustrated in Fig. 6 for two octahedra sharing an edge. A typical example of such sharing in nature is given by the structure of rutile, a stable modification of TiO_2. The oxygen octahedra coordinating Ti^{+4} form rows in which opposite edges are shared, and the shared edges are shortened. An alternative arrangement of TiO_2 octahedra results in the modification called anatase. In this structure the octahedra share two adjacent edges, and this structure is, therefore, less stable than the rutile structure.

Complex ions. Sometimes the same coordination polyhedra are found to occur in different structures. The example of silica tetrahedra has already been mentioned. If the forces that join the ions within such a polyhedron are greater than the forces joining the polyhedra to each other or to other atoms, such polyhedra are called *complex ions*. Another way of defining a complex ion is as a group of atoms joined by forces greater than those tending to pull the group apart. The complex-forming forces may be ionic or one of the other types of forces discussed in a later chapter. The distinguishing characteristic of complex ions is that their

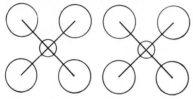 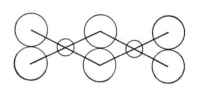

Fig. 6

packing in structures is entirely analogous to the packing of ordinary ions. Some of the more common complex ions and their configurations are given in Table 2.

Table 2
Possible polyhedra of complex ions

Polyhedron	CN	Examples
Triangle	3	BO_3^{-3}, CO_3^{-2}, NO_3^{-1}
Tetrahedron	4	AlO_4^{-5}, SiO_4^{-4}, PO_4^{-3}, SO_4^{-2}, ClO_4^{-1}
Square	4	$Ni(CN)_4^{-2}$, PdO_4^{-2}, $PtCl_4^{-2}$
Octahedron	6	NaO_6^{-5}, MgO_6^{-4}, AlO_6^{-3}, TiO_6^{-2}

Variations in atomic packings

General considerations. Having discussed some of the rules for packing atoms in crystals, it is reasonable to inquire at this time: What are the ways in which a collection of atoms can combine in an actual structure? To get an insight into the answer to this question, consider a simple compound composed of equal amounts of two kinds of atoms, say NaCl. The coordination numbers of the two kinds of atoms are determined by their radius ratio. According to the radii listed in

Appendix 3, $r_{Na}/r_{Cl} = 0.525$, so that according to Table 1 the coordination numbers of the ions are 6:6; that is, each sodium ion is octahedrally coordinated by six chlorine ions and each chlorine is similarly coordinated by six sodium ions. In considering the possible ways of packing these octahedra it is convenient to consider octahedra like Fig. 21 in Chapter 3, with sodium at their centers. It is fairly easy to show that the *only* way that such octahedra can be packed is according to the cubic closest packing shown in Fig. 25 of the previous chapter. An attempt to form the hexagonal closest packing leads to the sharing of faces by adjacent octahedra, in direct violation of Pauling's rules. Thus, unless the coordination numbers of Na and Cl are changed by some means, the only stable structure that NaCl can assume is that of a cubic closest packing of the larger chlorine ions with the sodium ions occupying all the octahedral voids. This structure is shown in Fig. 7.

Fig. 7. Halite, NaCl.

As another example of the possible ways of packing an *AB* compound, consider zinc sulfide. The radius ratio of zinc and sulfur, from Appendix 3, is $r_{Zn}/r_S = 0.402$ which, according to Table 1, means that zinc and sulfur are tetrahedrally coordinated, 4:4. Now, the question becomes:

Fig. 8

How can these tetrahedra be arranged in space, remembering that Pauling's rules require that corners only be shared?

A single layer of tetrahedra is shown in Fig. 8. Let this be a representation of zinc tetrahedra; that is, picture the zinc atoms at the centers and sulfur atoms at the corners of tetrahedra like the one shown in Fig. 19 of Chapter 3. Then, at each corner where three tetrahedra meet, a sulfur atom has three tetrahedrally disposed zinc neighbors. The above question, therefore, now becomes: How can such layers be stacked so that four tetrahedra share each corner and each corner atom has tetrahedral coordination? The two simplest ways that this can be done are shown in Figs. 9 and 10. It is easy to see that Fig. 9 shows the stacking of three tetrahedral layers in a cubic closest packing, and Fig. 10 shows the two-layer or hexagonal closest packing. This analysis could have been carried out equally well by starting with a cubic or hexagonal closest packing of the larger sulfur atoms. In order to satisfy the rule for ratios of coordination numbers, 4:4, only one-half of the tetrahedral voids

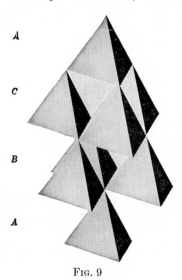

A

C

B

A

Fig. 9

between two closest-packed layers can be occupied. The stacking of such layers then obeys the rules developed in Chapter 3. The cubic closest packing is shown in Fig. 11. The reason that these two different kinds of structures are possible is that the larger atoms can pack in either of two closest packings. Thus, any *AB* compound having tetrahedral coordination can, in principle, assume either of these two forms, accordingly as to which closest packing the larger spheres assume. Such different structural arrangements of the same kind and number of atoms are called *polymorphs* or *polymorphic modifications* of a compound.

Polymorphism. The two possible polymorphs of ZnS shown in Figs. 9 and 10 are actually found in nature. The hexagonal polymorph is the mineral wurtzite, and the cubic one is called sphalerite or zinc blende. According to the rules of forming closest packings described in Chapter 3, other polymorphous modifications of ZnS should be possible also. Although some synthetic polymorphs of ZnS having larger stacking periods have been reported, none has been found to occur in nature. This does not mean that other polymorphic modifications do not, or cannot, occur but only that these other polymorphs are not as stable at

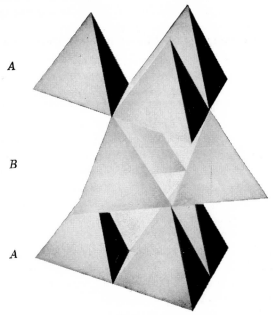

F‎IG. 10

ordinary pressures and temperatures. Any attempt to determine the most stable polymorphic form by direct calculation is futile because the errors introduced in such calculations are of the same order of magnitude as the differences sought. It is thus not possible to predict what the polymorphism of a particular compound will be. The relative thermodynamic stabilities of polymorphs are discussed in Chapter 8.

F‎IG. 11.   Sphalerite or zinc blende form of ZnS.

Isomorphism. It is possible that two or more compounds can assume the same structural arrangement. If two compounds have the same crystal structure but different chemical compositions, they are said to be *isostructural* or *isotypic*. If their structures are the same and their chemical compositions are similar, but not identical, so that they can form composite crystals called *solid solutions*, then they are said to be *isomorphous*.† For example, NiO, CoO, and PbS all have the structural arrangement shown in Fig. 7. The two oxides form solid solutions with each other but not with lead sulfide. Therefore NiO and CoO are isomorphous with each other but both are isotypic with PbS.

In forming solid solutions, the metal atoms of the two isomorphs usually distribute themselves randomly among the specified voids in the anion close packing. The replacement of the ions of one crystal by corresponding ions of the other can be likened to the solution of one crystal in the other, hence the name solid solution. If the two vicarious cations are dimensionally alike and have similar properties, then they are completely miscible; for example, NiO and CoO can be combined in any ratio of Ni to Co. On the other hand, KCl and NaCl are isomorphous, but the difference in the atomic size of K and Na prevents more than a small fraction of potassium atoms from entering the NaCl structure.

Solid solutions. Although it was not intended to apply to solid solutions, it can be said that solid solutions violate Dalton's law of subscripts of small whole numbers in chemical formulas. Nevertheless, solid solutions are very common among structurally related compounds. Minerals are notable examples because their structures usually consist of closest-packed anions containing cations in their interstices. Since the melts from which some minerals form contain a large variety of metal constituents, it is quite common to find nonstoichiometric ratios of metal ions in mineral crystals. The similarity between the structures and the properties of metals accounts for the ease of formation of metallic solid solutions. In fact, most metals used in industry are solid solutions.

There are several ways in which solid solutions can form. Accordingly, they are classified into the following:

1. *Substitutional solid solution* in which vicarious replacement of one atom for another takes place. Goldschmidt observed that substitutional solid solutions can occur only if the radius of the larger atom does not exceed the radius of the smaller atom by more than 15 per cent. Some of the other criteria for this type of solid solution are discussed for metals in Chapter 11.

---

† Strictly speaking, the term *isomorphous* means similar crystal forms (morphology). When two elements can substitute for each other in a crystal structure, they are best called *vicarious* elements.

2. *Interstitial solid solution* in which limited amounts of solute atoms occupy interstitial positions in the solvent crystal. For example, sphalerite can accommodate relatively large amounts of interstitial atoms because of its "open" structure. Similarly, certain metals can accommodate carbon atoms interstitially to form carbides, or nitrogen to form nitrides, and so on.

3. *Omission solid solution* in which the number of anions (or cations) is slightly less than that required by stoichiometry. This type of solid solution can occur only if the remaining cations can adjust their valencies to preserve charge neutrality. For example, transition-metal oxides can lose oxygen in small amounts without altering their structures. The name *defect structures* has been proposed to describe such crystals.

The three types of solid solutions can be readily distinguished if their composition and unit cell size are known. The density of a crystal can be computed for a given composition and cell size. It is possible, therefore, to prepare a graph showing the variation in density with change in composition, as shown in Fig. 12. Curve I illustrates what happens in the case of interstitial solid solution; as more atoms fill the interstices the density increases, so that the curve has a positive slope. The density change in a substitutional solid solution is shown by the other straight line (Curve II) having a positive slope, for the case in which the solute atom is heavier than the atom for which it substitutes. Finally, Curve III, calculated for an omission solid solution, has a negative slope because atoms are being removed from the crystal.

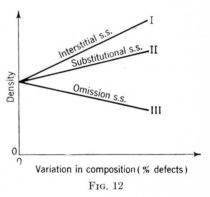

Fig. 12

Having prepared such a graph, it is possible to determine which type of solid solution exists in a crystal by measuring its density and noting on which of the three curves the measured density value falls.

Derivative structures. When a transition from one polymorphic modification to another takes place, the two polymorphic modifications have certain symmetry operations in common. Similarly, when two isomorphs form a solid solution, the symmetry of the resulting structure is related to that of either isomorph. The relationships between one crystal structure and another derived from it have been discussed by Buerger who proposed that the latter be called a *derivative structure*. The original structure is then called the *basic structure*. A derivative structure can be obtained by suppressing one or more symmetry operations in the basic structure or by suppressing a translation in the basic structure. Combinations of these two cases are possible also.

There are basically two mechanisms whereby a derivative structure can occur in nature. In one, the structure is distorted during a polymorphic transformation, as discussed further in Chapter 8. In the other, one or more different kinds of atoms are substituted for a specific kind of atom in the basic structure. These so-called *substitution* structures include the solid solutions already discussed and are frequently encountered in nature. As an example of a substitution structure that is not a solid solution, consider the basic structure of sphalerite (Fig. 11) and two of its possible derivative structures, chalcopyrite and stannite.

$$
\begin{array}{lll}
\text{Basic structure, } \textit{sphalerite} & \left|\ \text{Zn}\ \right|\ \text{S} & (Fm3m). \\[2ex]
\text{Substitution structure, } \textit{chalcopyrite} & \left|\ \begin{array}{c} \text{Cu}_{\frac{1}{2}} \\ \text{Fe}_{\frac{1}{2}} \end{array}\right|\ \text{S} & (I\bar{4}2d). \qquad (21) \\[3ex]
\text{Substitution structure, } \textit{stannite} & \left|\ \begin{array}{c} \text{Cu}_{\frac{1}{2}} \\ \text{Fe}_{\frac{1}{4}} \\ \text{Sn}_{\frac{1}{4}} \end{array}\right|\ \text{S} & (I\bar{4}2m).
\end{array}
$$

The two derivative structures in (21) are compared with two unit cells of the basic structure, sphalerite, in Fig. 13.

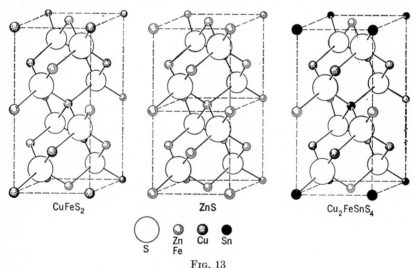

CuFeS$_2$ ZnS   Cu$_2$FeSnS$_4$

S Zn Cu Sn
   Fe

Fig. 13

Suggestions for supplementary reading

L. H. Ahrens, The use of ionization potentials, Part 1. Ionic radii of the elements, *Geochim. et Cosmochim. Acta*, vol. 2 (1952), pp. 155–169.

M. J. Buerger, Derivative crystal structures, *J. Chem. Phys.*, vol. 15 (1947), pp. 1–16.

R. C. Evans, *An introduction to crystal chemistry* (Cambridge University Press, London, 1939).

Linus Pauling, *The nature of the chemical bond*, 2d ed. (Cornell University Press, Ithaca, N.Y., 1948).

O. K. Rice, *Electronic structure and chemical binding* (McGraw-Hill Book Company, Inc., New York, 1940).

A. F. Wells, *Structural inorganic chemistry*, 2d ed. (Clarendon Press, Oxford, 1950).

Exercises

1. Calculate the radii of circular electron orbits in the ground state ($n = 1$) and the first excited state ($n = 2$) of hydrogen.

2. The relation between linear velocity and angular velocity is $v = \omega r$. Calculate the linear velocity of an electron in the ground state of hydrogen, assuming circular orbits.

3. Calculate the potential energies of the ground state and the first two excited states of hydrogen.

4. Suggest possible reasons why fluorine is more electronegative than chlorine.

5. Suggest possible reasons why fluorine is more electronegative than oxygen.

6. What is the coordination number of manganese in MnO if $r_{Mn} = 0.80$ Å and $r_O = 1.40$ Å?

7. What is the coordination number of iron in Fe_2O_3 if $r_{Fe} = 0.64$ Å and $r_O = 1.40$ Å?

8. What are the permissible ranges of the radius ratio in AB_2 compounds? Prepare a table similar to Table 1 in the text.

9. Prepare a graph like Fig. 3, showing the permissible ranges of the radius ratio for AB_3 compounds.

10. Illustrate, by means of a drawing like Fig. 4, the ionic bond strengths between all the atoms in the following compounds:

(a) $MgSiO_3$ (Mg^{+2} has 6-coordination, Si^{+4} has 4-coordination).

(b) Na_3AlF_6 (Na^{+1} and Al^{+3} have 6-coordination).

(c) $ZnFe_2O_4$ (Zn^{+2} has 4-coordination, Fe^{+3} has 6-coordination).

11. Can CsCl and NaCl form solid solutions? Explain.

12. The most stable manganese ion is Mn^{+2}. Would you expect to be able to dissolve any manganese in PbO? In PbO_2? Explain.

13. Zinc oxide is hexagonal, $a = 3.243$ Å, $c = 5.195$ Å, and it contains two formula weights in a unit cell. If the measured densities of two ZnO crystals are 5.470 and 5.606 g/cm³, determine which type of solid solution has occurred in each case.

14. Consider the plane group $p4m$. Show the derivative structures that can be obtained by suppression of the symmetry elements present, one at a time. (*Hint:* Start by replacing the 4 by a 2, etc.)

5

Imperfections in atomic packings

Types of imperfections

Discovery of imperfections. Laue's discovery of the diffraction of x-rays by crystals and the consequent elucidation of the structures of many solids greatly advanced man's understanding of the properties of solids. It soon became apparent, however, that certain observed properties such as plasticity, electrolytic conductivity, crystal strength, and others could not be explained on the basis of differences in structure alone. Consequently, it became necessary to postulate departures from the *ideally perfect* crystal in which the lattice arrays of atoms persist without flaws in all directions in the crystal. In fact, in order to explain certain aspects of the diffraction of x-rays by crystals, in 1914, C. G. Darwin was forced to postulate that the lattice arrays of atoms in real crystals are not continuous throughout the crystals but are broken up into blocks by discontinuities at the block boundaries. Such an *ideally imperfect* crystal was thought to be like a mosaic in which each part is perfect but tipped slightly, relative to its neighbors; hence the name *mosaic crystal* which has been more recently introduced. Although Darwin's postulate was purely imaginary, it was seized by later investigators to explain many solid-state phenomena. However, only a few of these explanations have survived the test of time. The reason that they failed has been that, even though actual crystals are not perfect, Darwin's ideally imperfect crystal is not an accurate representation of crystals existing in nature.

The present understanding of the nature of the deviations from perfect crystals really began in 1928–1929 when L. Prandtl and U. Dehlinger independently suggested that the mechanical properties of crystals were related to the presence of linear imperfections in such crystals. By 1934, three scientists, G. I. Taylor, E. Orowan, and M. Polanyi, working independently, proposed that linear deviations from true periodicity, now called *dislocations*, were responsible for the relative ease with which most crystals could be deformed by an externally applied stress. Soon thereafter, J. M. Burgers extended these notions, and within a few years a large body of evidence had been gathered, by many investigators, firmly establishing the existence of dislocations in crystals. At about the same time, A. Smekal pointed out that the explanation of such properties as electrolytic conductivity and diffusion required imperfections of a different kind. Although obviously dependent on the actual crystal structure, the motion of atoms through crystals cannot be explained without requiring an atom to leave its normal position in the structure. Such a displacement, therefore, produces an imperfection on an atomic scale as distinct from dislocations which affect large groups of atoms collectively. For example, diffusion experiments carried out at room temperature indicate that less than one atom out of a billion is actually displaced from its proper site at any instant of time.

Classification of imperfections. Before proceeding with the description of the various kinds of imperfections that are believed to exist in crystals, it is worthwhile to consider briefly just what an imperfection is. Ideally, a crystal consists of a perfectly periodic array of atoms whose arrangement conforms to the symmetry of one of the 230 space groups discussed in Chapter 2. The term *imperfection* or *defect* is generally used to describe any deviation from such an orderly array. If the deviation from a periodic arrangement is localized to the vicinity of only several atoms, it is called a *point imperfection* or a *point defect*. On the other hand, if the deviation extends through microscopic regions in the crystal, it is called a *lattice imperfection* because it produces a discontinuity in the lattice used to describe the actual periodicity of an atomic array in a crystal. There are essentially two types of lattice imperfections that can exist in crystals: *line defects*, so called because they propagate as lines in a crystal, and *plane defects* which have an areal extent. In addition to these defects, which are produced by atomic displacements in crystals, it is possible that imperfections can occur on a subatomic scale also. These so-called *electronic imperfections* are primarily necessary to explain electrical conductivity and related phenomena in solids.

Solid solutions provide examples of point imperfections that have been already described. The *interstitial* atoms present in interstitial solid solutions and the *anion vacancies* or *cation vacancies* in omission solid solutions are two types of imperfections usually invoked to explain diffusion and electrolytic conductivity in solids. Ion vacancies are also called *Schottky* defects, after their discoverer, and are presumed to be generated so that there are normally equal numbers of anion and cation

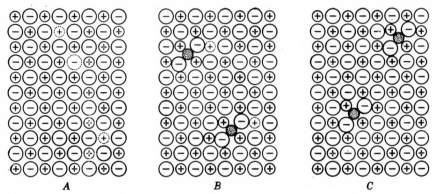

FIG. 1.   Point imperfections in crystals.
A. Schottky defects.
B. Frenkel defects.
C. Interstitials.

vacancies in a crystal.   It is also possible that an interstitial ion and a consequent ion vacancy are produced.   In fact, theoretical calculations indicate that these so-called *Frenkel defects* are more easily formed in certain crystals.   Several different kinds of point defects are pictured in Fig. 1.   Note in this figure that the three types of defects shown occur at a point in the crystal and produce strains nearby but do not affect the perfection of more distant parts of the crystal.   Such imperfections are usually called *point defects* for this reason.   When the density of point defects present in a crystal is relatively large, it is possible that the defects cluster together forming one large imperfection.   For example, a cluster of vacancies in one part of a crystal can form a large void.   It is usually convenient in such a case to think of the larger imperfection as a single entity rather than as a collection of individual point defects.

Another type of imperfection, namely, a *dislocation*, occurs when the periodicity of the atomic lattice array is interrupted along certain directions in a crystal.   For reasons that are discussed in a later section of this chapter, such dislocations occur along rows of the crystal structure and are commonly called *line defects*.   When such line defects cluster together in a plane, they can form a plane unit which is variously described as a *grain boundary*, *mosaic boundary*, or *lineage boundary*.   Similarly to the case of point-defect clusters, it is more convenient to think of these boundaries as separate entities having properties that are different from those of the individual defects composing them.   Plane defects can form in closest packings in still another way.   It is possible for "mistakes" to occur in the stacking sequence of hexagonal closest-packed layers. The plane separating two incorrectly juxtaposed layers is called a *stacking fault*.   The above listing is summarized in Table 1.

Table 1
Possible imperfections in crystals

Type of imperfection		*Description of imperfection*
Point defects:	Interstitial	Extra atom in an interstitial site
	Schottky defect	Atom missing from correct site
	Frenkel defect	Atom displaced to interstitial site creating nearby vacancy
Line defects:	Edge dislocation	Row of atoms marking edge of a crystallographic plane extending only part way in crystal
	Screw dislocation	Row of atoms about which a normal crystallographic plane appears to spiral
Plane defects:	Lineage boundary	Boundary between two adjacent perfect regions in the same crystal that are slightly tilted with respect to each other
	Grain boundary	Boundary between two crystals in a polycrystalline solid
	Stacking fault	Boundary between two parts of a closest packing having alternate stacking sequences.

At all temperatures above absolute zero, the atoms in a crystal are temporarily displaced from their ideal positions in the structure by the absorption of thermal energy. These displacements are relatively small, and interatomic forces obeying Hooke's law tend to restore the atoms to their proper positions. The resulting motion of each atom, therefore, consists of a vibration about a mean position which is the correct position of the atom in the ideal structure. It is most convenient to describe the elastic vibrations of atoms in a crystal by waves having specific wavelengths, frequencies, and velocities of propagation. Using this description, the vibrations of individual atoms can be likened to harmonic oscillators having three normal modes of vibration which, in the simplest case, correspond to one longitudinal mode and two mutually perpendicular transverse modes.

According to quantum mechanics, the energies that such oscillators can have are quantized. Specifically, the discrete energy values that are allowed are given by

$$E_n = (n + \tfrac{1}{2})h\nu \qquad (1)$$

where n = any positive integer including zero
  h = Planck's constant
  ν = mechanical frequency of vibration

The energy change accompanying a transition from one energy state described by the quantum number n_1 to the next highest energy state described by n_2 can then be written

$$E_{n_2} - E_{n_1} = (n_2 + \tfrac{1}{2})h\nu - (n_1 + \tfrac{1}{2})h\nu$$
$$E = (n_2 - n_1)h\nu. \qquad (2)$$

Since n_1 and n_2 can be any two integers differing by unity, the above transition is accompanied by the absorption of one quantum of thermal energy, $h\nu$.   If the transition takes place in the reverse order, that is, from a higher energy state to one of lower energy, a quantum of thermal energy is emitted.   This is entirely analogous to transitions involving the absorption or emission of photons (quanta of electromagnetic energy). Owing to this analogy, the name *phonon* has been proposed for quanta of thermal energy absorbed or emitted by a crystal.   The use of this somewhat artificial description has the great advantage that the results of the studies of interactions of electromagnetic radiation with solids can be transposed directly to yield results concerning the elastic vibrations in solids.

The absorption of phonons by a crystal produces atomic displacements in the crystal.   Hence, phonons can be classified as imperfections. Unlike point and line defects, however, phonons produce atomic displacements that vary with time, giving them a transientlike character.   If the temperature of the crystal's environment is increased, phonons flow into the crystal until the increased atomic vibrations produced thereby raise the crystal's temperature and equilibrium is again attained.   Conversely, decreasing the temperature of the crystal's environment causes the crystal to emit phonons.   As the phonons flow through the crystal they collide with atoms and with each other and are scattered in different directions.   Energy and momentum are conserved in the scattering process; however, the deviations from the original propagation directions caused by the scattering produce a resistance to thermal conductivity. The effect of these and other imperfections on the conductivity in crystals is considered further in later chapters.

In addition to phonon-phonon and phonon-atom interactions, it is also possible for a phonon to interact with the electrons in a crystal. Although the total energy of a phonon is usually much smaller than that of the electron, the energy gained by an electron in such a collision may be sufficient to raise the electron's energy to a higher energy state.   This produces an empty energy state in the crystal which is usually called a *hole*.   The excited electron and the hole are called *electronic imperfections*. Like all the imperfections in a crystal, electronic imperfections can interact with each other or with other imperfections present in the crystal. For example, it is possible for an excited electron and a hole to interact with each other, without completely losing their identity, to form an *exciton*.   Although this type of imperfection is not specifically discussed anywhere in this book, other interactions between electrons and holes are further described in chapters dealing with the electrical properties of solids.

Point defects

Schottky defects. Consider a perfect crystal composed of equal numbers of positively and negatively charged ions. In order for a cation vacancy to occur, a positive ion must somehow migrate out of its proper position in the structure to the crystal's exterior. If only positive ions migrate out of the crystal and collect on its surface, the surface will become positively charged. This positive surface charge opposes the migration of additional positive ions out of the crystal's interior. Simultaneously, the excess negative charge created inside the crystal is conducive to the formation of negative vacancies. In the absence of external forces, therefore, the number of oppositely charged vacancies inside a crystal tends to be equal.

Suppose that the crystal contains a total of N atoms and that n Schottky defects are produced by removing n cations and n anions from the crystal's interior. The different ways in which each kind of ion can be removed is given by

$$\frac{N(N-1)(N-2) \cdots (N-n+1)}{n!} = \frac{N!}{(N-n)!n!}. \tag{3}$$

The different ways in which n Schottky defects can be formed is then obtained by squaring the expression in (3), since the number of cation and anion vacancies are equal. The creation of n Schottky defects increases the crystal's entropy, according to the Boltzmann relation, by an amount

$$S = k \ln \left[\frac{N!}{(N-n)!n!} \right]^2. \tag{4}$$

This in turn produces a change in the Helmholtz free energy†

$$F = E - TS$$
$$= nE_p - kT \ln \left[\frac{N!}{(N-n)!n!} \right]^2 \tag{5}$$

where E_p is the energy required to remove a pair of atoms from the crystal's interior so that nE_p represents the total change in its internal energy.

The logarithmic term in (5) containing factorials can be simplified by using Stirling's formula, $\ln x! \simeq x \ln x - x$, so that

$$\ln \left[\frac{N!}{(N-n)!n!} \right]^2 \simeq 2[\ln N! - \ln (N-n)! - \ln n!]$$
$$= 2[N \ln N - N - (N-n) \ln (N-n)$$
$$+ (N-n) - n \ln n + n]$$
$$= 2[N \ln N - (N-n) \ln (N-n) - n \ln n]. \tag{6}$$

† The reader not familiar with thermodynamics will find a brief description of the relations between energy and entropy in Chapter 7.

When equilibrium is attained at a given temperature T, the Helmholtz free energy is constant and its first derivative is, therefore, equal to zero.

$$\left(\frac{\partial F}{\partial n}\right)_T = 0 = E_p - 2kT[\ln\,(N-n) - \ln n]$$

$$= E_p - 2kT \ln \frac{N-n}{n} \tag{7}$$

where the partial differentiation is with respect to n since the total number of atomic positions in the crystal N is not altered.

Rearranging the terms in (7),

$$E_p = 2kT \ln \frac{N-n}{n} \tag{8}$$

and
$$\frac{N-n}{n} = e^{E_p/2kT}. \tag{9}$$

The number of Schottky defects in a crystal is much smaller than the number of atoms; that is, $n \ll N$ and $N - n \simeq N$. It is possible, there-fore, to use equation (9) to de-termine the approximate num-ber of defects present at any temperature.

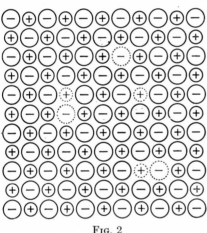

FIG. 2

$$n \simeq N e^{-E_p/2kT}. \tag{10}$$

For example, the energy to remove a pair of oppositely charged ions from a sodium chloride crystal is approximately 2 eV so that the number of Schottky defects pres-ent in NaCl at room temperature is approximately 10^6 defects/cm³. The number of Na^{+1} and Cl^{-1} ions in 1 cm³ of salt is approximately 10^{22} so that, on an average, there is one Schottky defect for each 10^{16} ions. Thus the neglect of n as com-pared with N in going from equation (9) to (10) is fully justified.

After a vacancy is created, it takes relatively little energy for an ion neighboring a vacancy to shift from its proper position to the vacant site. For example, such ionic movement can be produced by interactions with phonons. The resulting migration of ions through the crystal is called *diffusion* and is further discussed in Chapter 12. As shown there, two or more vacancies of opposite sign may come together to form a cluster. Figure 2 shows two kinds of Schottky defects most commonly found in crystals, namely, the individual positive and negative vacancy, presumed to form near each other, and a coupled pair.

Frenkel defects. In a perfect crystal, the energy required to displace an atom from its proper position to an interstitial position is E_i. Then, if there are N atoms in the crystal and N_i interstitial positions in its structure, there are

$$\frac{N!}{(N-n)!n!} \frac{N_i!}{(N_i-n)!n!} \tag{11}$$

ways in which n Frenkel defects can be formed. The change in the Helmholtz free energy produced by the creation of n Frenkel defects is

$$F = nE_i - kT \ln \frac{N!}{(N-n)!n!} \frac{N_i!}{(N_i-n)!n!}. \tag{12}$$

Proceeding as before, the factorial terms are simplified by using Stirling's formula.

$$\begin{aligned}
\ln \frac{N!}{(N-n)!n!} &+ \ln \frac{N_i!}{(N_i-n)!n!} \simeq N \ln N + N_i \ln N_i \\
&- (N-n) \ln (N-n) - (N_i-n) \ln (N_i-n) - 2n \ln n.
\end{aligned} \tag{13}$$

Substituting (13) into (12) and differentiating with respect to n,

$$\left(\frac{\partial F}{\partial n}\right)_T = E_i - kT \ln \frac{(N-n)(N_i-n)}{n^2}. \tag{14}$$

At equilibrium $(\partial F/\partial n)_T = 0$ and since $N \gg n$ and $N_i \gg n$,

$$\begin{aligned}
\frac{E_i}{kT} &\simeq \ln \frac{NN_i}{n^2} \\
&= \ln (NN_i) - 2 \ln n
\end{aligned}$$

which, after rearranging terms, becomes

$$\ln n = \tfrac{1}{2} \ln (NN_i) - \frac{E_i}{2kT}$$

so that

$$n = (NN_i)^{\frac{1}{2}} e^{-E_i/2kT}. \tag{15}$$

On the basis of both experimental evidence and theoretical calculations, it has been established that the predominant defects present in alkali halides are Schottky defects, whereas in silver halides the most prevalent defects below 700°K are Frenkel defects. Usually both kinds of defects are present in all solids; however, there is always a tendency for one type of defect to predominate since their energies of formation are usually unequal. Thus, in metals, it appears that the energy favors the formation of vacancies, although Frenkel defects undoubtedly also are formed. In this connection, it should be noted that interstitial atoms can interact with one another to form atom clusters in the same way that vacancies can combine to form voids. The size of the atom clusters, however, is more severely limited. In certain halides, the metal atoms may cluster together by occupying both the interstitial sites and vacancies to form clusters of colloidal proportions. Such a process is believed to take place in silver bromide grains after they have been exposed to electromagnetic radiation. The latent image formed in a grain of AgBr, contained in a photographic emulsion, consists of clusters of silver ions which are later reduced to metallic silver by the chemical action of the developer. When the suitably processed negative is viewed with visible light, the opaque image seen by the observer is formed by the free silver in the grains.

Disordered crystals. In the lowest energy state of a crystal, the atoms are arranged on the correct equipoints of the ideal structure. This is the atomic array, therefore, adopted by all crystals at very low temperatures. As the temperature increases, however, the Helmholtz free energy may be actually decreased if the atoms are displaced from their proper sites. The higher internal energy state of the crystal is stabilized by an increase in the entropy according to relation (9) and the crystal structure becomes *disordered*. Although the details of order-disorder transformations are discussed further in Chapter 8, it is appropriate to consider the mechanisms of disordering at this time.

Five basically different mechanisms of disordering can be distinguished in a stoichiometrically pure *AB* compound.

1. Displacement of *A* atoms to interstitial sites, leaving an equal number of *A*-type vacancies in the structure

2. Displacement of *B* atoms to interstitial sites, accompanied by the formation of an equal number of *B*-type vacancies

3. Creation of equal numbers of *A*- and *B*-type vacancies by the migration of the atoms to the crystal's surface

4. Creation of equal numbers of interstitial *A* and *B* atoms and *A*- and *B*-type vacancies

5. Interchange of *A* and *B* atoms in the structure so that some of the *A* atoms occupy *B* sites and an equal number of *B* atoms occupy *A* sites

The first two mechanisms lead to the formation of Frenkel defects whereas the third mechanism produces Schottky defects. The fourth mechanism probably never occurs as stated but can occur in combination with either of the first three. The name *antistructure* disorder has been suggested for the fifth mechanism. This type of disorder is rare in ionic crystals because it would bring ions of like charge next to each other in the structure. On the other hand, it occurs quite frequently in alloys at elevated temperatures.

Next, consider what happens when a nonstoichiometric crystal or a so-called solid solution is formed. Suppose that a small amount of $CdBr_2$ is added to a silver bromide crystal. The Cd^{+2} ions are known to enter the structure substitutionally for Ag^{+1} ions. The energy required to stuff the two relatively large Br^{-1} ions accompanying each cadmium ion into the interstices of the AgBr structure is quite large. The bromine ions can be pictured, therefore, as remaining on the crystal's surface occupying their appropriate equipoints in the AgBr structure. This situation is clearly unstable because the cadmium ions each have one more positive charge than the Ag^{+1} ions for which they are substituted whereas the added bromine ions produce an excess negative charge on the surface. It will be recalled, however, that AgBr crystals normally contain Frenkel defects, that is, interstitial Ag^{+1} ions and cation vacancies. It is believed that the interstitial silver ions diffuse to the surface where they neutralize the bromine ions while the cation vacancies that they leave behind balance the excess positive charge of the Cd^{+2} ions. At a given temperature, however, the number of Frenkel defects present in a crystal is constant and given by equation (15). This requires that, at equilibrium, new Frenkel defects be formed in order to replace the silver ions that diffused to the surface. Thus the result of adding $CdBr_2$ to silver bromide can be summarized as follows: The Cd^{+2} ions replace Ag^{+1} ions substitutionally. Charge neutrality is retained by the formation of cation vacancies in the AgBr structure. Consequently, a solid solution of cadmium bromide in silver bromide contains Schottky defects in addition to the Frenkel defects normally present.

Line defects

Dislocation types. Originally, dislocations were introduced in order to explain the plastic deformation of solids, notably metals. Since then it has been shown that dislocations are helpful in explaining crystal growth, electrical conductivity, and other phenomena as well. More recently, direct evidence of their existence has been produced. Individual dislocations have been observed in copper phthalocyanine crystals with electron microscopes having very high resolving power. One such electron micrograph is reproduced in Fig. 3.

A dislocation is a linear array of atoms each of which has a coordination differing from the normal coordination for such atoms in the structure.† Two basic kinds of dislocations can be distinguished. The first

† Since most metals have structures based on close packings in which one atom is associated with each lattice point, the terms *lattice* and *structure* have become hopelessly intertwined in common usage. Nevertheless, the distinction should be clearly made, since dislocations also occur in solids having more complicated structures. Like all defects, the dislocation itself is a local change in the structure; it produces an imperfection in the lattice by interrupting its periodicity.

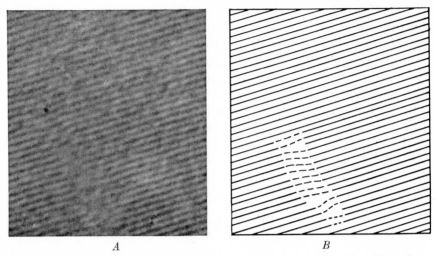

A   B

Fig. 3.   Portion of platinum phthalocyanine crystal showing two edge dislocations.
(Photograph by J. W. Menter.)
A. Electron micrograph magnified about 1,500,000 times.
B. Guide to finding the edge dislocations.

kind consists of a straight line of atoms, each of which has one less atom
coordinating it than is required by the crystal structure.   Such a dislocation is indicated by the symbol ⊥ in Fig. 4 in which the dislocation line
is normal to the pictured cross section of a hypothetical structure consisting of atoms in a simple cubic array.   As can be seen in this figure,
the dislocation line appears to mark the edge of a plane of atoms that has

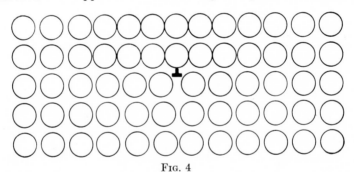

Fig. 4

been inserted part way into the crystal.   Such dislocations are therefore
called *edge dislocations*, also sometimes *Taylor* dislocations, or *Taylor-
Orowan dislocations*, after their discoverers.   The second type of dislocation was introduced by Burgers in 1939 and is called a *screw dislocation*
or *Burgers dislocation*.   It consists of a line of atoms each of which has
the correct number of atoms coordinating it; however, the coordination

polyhedron is distorted. The genesis of a screw dislocation is most clearly seen in a three-dimensional view of the crystal. Figure 5 shows what happens when one part of the crystal is displaced relative to the rest of the crystal and the displacement terminates within the crystal. The row of atoms marking the termination of the displacement is the Burgers dislocation. Note that in the region surrounding the dislocation the atoms are in their correct array, as can be seen, for example, on any of the vertical faces in Fig. 5. Along the dislocation line, however, the coordination polyhedra of the atoms have become distorted by the displacement. The nature of the distortion can be seen in Fig. 6 which

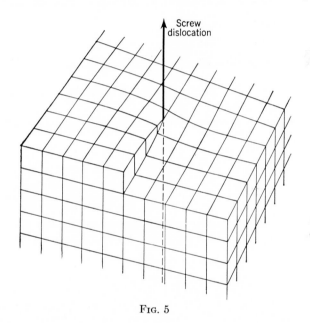

Fig. 5

shows a side view of the dislocation and the two sets of atom rows lying in the planes just above and below the plane along which the displacement occurred. (The atoms in the upper layer are represented by slightly smaller solid circles in Fig. 6 while the atoms in the lower layer are represented by open circles.) To the left and to the right of the dislocation line each atom is coordinated by four atoms in the same plane (joined by solid lines) and by two atoms, respectively, lying in the planes directly above and below (shown by the dotted vertical line), forming a regular octahedron. In the disturbed region, however, the octahedron is no longer regular, as can be seen by noting the shape of the bottom half of the distorted octahedron. On the other hand, the atoms, in the next layer above, are arranged according to the array of solid circles so that the amount of distortion gradually disappears with increasing distance from the dislocation line.

A dislocation can be described alternatively by means of a closed loop surrounding the dislocation line. This loop, or *Burgers circuit*, is formed by proceeding through the undisturbed region surrounding a dislocation in steps which are integral multiples of a lattice translation. The loop is completed by going an equal number of translations in a positive sense and negative sense in a plane normal to the dislocation line. Such a loop

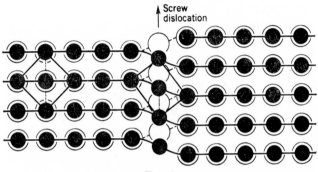

Fig. 6

must either close upon itself (if it does not enclose a dislocation) or fail to do so by an amount called a *Burgers vector*

$$s = n_a \mathbf{a} + n_b \mathbf{b} + n_c \mathbf{c} \tag{16}$$

where n_a, n_b, n_c are equal to integers or zero and $\mathbf{a}$, $\mathbf{b}$, $\mathbf{c}$ are the three primitive lattice translations. The Burgers circuit for a screw dislocation is shown in Fig. 7. Starting at some lattice point at the front of the crystal, the loop fails to close on itself by one unit translation parallel to the dislocation line. This is the Burgers vector s which always points in a direction parallel to the screw dislocation. Note that, if the loop is continued, it will describe a spiral path around the Burgers dislocation similar to the thread of a screw.

A Burgers circuit surrounding an edge dislocation is shown in Fig. 8. Note that in this case the Burgers vector is perpendicular to the edge dislocation. It is thus possible to distinguish the two kinds of dislocations according to the direction of their respective Burgers vectors. Also note in Fig. 8 that the atoms in the upper half of the crystal, that is, above the plane containing the edge dislocation, are in a state of compression which is largest at the edge dislocation itself. Conversely, directly below the dislocation, the atoms have larger than normal separations. In general, a dislocation may be a curved line. Such a dislocation can always be analyzed in terms of how much edge character and screw character it has by drawing a Burgers circuit around it.

Dislocation theory. The simplest way to describe dislocations is to consider the relative displacements of the parts of the crystal necessary to produce them. For example, an edge dislocation can be produced by applying a shear couple to the crystal, as shown in Fig. 9. The relative displacement produced can be described by the appropriate Burgers vector. Since there are certain equilibrium positions that the atoms in a

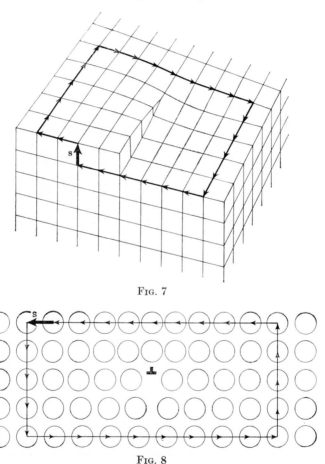

FIG. 7

FIG. 8

crystal prefer to occupy, the net displacement of atoms in one part of the crystal relative to the others is equal to one of the distances separating adjacent equilibrium positions. When this distance equals a translation in the crystal's lattice, the dislocation is called a *unit* dislocation. If the Burgers vector is shorter than a unit translation, then the dislocation is called a *fractional* or *partial* dislocation. Conversely, dislocations having Burgers vectors that are longer than a unit translation are not stable, since it can be shown that such displacements actually consist of several dislocations, each of unit length or less.

Figure 10 shows the dislocation line enclosing a displaced region in a crystal (stippled area). The relative motion of the atoms in this region is described by the Burgers vector **s**, which indicates the amount and direction of displacement of the atoms lying above the plane containing

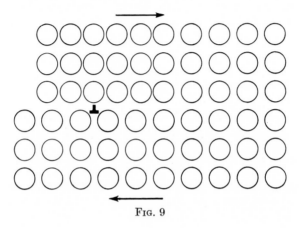

Fig. 9

the dislocation line relative to the undisplaced atoms lying below this plane. The atoms lying in the region outside the dislocation line have not been displaced. The plane containing the dislocation line is called the *slip* plane. The Burgers vector is the same for all parts of the dislocation line so that those parts for which the Burgers vector is perpendicular to the dislocation line are edge dislocations, whereas those parts for which the Burgers vector is parallel to the dislocation are screw dislocations. All other parts of the dislocation line are *mixed* dislocations. These mixed dislocations can be resolved into two components, one perpendicular and one parallel to the dislocation line, as shown in Fig. 10. The relative magnitudes and directions of these components can vary as

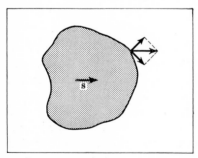

Fig. 10

long as their vector sum equals the vector **s** which connects the two equilibrium positions in a crystal. It should also be noted that the atomic displacements pictured in Fig. 10 can be described either as a motion of the upper part of the crystal to the right (+**s**) while the bottom part remains unmoved or as a motion of the lower part to the left (−**s**) while the upper part is motionless. These two types of motion are equivalent and can be described by the two schemes A and A' indicated below.

Displacement scheme	A	A'	B	B'	
Upper part moves by	$+s$	0	$-s$	0	(17)
Lower part moves by	0	$-s$	0	$+s$	

Relative motions in the opposite direction are indicated in scheme B and B' of (17), and these motions are said to produce a dislocation having an opposite sign. Although this distinction is not important when only one dislocation is considered, it takes on a real significance if two or more dislocations are present in the same crystal. In this connection it is usual to speak of a *dislocation density* $\rho = l/V$, where l is the total length of all dislocations present in a crystal and V is the total crystal volume. If a crystal is presumed to contain a number of parallel dislocation lines extending from one face of the crystal to the other, then the dislocation

A   B

FIG. 11

density is given by the number of such dislocations crossing a unit area perpendicular to the dislocation lines.

When a shear stress is applied to a crystal, the dislocations present in the crystal can move in certain directions specified by the crystal structure. It can be shown that the force per unit length acting on the dislocation perpendicular to the dislocation line is

$$\mathbf{F} = \tau\mathbf{s} \tag{18}$$

where τ is the stress acting on the slip plane and $\mathbf{s}$ is the Burgers vector of the dislocation. When a uniform stress is applied, therefore, the force acting on the dislocation is the same everywhere along the dislocation line since $\mathbf{s}$ is everywhere the same. That a dislocation can indeed move under the applied stress can be qualitatively justified as follows: The atoms in the immediate vicinity of the dislocation are displaced from their equilibrium position. If the dislocated atoms are stabilized by the attractive and repulsive forces of the atoms adjacent to them, these forces must approximately balance each other. A displacement of these atoms to an adjacent set of equilibrium positions therefore requires relatively little force.

The atomic displacements involved in the motion of a dislocation can be seen with the aid of Fig. 11 which shows two atom rows before and after the dislocation has moved one translation. The top row contains one more atom than the bottom row. The relative displacements of the atoms before the dislocation has moved are shown in Fig. 11*A* (also by open circles in Fig. 11*B*). After the dislocation has moved, the atoms on one side of the dislocation have moved nearer to their correct equilibrium sites (shown by the dashed lines), whereas the atoms lying to the right of the dislocation have moved farther away from their equilibrium positions. To a first approximation, the increase in the attractive forces for the atoms on the left just equals the increase in the repulsive forces for the atoms on the right, so that the forces just balance, and the dislocation can move without encountering resistance to its motion.

Because the coordination of the atoms in an edge dislocation is different from other parallel atom rows in the crystal, an edge dislocation is free to move only in its slip plane (Fig. 9). By comparison, a screw dislocation can move in any plane parallel to itself. This is so because the

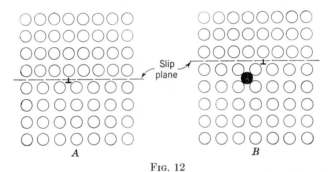

Fig. 12

motion of a screw dislocation consists of producing a slight distortion along successive parallel atom rows while the previously distorted regions return to their correct configuration. When an edge dislocation moves out of its slip plane, a process called *climb*, such motion must be accompanied by the creation of interstitials (or vacancies). That this is so can be seen in Fig. 12 which shows the original dislocation in Fig. 12*A* and its position after it has moved in Fig. 12*B*. The row of atoms removed from the edge of the extra half-plane is shown by the black circle in an interstitial position. Actually, this situation is not very stable, and such motion of dislocations is usually accompanied by the diffusion of the interstitial atoms to other parts of the crystal.

When dislocations move in a crystal, it is quite likely that they will intersect. One possible consequence of such an intersection is shown in Fig. 13. When the two mutually perpendicular screw dislocations, denoted by their Burgers vectors s_1 and s_2 in Fig. 13*A*, intersect, each produces a kink or *jog* in the other, as shown in Fig. 13*B*. The jogs produced in this case are edge dislocations because their Burgers vectors

(equal in magnitude and direction to the Burgers vectors of the dislocations producing the jog) are at right angles to the original dislocation line.
Any further movement of the screw dislocations along the dashed line in
Fig. 13 means that these newly formed edge dislocations must move out
of their slip planes so that such motion is accompanied by the formation
of interstitials or vacancies. Another type of jog is shown in Fig. 14, in

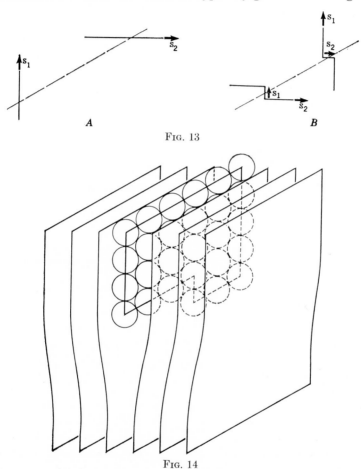

Fig. 13

Fig. 14

this case at the edge of the extra half-plane forming an edge dislocation
in a crystal. The atom at the corner of the jog has only two nearest
neighbors whereas all the other atoms along the edge dislocation have
three nearest neighbors in the extra plane so that this atomic site is
energetically not as stable as the others. One of two things can happen
therefore. The jog serves to attract another atom from the host crystal,
forming a vacancy thereby, or the corner atom can move into an inter-

stitial position. This is another way in which the motion of a dislocation can produce other kinds of imperfections in a crystal, since either of the above two mechanisms acts to displace the dislocation by one interatomic separation.

Plane defects

Large-angle boundaries. The imperfections discussed above can exist inside individual crystals. Most common materials consist of many small interlocking crystals or *grains* having random orientations. The boundary between two adjacent grains, therefore, must have a structure that somehow conforms to the structures and orientations of both grains. It is obvious from this that the grain boundary forms a discontinuity in the periodicity of the lattice of either crystallite or grain and is, therefore, a type of lattice imperfection. The nature of the atomic arrangement in the boundary can be deduced from the following reasoning. The forces exerted by individual atoms can extend to other atoms over distances that are comparable to atomic dimensions. If two grains are separated by a fairly thick noncrystalline layer, each grain should continue to grow in size by forcing the atoms at its surface to assume positions consistent with its crystal structure, thereby lowering the energy of the assembly. This process continues until two grains are separated by only a few atoms. At this distance each competing grain pulls on the boundary-layer atoms with comparable forces, making the atoms assume positions that are some kind of compromise between the requirements of the structures of either grain.

This view is supported by experimental observations. The energies of grain boundaries have been measured for several metals. It is possible to compute what the energies of the grain boundaries are by assuming that the boundary structure corresponds to a series of regularly spaced dislocations. When this is done, it turns out that the experimental and theoretical values are in very good agreement for misorientations of identical planes in two adjacent crystals by as much as 30°. For such *large-angle boundaries*, the grain-boundary structure more nearly approximates that of a liquid. It has been shown, for example, that the viscosity of grain boundaries in aluminum is comparable to that of liquid aluminum if the boundary is assumed to be 4 Å thick. This is additional proof that grain boundaries are only a few atoms in thickness.

The shapes of grains generally bear no relation to the crystal structures of the individual crystallites. Similarly, the shapes of grains formed during the solidification process are not appreciably affected by the properties of the grain boundaries. When the solid is heated, however, the increased mobility of all atoms, and particularly those near the surface of each grain, is influenced by the surface tension at the grain boundaries.   Cyril S. Smith has shown that, because of the surface tension, large-angle grain boundaries prefer to form common corners between three grains so that the interboundary angles equal 120°.   Now, although it is possible to form such ideal boundaries in two dimensions, it is not possible to fill space completely with polyhedra whose terminal planes form 120° angles with each other.   Consequently, the effect of surface tension is to make the interboundary angles tend toward 120° with the result that the individual grains have somewhat irregular forms.

The properties of grain boundaries also have a pronounced influence on the mechanical, electrical, and other properties of polycrystalline solids.   A polycrystalline solid forms by the simultaneous formation of a large number of randomly oriented crystallites.   This has several important consequences.   As the individual grains grow in size, they tend to expel all foreign atoms, interstitials, etc., which, therefore, must collect at the boundaries.   This means that the grain boundaries may contain a variety of imperfections, so that it is very difficult properly to evaluate their influence on the mechanical and physical properties of materials. As discussed in the next section, it is possible to construct an accurate model of a grain boundary only when the misorientation between adjacent grains is limited to a small number of degrees.   The random orientation of the initial grains, however, means that the grain boundaries in most solids are large-angle boundaries.   Since most materials of practical importance are polycrystalline aggregates rather than single crystals, the difficulties attendant on the analysis of grain-boundary effects handicap the understanding of what actually happens in polycrystalline solids. Thus many properties deduced from the study of single crystals show marked differences when polycrystalline materials are examined.

Small-angle boundaries.   Two similar models of grain boundaries based on two-dimensional arrays of dislocations were independently proposed by Bragg and by Burgers in 1940.   Suppose that the structures of two adjacent grains are tilted by a few degrees relative to each other, as shown in Fig. 15A.   Provided that the angle of tilt ψ is not too large, these two grains can be joined as shown in Fig. 15B.   The result is that a series of parallel edge dislocations is formed along the boundary.   The spacing D between adjacent dislocations is readily deduced from Fig. 15. Consider the arc defined by the angle of tilt ψ in a circle whose radius is D. If the translation normal to the boundary $b \ll D$, then it is very nearly equal in length to such an arc length.   It is possible to write, therefore, that

$$b \simeq D\psi \tag{19}$$

where b and D are measured in the same units of length and ψ is expressed in radians.

When a small-angle boundary intersects the surface of the material, the presence of edge dislocations in this boundary can be observed by *etching* a thin layer of the surface in such a way as to produce small pits at the sites of emergence of dislocation lines.   The appearance of a row of such *etch pits* along a grain boundary is shown in Fig. 16.   It is possible

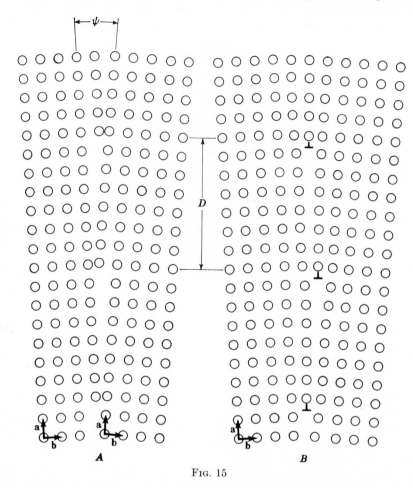

Fig. 15

to confirm (19) experimentally, therefore, by first measuring the spacing D between the etch pits.   Next, the relative angles at which the two grains on each side of the boundary diffract x-rays are determined.   The relative difference between the two diffraction angles is a direct measure of the angle ψ by which the two grains are tilted with respect to each other. Since the translation normal to the grain boundary can be similarly determined by means of x-ray diffraction, it can be shown that the spacing calculated from the ratio b/ψ just equals the value of D determined from the distance between adjacent etch pits.

The misfit between the two grains meeting at the boundary is partially relieved by an elastic deformation extending over an area several interatomic spacings wide. It is possible to calculate the elastic energy of a small-angle boundary, that is, a two-dimensional array of dislocations, from the known elastic stress field surrounding a single dislocation. It

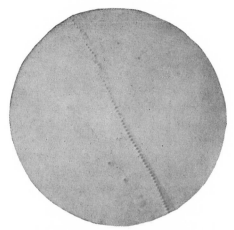

Fig. 16. Array of etch pits along a small-angle boundary in a germanium crystal. The tilt between the two regions is slightly more than 1′ of arc. (Photographed by F. Lincoln Vogel; shown magnified approximately 750 times.)

has been shown by several investigators that the energy E per unit area of boundary depends on the tilt or misfit ψ according to

$$E = E_0\psi(A - \ln \psi) \tag{20}$$

where E_0 is the elastic strain energy of the dislocation and A is a constant that expresses the energy of the misfit. A plot of E/ψ against $\ln \psi$ is a straight line. According to (20), the slope of the line is $-E_0$, and the value of A can be determined from the intercept of the line on the E/ψ axis.

It is also possible for two-dimensional boundaries to form within a single crystal. (The boundary shown in Fig. 16 actually was observed in a single crystal of germanium.) The strain field surrounding each edge dislocation tends to bend the crystal around the dislocation line in such a way that the interatomic distances more nearly equal the equilibrium separations of the structure. This is shown by the thin crystal strips in Fig. 17. Since the easiest way for such thin strips to combine, when forming a large crystal, is to fit together so that the bends superimpose, it is reasonable to suppose that the energy of a crystal containing many edge dislocations is lowered when the dislocations stack above each other in a plane. Such a plane of dislocations is sometimes called a *dislocation wall* and is very similar to the small-angle boundary depicted in Fig. 15*B*. These walls are frequently found to form when a plastically deformed crystal is annealed. Phonons interact with the edge dislocations and provide the dislocation lines with the energy necessary to migrate through the crystal and to collect in walls, forming *subboundaries* frequently called *polygonization boundaries*. When this polygonization process occurs, it usually can be observed by x-ray diffraction methods.

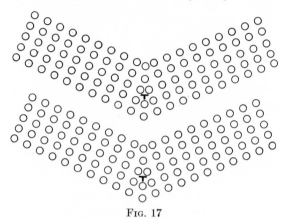

FIG. 17

Stacking faults. Suppose that the *n*th layer in a closest packing is an *A* layer and the $(n + 1)$th layer is supposed to be a *B* layer but because of a "mistake" in the stacking sequence it is a *C* layer instead. It is said that a *stacking fault* has been introduced between the *n*th and $(n + 1)$th layer in that case. For example, consider the stacking sequences

$$\ldots ABABABCBCBC\ldots \qquad \ldots ABCABCBCABCA\ldots$$
$$\ldots h\,h\,h\,h\,h\,c\,h\,h\,h\,h\,h\ldots \qquad \ldots c\,c\,c\,c\,h\,h\,c\,c\,c\,c\,c\ldots \qquad (21)$$

In the first case, a stacking fault has occurred on one side of the *c* layer. (The choice of the side is based on which sequence is deemed to be the correct one.) In the second case, the stacking fault clearly lies between the two *h* layers. Note that the two parts of the closest packings in (21) are centrosymmetric. In the first case, the symmetry centers lie in the *c* layer, whereas in the second case they lie between the two *h* layers. Because the stacking fault marks a plane separating two identical structures, it is, in fact, a *twin* plane.

The stacking fault can be produced by at least two distinct mechanisms. As discussed in Chapter 7, when a closest packing of atoms forms in a crystal during its growth, it is possible for a new layer to start incorrectly;

that is, a C layer can start to grow instead of the B layer required by the preceding stacking sequence. If the crystal grows sufficiently rapidly, this so-called *growth fault* is incorporated in the final crystal. Similarly, it is possible to displace the atoms in, say, a B layer to the sites of a C layer during plastic deformation of the crystal. (This actually takes place by the relative motion of the two parts of the crystal.) After the forces producing the displacement are removed, the so-called *deformation fault* can persist in the crystal because the immediate coordination of each atom is not changed (the CN remains at 12 regardless of the stacking sequence). Thus only the forces between next-nearest neighbors favor the return of the atoms to their original sites. The energy of a stacking fault, therefore, can be calculated by taking into account interactions between next-nearest neighbors only. (The contribution due to next-next-nearest neighbors is small so that it can be neglected.) The measured values of this energy are 19 ergs/cm² in copper and between 100 to 200 ergs/cm² in aluminum.

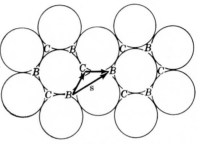

Fig. 18

It is also possible to describe the production of deformation faults in terms of dislocations. Consider the hexagonal closest-packed layer, say the A layer shown in Fig. 18. Suppose that the next layer above is a B layer. It can be displaced along the Burgers vector **s** to produce a unit dislocation. Actually, it is much easier to displace the layer to the neighboring C sites. (Remember, the nearest-neighbor forces acting on each atom are not affected by this change.) When such a *partial* dislocation is formed in a closest packing, a stacking fault is produced. For example, in cubic closest packings of metals, the slip planes are the hexagonal closest-packed planes ((111)). The observed slip directions in these crystals are [[110]], the directions along rows of closest-packed atoms. From the foregoing discussion (Fig. 18), it is evident that the atoms probably move in a zigzag path so that it is not surprising that stacking faults have been found to exist in plastically deformed face-centered cubic metals. A further discussion of plastic deformation is given in the next chapter.

Suggestions for supplementary reading

H. G. van Bueren, Lattice imperfections and plastic deformation in metals, I. Nature and characteristics of lattice imperfections, notably dislocations, *Philips Tech. Rev.*, vol. 15 (1954), pp. 246–257.

A. H. Cottrell, *Theoretical structural metallurgy*, 2d ed. (St. Martin's Press, Inc., New York, 1957), especially pp. 36–43 and pp. 222–239.

A. H. Cottrell, *Dislocations and plastic flow in crystals* (Oxford University Press, London, 1956).

W. Shockley, et al., *Imperfections in nearly perfect crystals* (John Wiley & Sons, Inc., New York, 1952).

W. T. Read, Jr., *Dislocations in crystals* (McGraw-Hill Book Company, Inc., New York, 1953).

Suggestions for further reading

Frederick Seitz and David Turnbull (eds.), *Solid state physics*, vol. 3 (Academic Press, Inc., New York, 1956), especially the following articles:

J. D. Eshelby, The continuum theory of lattice defects, pp. 79–145.

F. A. Kröger and H. J. Vink, Relations between the concentrations of imperfections in crystalline solids, pp. 310–438.

Exercises

1. Derive the equation relating the number of vacancies n found in a monoatomic crystal to the energy E_a required to remove one atom to the crystal's exterior.

2. The relation to be derived in Exercise 1 is $n = Ne^{-E_a/kT}$. If 1 eV is required to move an atom from the crystal's interior to the surface, what is the proportion of vacancies present in the crystal at 1000°K? At 300°K?

3. Starting with an ideally perfect crystal, make a plot of the density (specific gravity) of the crystal as a function of the number of defects present for the case of

(a) Frenkel defects.
(b) Schottky defects.

(Such a plot can be prepared without knowing the actual numbers involved by indicating what the curves would look like and what their probable slopes are.)

4. On the basis of a plot like the one described in Exercise 3, do you think it is possible to distinguish the two kinds of point defects that may be present in a crystal? If densities of crystals can be measured to four decimal places, what is the smallest ratio of defects that can be detected by such methods

(a) In a simple metal?
(b) In an alkali halide?

5. Using the five types of mechanisms for defect formation, explain the formation of the three types of solid solutions described in the previous chapter. List the defects present in each.

6. A common method for observing edge dislocations in crystals is to expose the crystal to a solvent or etchant. The resulting *etch pits* are believed to form at places where an edge dislocation intersects the crystal's surface. List some possible reasons for this belief.

7. What combinations of dislocations can you postulate around which the Burgers circuit closes upon itself, that is, the Burgers vector is zero? Use sketches to illustrate your answer.

8. Four schemes for producing an edge dislocation are listed in (17). By means of drawings, show that the schemes A and A' are equivalent and opposite in sense to the dislocations described by schemes B and B'. Use arrows to indicate the direction of slip of the displaced region.

9. Draw a primitive cubic lattice array containing one positive and two negative edge dislocations. (Assume that the three dislocations are parallel.)

10. Show the structure of the (110) plane of NaCl containing an edge dislocation parallel to [110] by inserting an extra ($1\bar{1}0$) plane halfway into the crystal. How can such a dislocation be created without placing like atoms next to each other? What would happen if like ions were placed next to each other?

11. Consider a crystal containing two parallel edge dislocations which move in two parallel slip planes. Assume that the lattice of the crystal is primitive cubic and each unit cell contains one atom. If the edge dislocations lying, respectively, above and below their associated slip planes move toward each other, what will happen when they meet if

(a) The slip planes are separated by one vertical translation?
(b) The slip planes are separated by two vertical translations?
(c) The extra half-planes of each dislocation overlap by one vertical translation?

Hint: This is an example of the relation between edge dislocations and the generation of point defects.

12. Plot the energy of a grain boundary determined by relation (20) by

(a) Plotting E/ψ versus ln ψ.
(b) Plotting E versus ψ.

The plot in (b) is a curve which reaches a maximum energy E_m at a specific value of the tilt angle ψ_m.

13. The parameters E_0, E_m, and ψ_m in Exercise 12 are related by $E_m = E_0\psi_m$. If typical values of E_m and ψ_m are 600 ergs/cm² and 0.5 radian, respectively, what are the corresponding values of E_0 and A in relation (20)?

14. Draw a side view of a stacking fault in a cubic closest packing. Do this by showing two layers of atoms (use circles and dots to distinguish them) in planes normal to [111].

15. Using a drawing like the one in Exercise 14, show that there are three ways to produce a stacking fault:

(a) Let slip occur in the [$11\bar{2}0$] direction between two parallel hexagonal closest-packed layers.
(b) Remove a hexagonal closest-packed layer from the stack and close the gap by bringing together the layer above and below the missing layer.
(c) Insert a hexagonal closest-packed layer between any two layers in the stack. Show that this is equal to a combination of two slips like that in part (a) on two adjacent slip planes.

6

Mechanical properties of crystals

Classification of properties

The largest utilization of crystalline solids is in the construction of various objects used by men in their daily lives. These may range in size from pins to skyscrapers and differ in their complexity from simple articles, formed of one kind of material only, to complex machines consisting of many different intermeshed components. The suitability of a given material to construction purposes is determined by the so-called *mechanical* properties of the solid. On the other hand, components for electric circuits, optical systems, or similar devices are selected on the basis of their *physical* properties, for example, conductivity, opacity, magnetism, and so forth. A more meaningful classification for the purposes of this book is to distinguish between those properties that are determined by the actual crystal structure, the so-called *structure-sensitive* properties, and those that are independent of the crystal structure, namely, the *structure-insensitive* properties. The distinction between these two categories is usually not clear-cut and is primarily one of degree of importance. For example, consider some of the physical properties discussed in Chapter 10. It can be shown that electrical conductivity in most metals is completely explained by the so-called free-electron theory that does not take the crystal structure into account. On the other hand, it is not possible to explain the electrical properties of nonmetals without considering their crystal structures. Similarly, paramagnetism is a structure-insensitive property, but ferromagnetism is strongly structure-dependent. Finally, as indicated in the previous chapter, the movement of atoms through a crystal, called diffusion, depends on the type of imperfections present in the crystal rather than on its structure. Yet it should be obvious that the same number of the same type of imperfections leads to different diffusivities if two totally different kinds of crystals are considered. As might be expected, the same types of imperfections do not account for the diffusion process in all different crystals, so that the very need to invoke different types of imperfections implies that diffusion is also structure-sensitive in this sense.

Usually, the physical and mechanical properties of crystals must exhibit the same symmetry as that of the crystal structure itself. This is so because they depend on the types of forces that exist between atoms, which are also responsible for the particular crystal structure adopted. It is not surprising, therefore, that most properties of interest to engineers are structure-sensitive. In this connection, it should be noted that the word *structure* is sometimes used in two different ways: One is the meaning employed in this book, that is, the crystal structure; the other is used to describe the nature of a polycrystalline specimen as seen with the aid of a microscope, that is, whether it is coarse-grained or fine-grained, etc. It is probably better to use the term *microstructure* to describe the second case. The important properties for engineers include most of the mechanical and physical properties of usual interest. The fact that such properties are structure-sensitive does not mean that once a crystal's structure is known its properties can be uniquely determined. Unfortunately, this is so because the theoretical treatment of this problem is not as yet sufficiently far advanced. On the other hand, enough is known to allow certain predictions to be made whenever the crystal structure is known.

Properties of engineering importance. Because of the present theoretical limitations in accounting for the many different properties that solids can have, it is usual practice to determine the properties of a solid experimentally. As long as the results are reproducible, such experimental values can then be used to determine the design specifications for a particular purpose. This leads one to wonder why it is necessary to seek a theoretical understanding at all, when most of the necessary data are readily available in handbooks and similar compilations. The reason is, simply, that materials presently available can be thus utilized, but new materials possessing as yet undetermined properties can be developed only following the elucidation of the relations between the structure and properties of solids. Moreover, new applications for old materials are also discovered in this way. Some of the specific mechanical properties of solids are briefly discussed below.

Virtually all solids undergo some deformation in their daily use. One of the criteria for selecting construction materials, therefore, is their ability to withstand such deformation. Two principal types of deformation can be distinguished, depending on whether the deformation produced is permanent or not. If the deformation produced by an external stress disappears after the force has been removed, the material is said to have deformed elastically. Such *elastic deformation* is caused by strains which obey Hooke's law; that is, the atomic displacements are proportional to the applied force. On the other hand, when the *elastic limit* of a solid is exceeded, permanent or *plastic deformation* sets in. In practice, the elastic limit is very hard to determine. In most experiments either it is not reached or else it is exceeded, as evidenced by the occurrence of plastic deformation. Furthermore, most actual tests are performed on polycrystalline materials so that it is tacitly assumed in such experiments that the material tested is homogeneous and isotropic. As shown in subsequent sections, this is not usually the case, so that the measurements are subject to a number of experimental errors that cannot be exactly evaluated. It should also be noted that it is possible to deform a solid, below its elastic limit, in such a way that deviations from Hooke's law may be observed. For example, when a wire is suddenly twisted, it does not immediately reach its full distortion but approaches the final state asymptotically. Nor does the wire immediately regain its original form upon removal of the deforming torque. This is called *anelastic deformation*.

Hardness is another property of common importance that is difficult to define on an absolute basis. Mineralogists usually use the so-called Mohs scale in which diamond has a hardness of 10, corundum of 9, all the way down to talc, which has a hardness of 1. The hardness of any other mineral is then determined by a scratch test, that is, by establishing which of the minerals in the Mohs scale can scratch the unknown or which in turn can be scratched by the unknown. Metallurgical and other engineers more commonly use penetration tests such as the Brinell hardness test or the Rockwell hardness test. In these tests, a suitably weighted plunger bears down on the specimen which deforms first elastically and then plastically. The depth or diameter of the indentation produced by a known load is then used as an indication of the hardness of the material. Although it is not possible to calculate what the hardness of a particular crystal should be on purely theoretical grounds, it is generally possible to predict its relative hardness. This is so because hardness is a measure of the resistance to deformation, which is directly related to the forces that exist between atoms in the solid. Since these forces are determined by the type of atoms present and their array or crystal structure, it is possible to predict not only the relative hardness of a solid but also related properties such as ductility, melting point, and others whenever the structure is known.

Anisotropy in crystals. When the properties of a solid do not depend on the direction in the solid along which they are measured, the solid is said to be *isotropic*. Thus, *anisotropy* is defined as the variation of a particular property with direction. Whether a solid is isotropic or not, therefore, depends on the property being observed and on the structure of the solid. For example, all single crystals belonging to the cubic system transmit light isotropically; that is, the velocity of the light is independent of direction in the crystal. On the other hand, the elastic properties of cubic crystals are anisotropic. When such cubic crystals make up a polycrystalline solid, however, the solid can be elastically isotropic provided that the orientation of the individual crystallites is completely random so that their individual anisotropies cancel out for each direction. Conversely, when their orientations are not random, the polycrystalline solid is anisotropic, as discussed in the next section. Noncubic crystals are anisotropic in all their properties, and the degree of their anisotropy is directly related to their crystal structure. As an example of extreme anisotropy, consider the micas whose layer structures are responsible for their pronounced cleavage parallel to these layers.

The directional dependence of properties in single crystals suggests that these properties can be best expressed in terms of vectors having certain components along the three crystallographic axes. The coefficients of each component then specify the magnitude of the property while their vector sum describes the direction. The specification of many properties of crystals, however, requires more than three coefficients. When the response of the crystal to the conditions imposed on it is a linear function of these conditions (for example, when Hooke's law is obeyed in elastic deformation), it is most convenient to express this relation by means of a *tensor*. Electrical conductivity obeying Ohm's law also can be used to illustrate this usage. Suppose that the electric field at a given point in the crystal is $\mathbf{E}$. The current produced by this field is, in general, not the same for all directions in the crystal. If one chooses a cartesian (mutually orthogonal) coordinate system, the current components, $\mathbf{I}_1$, $\mathbf{I}_2$, $\mathbf{I}_3$, along the three reference axes can be related to the three components of the field, $\mathbf{E}_1$, $\mathbf{E}_2$, $\mathbf{E}_3$, by

$$\mathbf{I}_1 = k_{11}\mathbf{E}_1 + k_{12}\mathbf{E}_2 + k_{13}\mathbf{E}_3$$
$$\mathbf{I}_2 = k_{21}\mathbf{E}_1 + k_{22}\mathbf{E}_2 + k_{23}\mathbf{E}_3 \qquad (1)$$
$$\mathbf{I}_3 = k_{31}\mathbf{E}_1 + k_{32}\mathbf{E}_2 + k_{33}\mathbf{E}_3$$

where the nine coefficients represented collectively by k_{ij} are called the *conductivity tensor*. Unless certain relations exist between these nine coefficients, all nine must be known in order to specify the current. Because of the inherent symmetry of crystals, however, it usually turns out that some of the coefficients are equal to each other or to zero, so that a much smaller number of coefficients is actually required to describe a particular property. For example, it can be shown that the tensor in equations (1) is a symmetric tensor, that is, $k_{ij} = k_{ji}$. In fact, it turns out that, if the three reference axes are properly chosen, only three independent coefficients are required to describe the current in any crystal. Denoting these coefficients σ_1, σ_2, and σ_3, the current can be expressed by the relation

$$
\begin{aligned}
\mathbf{I} &= \mathbf{I}_1 + \mathbf{I}_2 + \mathbf{I}_3 \\
&= \sigma_1\mathbf{E}_1 + \sigma_2\mathbf{E}_2 + \sigma_3\mathbf{E}_3 \\
&= \sum_{i=1}^{3} \sigma_i\mathbf{E}_i.
\end{aligned} \tag{2}
$$

The electrical properties of any crystal, therefore, can be expressed in terms of its three conductivities σ_i or its three resistivities ρ_i, since $\sigma = 1/\rho$. Consequently, it is a vector property rather than a tensor property. (A vector is sometimes referred to as a first-order tensor, since the order of a tensor n is determined by the maximum number of coefficients 3^n, required to specify the tensor.)

Preferred orientation in polycrystalline aggregates. Because many materials, notably metals, are formed under anisotropic conditions,

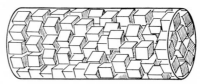

Fig. 1

the grains composing them tend to orient themselves in a nonrandom fashion. The resulting *preferred orientation* or *texture* is, of course, due to the anisotropies of the individual crystallites. For example, when a metal wire is drawn through a die, the deformation of the metal causes the crystallites to align in such a way that a particular crystallographic direction in each grain is parallel to the drawing direction. The resulting *fiber* texture of the wire then consists of one common direction in each grain parallel to the wire axis and a random orientation of the grains about this common direction. Figure 1 illustrates the case of preferred orientation of cubic crystallites in which the wire axis is parallel to their [[100]] directions. (The cross-sectional view in Fig. 1 shows the randomness of their orientation around the wire axis.) When a metal is deformed biaxially, say in the rolling of a sheet, the crystallites align preferentially along two directions. In the resulting *sheet* texture, one direction is normal to the plane of the sheet, that is, certain crystallographic planes tend to lie in the plane of the sheet, and the other direction is parallel to the rolling direction. Preferred orientation can be produced in other ways also. For example, certain substances tend to form crystals having needlelike or platelike habits. When such crystallites are compacted or sintered in order to produce a larger solid, they tend to have certain directions in common.

The presence of preferred orientation can produce undesirable consequences. The strength and related properties of devices formed from such materials reflect the anisotropy of the individual crystallites comprising them. For example, when circular cups are stamped from metal sheets having preferred orientation, the sides of the cups produced are not even, an effect called "earing." In many applications, therefore, preferred orientation is to be avoided whenever possible. Sometimes it can be removed from metals by proper annealing following the working of the metal. Conversely, it is possible that certain applications require the presence of preferred orientation. As discussed in a later chapter, the ease of magnetization of a crystal depends on the crystallographic direction that is parallel to the magnetic field. Depending on the desired end result, it may be required to have an easy or a hard direction of magnetization parallel to a particular direction in the final device.

Elastic deformation

Single crystals. The application of an external stress to a single crystal can produce a temporary deformation which disappears when the stress is removed. Whether a stressed crystal deforms elastically or whether it deforms plastically depends on the magnitude of the stress and the nature of the interatomic bonds in the crystal. Under normal loads, metal crystals rarely deform elastically without some plastic deformation also taking place. On the other hand, many nonmetallic crystals can be deformed elastically quite easily.

When a crystal is stressed, it exerts equal and opposite forces that resist further deformation so that, at equilibrium, the two sets of forces are balanced and equal. If a particular plane in the crystal is considered, it is possible to resolve the external stress into three mutually orthogonal components. The one that is normal to the plane is called the *normal stress* σ while the two lying in the plane are called the *shear stresses* τ. It is always possible to select three mutually perpendicular planes such that the shear stress for these planes is zero. These three planes are called the three *principal planes*, and the normal stresses acting on each plane are called the three *principal stresses* of the crystal. For example, consider a cylindrical crystal that is being compressed along the cylinder axis. The plane normal to the compressive stress and any two mutually orthogonal planes that are parallel to the compression direction can be selected as the principal planes. In this simple example, the principal stresses on the last two planes are zero, while the principal stress on the plane normal to the compression direction is equal to the applied force divided by the area of the plane. If any other plane in this crystal is selected, both the normal and the shear stresses have nonzero values. Consider a plane inclined at $90° - \phi$ to the compression direction, as shown in Fig. 2. The normal stress on this plane is determined by dividing the force component normal to the face, $F \cos \phi$, by the area of the plane $A/\cos \phi$, where A is the cross-sectional area of the crystal.

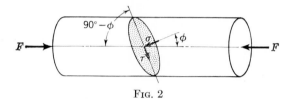

FIG. 2

Similarly, the shear stress is obtained by dividing the force component parallel to the plane by its area so that

$$\sigma = \frac{F}{A} \cos^2\phi \qquad (3)$$

and

$$\tau = \frac{F}{A} \sin \phi \cos \phi.$$

The *normal strain* in the crystal, ε, is defined as the ratio of the change in its length Δl to the original length l,

$$\varepsilon = \frac{\Delta l}{l}. \qquad (4)$$

According to Hooke's law, the normal strain produced by an applied stress $\sigma = F/A$ is

$$\varepsilon = \frac{\sigma}{E} \qquad (5)$$

where E is *Young's modulus*. The *shear strain* γ is similarly given by

$$\gamma = \frac{\tau}{G} \qquad (6)$$

where G is the *shear modulus* of elasticity, also called the torsion modulus.

Consider the infinitesimal cubic element of volume within a crystal shown in Fig. 3. The equilibrium normal stresses acting on each cube face can be denoted σ_x, σ_y, and σ_z, respectively. In order to describe the shear stresses, two subscripts are used. The first subscript denotes the plane within which the stress lies by naming the axis which the plane intersects, and the second subscript denotes the shear-stress direction.

An inspection of Fig. 3 shows that if the shear stresses are in equilibrium, that is, if the cube does not rotate, then

$$\tau_{yz} = \tau_{zy} \qquad \tau_{zx} = \tau_{xz} \qquad \tau_{xy} = \tau_{yx}. \tag{7}$$

Six stress components, σ_x, σ_y, σ_z, τ_{xy}, τ_{yz}, τ_{zx}, therefore, are sufficient to describe the state of stress at any point in the crystal. If these stresses are the same at every point in the crystal, it is said to be *homogeneously*

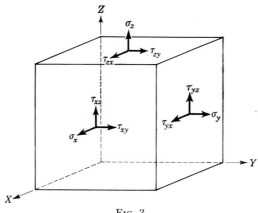

FIG. 3

stressed. For such a crystal, the relations between stress and strain are given by the generalized form of Hooke's law (5). The six strains are

$$
\begin{aligned}
\varepsilon_x &= s_{11}\sigma_x + s_{12}\sigma_y + s_{13}\sigma_z + s_{14}\tau_{yz} + s_{15}\tau_{zx} + s_{16}\tau_{xy} \\
\varepsilon_y &= s_{21}\sigma_x + s_{22}\sigma_y + s_{23}\sigma_z + s_{24}\tau_{yz} + s_{25}\tau_{zx} + s_{26}\tau_{xy} \\
\varepsilon_z &= s_{31}\sigma_x + s_{32}\sigma_y + s_{33}\sigma_z + s_{34}\tau_{yz} + s_{35}\tau_{zx} + s_{36}\tau_{xy} \\
\gamma_{yz} &= s_{41}\sigma_x + s_{42}\sigma_y + s_{43}\sigma_z + s_{44}\tau_{yz} + s_{45}\tau_{zx} + s_{46}\tau_{xy} \\
\gamma_{zx} &= s_{51}\sigma_x + s_{52}\sigma_y + s_{53}\sigma_z + s_{54}\tau_{yz} + s_{55}\tau_{zx} + s_{56}\tau_{xy} \\
\gamma_{xy} &= s_{61}\sigma_x + s_{62}\sigma_y + s_{63}\sigma_z + s_{64}\tau_{yz} + s_{65}\tau_{zx} + s_{66}\tau_{xy}
\end{aligned}
\tag{8}
$$

and the six stresses are

$$
\begin{aligned}
\sigma_x &= c_{11}\varepsilon_x + c_{12}\varepsilon_y + c_{13}\varepsilon_z + c_{14}\gamma_{yz} + c_{15}\gamma_{zx} + c_{16}\gamma_{xy} \\
\sigma_y &= c_{21}\varepsilon_x + c_{22}\varepsilon_y + c_{23}\varepsilon_z + c_{24}\gamma_{yz} + c_{25}\gamma_{zx} + c_{26}\gamma_{xy} \\
\sigma_z &= c_{31}\varepsilon_x + c_{32}\varepsilon_y + c_{33}\varepsilon_z + c_{34}\gamma_{yz} + c_{35}\gamma_{zx} + c_{36}\gamma_{xy} \\
\tau_{yz} &= c_{41}\varepsilon_x + c_{42}\varepsilon_y + c_{43}\varepsilon_z + c_{44}\gamma_{yz} + c_{45}\gamma_{zx} + c_{46}\gamma_{xy} \\
\tau_{zx} &= c_{51}\varepsilon_x + c_{52}\varepsilon_y + c_{53}\varepsilon_z + c_{54}\gamma_{yz} + c_{55}\gamma_{zx} + c_{56}\gamma_{xy} \\
\tau_{xy} &= c_{61}\varepsilon_x + c_{62}\varepsilon_y + c_{63}\varepsilon_z + c_{64}\gamma_{yz} + c_{65}\gamma_{zx} + c_{66}\gamma_{xy}
\end{aligned}
\tag{9}
$$

where the s_{ij}'s are the *elastic constants* and the c_{ij}'s are called *elastic moduli*. Fortunately, many of these constants equal each other or are zero. Also, in crystals, the tensors in (8) and (9) are symmetric tensors; that is, $s_{ij} = s_{ji}$ and $c_{ij} = c_{ji}$. This reduces the total number of elastic constants from thirty-six to twenty-one in the triclinic system. If the crystal has additional symmetry, the total number is decreased still further, to five in the hexagonal system and to three in the cubic. In the cubic system, the elasticity tensor in (8) is

$$
\begin{array}{cccccc}
s_{11} & s_{12} & s_{12} & 0 & 0 & 0 \\
s_{12} & s_{11} & s_{12} & 0 & 0 & 0 \\
s_{12} & s_{12} & s_{11} & 0 & 0 & 0 \\
0 & 0 & 0 & s_{44} & 0 & 0 \\
0 & 0 & 0 & 0 & s_{44} & 0 \\
0 & 0 & 0 & 0 & 0 & s_{44}.
\end{array}
\tag{10}
$$

The value of the three elastic constants, s_{11}, s_{12}, s_{44}, must be determined experimentally for a cubic crystal. Once these constants have been determined, it is possible to calculate the strains produced by any set of applied stresses.

The principal stresses σ_1, σ_2, σ_3 in an isotropic body are related to the principal strains by

$$
\varepsilon_1 = \frac{1}{E}[\sigma_1 - \nu(\sigma_2 + \sigma_3)]
$$

$$
\varepsilon_2 = \frac{1}{E}[\sigma_2 - \nu(\sigma_3 + \sigma_1)]
\tag{11}
$$

$$
\varepsilon_3 = \frac{1}{E}[\sigma_3 - \nu(\sigma_1 + \sigma_2)]
$$

where ν is Poisson's ratio,

$$
\nu = \frac{E}{2G} - 1.
\tag{12}
$$

In an isotropic body (usually noncrystalline) $s_{44} = 2(s_{11} - s_{12})$, and there are only two independent elastic constants so that $E = 1/s_{11}$, $G = 1/s_{44}$, and $\nu = -s_{12}/s_{11}$. Because most practical materials are polycrystalline, the above relations for isotropic bodies can be applied to such materials provided only that the crystallite size is very small and their orientation is completely random.

Polycrystalline aggregates. When a polycrystalline material is deformed elastically, the above relations are obeyed only approximately. The reason for this is that the elastic properties of a polycrystalline aggregate are the averages of the individual properties of the crystallites comprising it. One of the principal factors that complicates the situation is that the crystallites usually are not oriented completely at random. An example of the anisotropy produced by preferred orientation is given in Fig. 4 which shows the variation of Young's modulus for a rolled sheet. As might be expected, the variation is symmetrical about the rolling direction. Another factor that affects the elastic properties of polycrystalline aggregates is that the grain boundaries have different moduli than the crystallites.   The large concentration of imperfections at grain boundaries also means that some plastic deformation invariably occurs under an applied stress.   The consequence of this is that the only meaningful calculations possible are based on averaging processes which take the various factors into account in an approximate way.   Finally, it

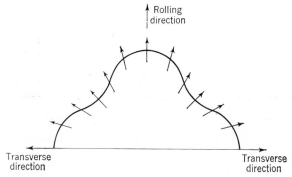

Fig. 4.   Anisotropy in a polycrystalline sheet.   The arrows indicate the direction along which Young's modulus has the value shown by the curved line.

should be noted that the preferred orientation and crystallite size usually change during the annealing of a metal so that the elastic moduli before and after annealing may be different.

Plastic deformation

Slip in single crystals.   Plastic deformation of a crystal takes place through a relative motion of the constituent atoms under an applied stress.   It can be shown by direct calculation, based on the interatomic forces between the atoms in a crystal, that the stress needed to produce this motion in an ideal crystal is several orders of magnitude greater than that actually applied.   Thus the assumption of a perfect crystal structure leads to an erroneous result indicating that some deviations from perfection must be present in real crystals.   The imperfections that have been postulated to explain this anomaly are either dislocations already present in the crystal or else new dislocations generated by the applied stress.   Alternatively, one can postulate that internal flaws such as tiny cracks or intracrystalline boundaries may help to "weaken" the crystal. In any case, if the plastic deformation can be pictured as a displacement of atoms lying in one plane relative to the atoms lying in an adjacent parallel plane, the process can be best described in terms of the movement of dislocations separating the displaced region from the undisplaced one. The relative atomic displacement involved can be thought of as a *slip* or *gliding* of certain atomic planes past each other.   The planes along which the resulting displacement occurs are usually called *slip planes* by metallurgists and *glide planes* by mineralogists.† The direction within the slip plane along which the atoms move is called the *slip direction*. The most frequently occurring slip planes and slip directions in simple metals are given below.   Note that generally the slip planes are among the densest planes in these close-packed structures.

	Hexagonal closest packing	Face-centered cubic	Body-centered cubic	
Slip planes	(0001)	((111))	((112)),((110)),((123))	(13)
Slip directions	[[2$\bar{1}\bar{1}$0]]	[[110]]	[[111]]	

When a crystal deforms elastically, the individual atomic displacements must be small so that the elastic restoring forces between the atoms are not disrupted.   Conversely, in the case of plastic deformation, the atoms must move from one equilibrium position to another.   Since a motion of all the atoms lying in the slip plane is involved, the displacement of the atoms must equal an integral number of translations in the slip direction.   Normally, slip does not occur on all the parallel planes in the crystal but rather along those planes on which the resistance to deformation is decreased by the presence of structural irregularities (dislocations).   Thus the deformation can be pictured as a relative displacement of thin undeformed layers called *glide packets*.   The thickness of these packets varies from crystal to crystal but is usually of the order of 10^{-3} to 10^{-5} cm.   The presence of undeformed regions in the crystal is attested to by the appearance of *slip striae* on the surface of the crystal marking the intersections of the slip planes with the crystal's surface.   The slip striae appear only on faces that are nonparallel to the slip direction.   Suppose that a crystal is deformed as shown in Fig. 5*A*. The protrusions of each glide packet are equal to only one or two translations in the slip direction, so that they cannot be directly observed, and only the slip striae are visible, as shown in Fig. 5*B*.   Since the slip striae are manifest on all the planes of one zone, it is not possible to determine the actual slip direction for such a crystal, only the slip plane.   On the other hand, consider a crystal deformed as shown in Fig. 6*A*.   Since the atoms move from one translation-equivalent position to another, parallel to a crystal face, the crystal faces parallel to the slip direction [*uvw*] do not show slip striae and the crystal appears as shown in Fig. 6*B*.

† The term *glide plane* has another meaning in crystallography, introduced in the discussion of symmetry elements in Chapter 2.   For this reason, the term *slip plane* is used in this book in the discussion of plastic deformation.

It is possible to determine the slip direction, therefore, by finding unstriated faces parallel to the slip direction. In the absence of natural faces, it is still possible to make the observations by artificially grinding such faces. In the cubic system, [*hkl*] is normal to (*hkl*) so that slipping can occur along several planes simultaneously. When such *multiple* slipping occurs, all the crystal faces will exhibit slip bands except when the so-called *active slip systems* have parallel slip directions.

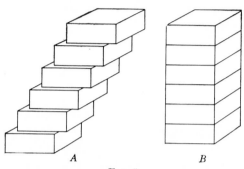

A   B

FIG. 5

Multiple slip occurs in sodium chloride, for example. The slip plane in NaCl is (110), and two adjacent (110) planes are shown in Fig. 7. Note that the (110) planes consist of alternating parallel rows of sodium and chlorine atoms. If slip were to occur in any direction but [1$\bar{1}$0], like atoms in adjacent sheets would pass over each other so that the repulsive forces between them oppose such movement. This does not occur for slip along [1$\bar{1}$0], which is believed to be the reason why the slip system in NaCl and other alkali halides is (110) · [1$\bar{1}$0]. Similarly, it is possible for slip to occur along any of the [[110]] directions in the ((001)) planes of other crystals having this structure. Again, the explanation of the slip system is that unlike atoms pass over each other and it is not necessary to break all the first coordination bonds formed by each atom. As the

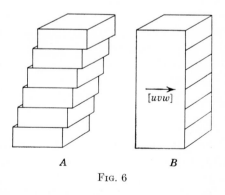

A   B

[*uvw*]

FIG. 6

bonds on one side of the moving atoms are broken, identical bonds are formed on the other side of each atom. By comparison, the bonding in metal crystals is due to an electrostatic attraction between the valence electrons, which are not localized at the sites of their parent atoms but are free to permeate the crystals as a whole, and the positive ion cores

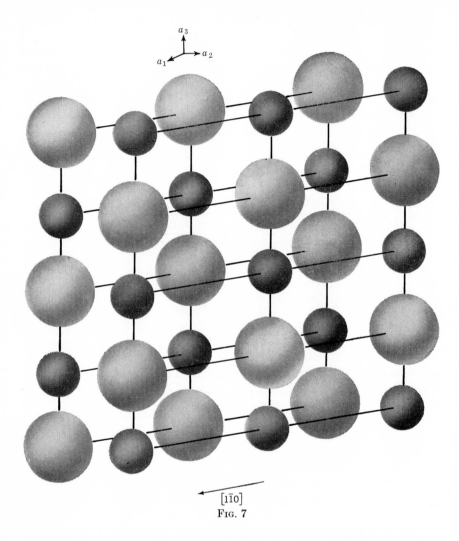

a_3
a_1 a_2

$[1\bar{1}0]$

Fig. 7

of each atom. The electrons, therefore, act as a sort of "lubricant" during deformation. Consequently, metal crystals are highly plastic, and slip is likely to occur along any densely packed plane. For example, the slip planes in body-centered cubic α iron are ((110)), ((112)), and ((123)).

Mechanism of deformation. Before considering the detailed mechanisms responsible for the deformation of crystals, it is of interest to determine the value of the stress necessary to produce deformation. Slip occurs when the shear-stress component parallel to a favorably oriented plane (in the slip direction) reaches a critical value. (The actual magnitude of this shear stress depends on the temperature.) As discussed later, it is possible that a weaker stress can also produce plastic or permanent deformation; in that case, however, the deformation proceeds very sluggishly, and the process is called *creep*. Regardless of the direction of the applied force, slip occurs on the potential slip plane in a crystal at the same *critical resolved shear-stress* value. Consider the cylinder-shaped crystal with a cross-sectional area A as shown in Fig. 8. The slip plane is shaded in this figure, and since it is inclined by an amount ϕ to the cross section of the crystal, its area is $A/\cos \phi$. If the

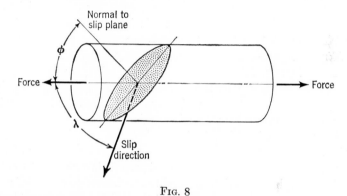

Fig. 8

slip direction forms the angle λ with the direction of the applied force, the force component in the slip direction is $F \cos \lambda$. The critical resolved shear stress then becomes

$$
\begin{aligned}
\tau &= \frac{\text{force}}{\text{area}} \\
&= \frac{F \cos \lambda}{A/\cos \phi} \\
&= \frac{F}{A} \cos \phi \cos \lambda.
\end{aligned}
\tag{14}
$$

The value of τ for most metal crystals is 10 to 100 g/mm^2. Numerous experiments have shown that this is the only stress component that affects slip in most metal crystals. The stress component normal to the slip planes has no observable effect, as has been demonstrated by loading different crystals hydrostatically. The importance of equation (14) was first pointed out by E. Schmid, and it is often called *Schmid's law*.

When an external force is applied to a crystal, the type of deformation produced also depends on the way in which the force is applied. The simplest way to produce deformation is to apply a shear couple parallel to a slip direction. Deformation then proceeds by the slipping of parallel

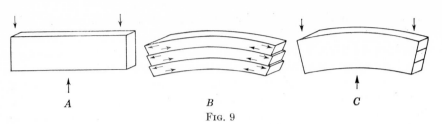

A B C

Fɪɢ. 9

glide packets by one or more translations parallel to the slip direction, and the process is called *translation gliding*. If the amount of slip is less than a translation, a deformation twin results, as discussed in a later chapter. Alternatively, if a force couple is applied so as to bend the crystal, shear can take place between adjacent glide packets to produce *bend gliding*. Suppose that the forces acting on a rectangular crystal are as shown in Fig. 9A. The bottoms of each glide packet are then stressed in compression and the tops in tension, as shown in Fig. 9B. The final appearance of the crystal is as shown in Fig. 9C. Usually the two ends of the crystal show the slip bands.

The stresses in the individual glide packets can be relieved by inserting extra planes, as shown in Fig. 10. This produces a number of equally spaced edge dislocations of the same sign. It is possible to calculate the number of such dislocations needed to produce a curvature of radius r.

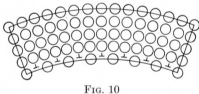

Fɪɢ. 10

If the thickness of the glide packet is T, the circumferential strain at each surface is $\pm T/2r$. Between two adjacent packets, the total length of the misfit produced per unit length in the slip direction is T/r. If the Burgers vector of the dislocations producing this misfit is s, then there are T/rs dislocations present per unit length. Finally, the dislocation density, ρ, in the entire crystal can be determined by noting that

$$\rho = \frac{\text{number of dislocations}}{\text{in glide packet}} \times \frac{\text{number of glide packets}}{\text{in unit thickness}}$$
$$= T/rs \times 1/T$$
$$= \frac{1}{rs}. \tag{15}$$

When a crystal is stressed in one of the ways described above it is doubtful that slip occurs by a simultaneous displacement of all the atoms in the slip plane. It is far more likely that the atomic displacements proceed consecutively so that at any instant of time some of the atoms in the slip plane are displaced while others are not. The boundary between the slipped and unslipped regions is called a *slip dislocation*, and the dislocation line must be either a closed loop within the crystal or else terminate on one or two of its faces. Slip can proceed, therefore, by the movement of the slip dislocation along the slip plane and in the slip direction. In order for the deformation process to continue, many new dislocations are produced in a region where the stress concentration is exceptionally high. Such a region may be produced around an inclusion in the crystal or at an internal crack or intracrystalline boundary. When a unit dislocation moves through a crystal, it produces a unit of slip. To account for the observed slip in crystals, therefore, it is necessary to postulate the existence of a source that continuously produces new dislocations. Similar mechanisms for doing this were independently conceived by Frank and Read. If a dislocation is anchored at two imperfections in the crystal, it is driven by the applied stress through the slip plane by forming an ever-increasing loop, as shown by the stages 1 to 4 in Fig. 11. As can be seen in this figure, at stage 4, the dislocation loop has closed in on itself. Further motion then results in a growth of the external part of

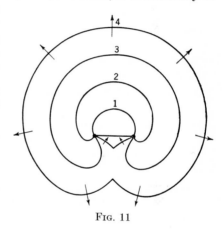

Fig. 11

the loop while the inner portion returns to stage 1, ready to resume the process. The existence of such sources in actual crystals was recently demonstrated by W. C. Dash. Figure 12 shows a photograph of a Frank-Read source obtained by Dash by diffusing Cu into a silicon crystal. The copper has precipitated along the discontinuities produced by several dislocation loops emanating from a common source and renders them visible when the crystal is viewed with infrared light. It is also possible to produce dislocations by a similar mechanism when only one end of a dislocation is anchored within the crystal, say at a screw dislocation crossing the slip plane. In this case, the dislocation moving in a slip plane has the shape of a spiral continuously winding around the point where it is anchored. Other mechanisms for generating dislocations may also be possible; however, theoretical calculation of the propagation of dislocations is so complicated that it is currently possible to present only a semiquantitative picture of the slip mechanism.

F. C. Frank has shown that the strain energy of a dislocation is propor-

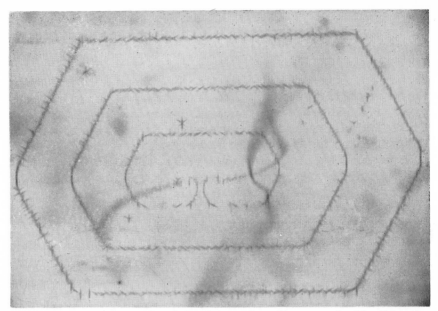

FIG. 12.   Photograph of a Frank-Read source in a silicon crystal.   The dislocation loops are rendered visible by the precipitation of copper atoms along the dislocations. (Photograph taken with infrared by W. C. Dash.)

tional to the square of the length of its Burgers vector.   Thus the energy of a dislocation whose Burgers vector is two translations long can be reduced by half by dissociating the dislocation into two separated unit dislocations.   In a crystal, the unit dislocations of lowest energy are determined by its structure.   A unit dislocation has a low energy when its Burgers vector is parallel to a direction of closest packing in the structure.   Since the Burgers vector is also parallel to the slip direction, this is the reason why slip usually occurs along directions of closest packing in crystals.   In case the crystal structure is a closest packing, therefore, it is possible for a unit dislocation lying in a closest-packed plane, but not parallel to a closest-packed direction, to dissociate into two half-dislocations that are parallel to two closest-packed directions.   This occurs, for example, when one closest-packed layer glides past another.   Instead of moving directly from one equivalent position to another, the layer slips first to an adjacent nonequivalent position and then slips to the transla-tion-equivalent site.   If slip is arrested before the translation-equivalent site is reached, a stacking fault is produced, as shown in the previous chapter.

Continued working or deformation of a solid produces large numbers of dislocations in the various slip planes that are active.   As the disloca-tions move under an applied stress, they intersect each other, producing jogs, and otherwise interfere with each other's motion. Continued working of a solid, therefore, ultimately decreases its plasticity by increasing the dislocation density, leading to what is commonly called *work-hardening*. It can be shown that this effect becomes important when the forces between dislocations are, on an average, of the same order as the forces due to the applied stress. This is the case when the density of dislocations becomes fairly large. Calculations of the distances between two dislocations when this stage is reached show that work-hardening occurs when the dislocation density is of the order of 10^8 dislocations/cm². The motion of dislocations is also impeded by the presence of other kinds of imperfections in the crystal, say foreign atoms included substitutionally or interstitially, so that additional energy is required for a dislocation to move past such an obstruction. Nevertheless it is possible for plastic deformation to occur even when the applied stress is less than the critical resolved shear-stress value (14). This type of deformation is called *creep* and is explained by postulating that the additional energy required to move a dislocation is supplied by the phonons present in a crystal. Because the number of cooperative phonon-dislocation interactions needed to move a dislocation through the crystal is, of necessity, a large one, creep proceeds relatively slowly at ordinary temperatures. In most commercial alloys, after a slight initial deformation, creep due to a static load becomes so small as to be negligible for most purposes. (This is not true of very pure metals or of elements like lead.) On the other hand, creep can become a serious problem at elevated temperatures. In polycrystalline materials, creep can occur by a relative movement of two neighboring grains along their boundary or by the diffusion of vacancies from one side of a grain to the other. Several specific models employing dislocations also have been proposed to explain creep and are described in some of the references given at the end of this chapter.

Fracture. When the stress normal to a crystallographic plane exceeds a critical value, the planes part and the crystal breaks. In single crystals, this is called *cleavage* when it occurs along well-defined planes so that the two halves of the fractured crystal are bounded by flat faces. The cleavage planes are usually planes separated by large interplanar spacings such as the ((100)) planes in NaCl or α-Fe. On the other hand, the nature of the interatomic forces in crystals can modify this generalization. For example, crystals having layered structures cleave along planes parallel to the layers because the forces between layers are frequently weaker than those within a layer. Because crystals tend to cleave along certain planes only, the critical stress necessary to produce cleavage depends on the crystal's orientation relative to the stress direction.

The fracture of polycrystalline materials is called *brittle fracture* if no plastic deformation preceded it, or *ductile fracture* if it follows pronounced plastic deformation. There exist a number of theories that attempt to explain the fracture of polycrystalline aggregates, specifically metals, in which ductile fracture is most common; they are, however, only moderately successful. A discrepancy arises when the predicted critical value of the *normal fracture stress* is compared with the experimentally observed value which is usually less by a factor of 100 or even 1000. The reason for this is the difficulty in taking account of all the imperfections that are present in the material and tend to weaken it. In explaining the fracture of glasses, Griffith postulated that fracture occurs because of the presence of small cracks normal to the tensile stress. Thus, the very high tensile strength of freshly drawn glass fibers is explained by assuming that such fibers do not contain cracks favorably oriented for fracture, since cracks that are parallel to the fiber axis do not affect the tensile strength appreciably. When such reasoning is applied to metals, however, the problem is further complicated by the fact that cracks can be produced during the plastic deformation prior to ductile fracture. Fracture can also occur by a shearing along a slip band. *Shear fracture* can be distinguished from cleavage because it leaves a nonplanar, usually concoidal, surface. Both types of fracture can occur in polycrystalline materials and are easily distinguishable by the appearance of the fractured surfaces. If a material is subjected to a series of consecutive stresses even of relatively low magnitude, particularly if the stresses are cyclically repeated, *fatigue fracture* can occur. This type of fracture is believed to be produced as a consequence of the formation of cracks at the points of stress concentration. A common example of fatigue fracture is the breaking of a wire or a metal strip by repeated bending in opposite directions.

Another way that a crystal can deform is by the formation of one or more *twins* in which the two parts of the crystal are so displaced that they appear to be mirror images of each other. (Other possible relations between twins are discussed in Chapter 7.) It can be shown that there is a critical-stress value for twinning similar to the critical-stress value for slip or for fracture. Unlike the normal fracture stress, the critical stresses for slip and for twinning depend not only on their orientations relative to the slip or twin planes but also on their orientations relative to the slip direction within these planes. It follows from this that, when a single crystal is stressed beyond its elastic limits, deformation may occur in one or more of these three ways, depending only on which direction is most favorably oriented relative to the stress direction and on the resistances of the various mechanisms. It is thus possible to account for the brittleness of certain crystals by comparing the cohesion across cleavage planes with their resistance to plastic deformation.

Suggestions for supplementary reading

Charles S. Barrett, *Structure of metals*, 2d ed. (McGraw-Hill Book Company, Inc., New York, 1952), especially pp. 316–319, 336–392, and 531–536.

W. Boas and J. K. Mackenzie, Anisotropy in metals, in *Progress in metal physics*, vol. 2 (Pergamon Press Ltd., London, 1950), pp. 90–119.

H. G. van Bueren, Lattice imperfections and plastic deformation in metals, II. Behavior of lattice imperfections during deformation, *Philips Tech. Rev.*, vol. 15 (1954), pp. 286–295.

A. H. Cottrell, *Dislocations and plastic flow in crystals* (Oxford University Press, London, 1956).

W. T. Read, Jr., *Dislocations in crystals* (McGraw-Hill Book Company, Inc., New York, 1953).

W. A. Wooster, *A textbook on crystal physics* (Cambridge University Press, London, 1938).

C. Zener, *Elasticity and anelasticity of metals* (University of Chicago Press, Chicago, 1948).

Exercises

1. In the Mohs scale, the hardness of a fingernail is ~ 2, of a pocketknife ~ 5, of ordinary glass $5\frac{1}{2}$, and of a steel file $6\frac{1}{2}$. Using these implements, determine the relative hardness of three kinds of metals.

2. List some possible reasons why coarse-grained polycrystalline solids should have a lower tensile strength than fine-grained solids of the same material.

3. Make a sketch of the sheet texture found to occur most commonly in face-centered cubic metals. In this texture, the crystallographic planes parallel to the sheet are ((110)) with [[112]] parallel to the rolling direction.

4. What are the principal planes in a square prism being stressed in tension along the prism axis? In a rectangular prism being compressed along the shortest axis?

5. Calculate the three principal stresses in an aluminum crystal, assuming that relation (11) applies. For aluminum, $E = 7700$ kg/mm^2, $G = 2900$ kg/mm^2, $s_{11} = 1.59 \times 10^{-12}$ cm^2/dyne, $s_{12} = -0.58 \times 10^{-12}$ cm^2/dyne, $s_{44} = 3.52 \times 10^{-12}$ cm^2/dyne.

6. It can be shown that a dislocation starts to move in its slip plane when the applied stress $\tau \sim Gs/L$, where G is the average shear modulus, s is the Burgers vector of the dislocations, and L is the diameter of the dislocation loop. If L can be used as a measure of the length of a Frank-Read source (Fig. 11), what is the minimum value that L can have for slip to occur in the [110] direction of a copper crystal under an applied stress of 5.00 kg/mm^2 ($G = 2900$ kg/mm^2, $a = 3.615$ Å).

7. Consider the slip system of NaCl (110) · [1$\bar{1}$0]. Show how it is possible for slip according to the above scheme to initiate slip in the slip system (1$\bar{1}$0) · [110]. (Do this by considering an edge dislocation parallel to [001] in a unit cube.) If slip occurs on both of these slip systems, it is called *double* slip.

8. An iron plate is bent to a radius of 10 cm. What is the dislocation density in this plate after bending if the dimensions of the plate are 0.4 × 3.0 × 12 cm and the unit translation parallel to the curvature is 2.5 Å?

9. Although the shortest unit translation in a body-centered cubic crystal is parallel to [111], an edge dislocation having a unit Burgers vector parallel to [100] does not dissociate into two dislocations whose Burgers vectors are parallel to [111]. Conversely, if two dislocations with Burgers vectors parallel to [100] and [010] cross, they can dissociate into two [111] dislocations. Prove the above two statements by using energy considerations.

7

Formation of crystals

Crystal growth

The beauty and sparkle of many-faceted crystals found all over the earth's crust have attracted man's interest since the beginning of recorded history. During most of this history, crystals have been treasured primarily because of their ornamental value. More recently, however, new applications for single crystals have been discovered in what are loosely called solid-state devices. Because many properties of solids are best studied with single crystals, the increasing interest in the nature of solids also has required that crystals be grown under controlled conditions for a variety of investigations. To date, almost all naturally occurring crystals of interest have been synthesized successfully in the laboratory. In the course of such syntheses, a great deal has been learned about the growth process itself. Some of the highlights of the growth of single crystals are reviewed below. It often happens that what appears to be a single crystal is actually a *twin* composed of two or more single entities bearing specific orientations to each other. Some of the processes whereby twins are produced, therefore, are also discussed in this chapter.

Velocity of growth. The world of minerals provides many examples of crystals bounded by well-developed plane *faces* which exhibit the point-group symmetry of the crystal structure. It was the observation of the regularity of these faces that led R. J. Haüy to declare in 1772 that *similar faces on different crystals of the same mineral form identical angles.* This so-called *law of Haüy* further states that these angles are characteristic of each different kind of crystal. In fact, this law may be considered to have laid the foundation of the science of crystallography. It was not until the beginning of the twentieth century, however, that the first accurate experiments were conducted to determine the process by which these faces were developed by crystals. In a rather ingenious experiment, G. Wulff immersed a transparent crystal seed in a liquid containing an isomorphous salt in solution. As the crystal grew by addition of the isomorphous salt, he measured the thicknesses of the new layers deposited on different faces of the crystal and established thereby the relative growth velocities of the different faces. From that experiment through to the present time, a great deal of research has gone into the study of the various factors that affect the growth rate of crystal faces.

If the velocity of growth of a number of crystal faces is known, it is possible to use a simple geometrical construction to predict the faces that will predominate as the crystal continues growing. Draw two vectors from a common point O normal to any two crystal faces so that

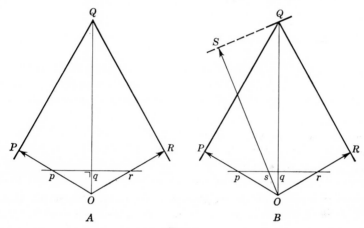

Fig. 1

their lengths are proportional to the relative growth velocities of these faces. Then draw the faces and connect their intersection to the origin, as shown in Fig. 1A. Finally, draw a line intersecting the growth-velocity vectors normal to this construction line. The following relations now can be deduced from an analysis of similar right triangles in Fig. 1A. From the similar right triangles OPQ and Oqp

$$OP:Oq = OQ:Op \qquad (1)$$

and from the similar right triangles ORQ and Oqr

$$OR:Oq = OQ:Or. \qquad (2)$$

Relations (1) and (2) can be alternatively written

$$Op = \frac{1}{OP}(OQ \cdot Oq)$$

$$Or = \frac{1}{OR}(OQ \cdot Oq). \qquad (3)$$

As can be seen in (3), the lines Op and Or are respectively proportional to the reciprocals of the growth-velocity vectors. These lines are called *index vectors* because they can be used to indicate when a particular face is present on the crystal.

Consider Fig. 1B which shows the same two faces of Fig. 1A except that a virtual third face has been added at S. It follows from the analysis leading to (3) that the index vector of the new face is related to its growth-velocity vector by

$$Os = \frac{1}{OS}\,(OQ \cdot Oq). \tag{4}$$

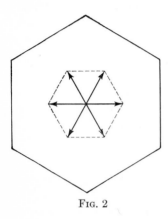

Now it is easy to see that, if the index vector of this face, Os, lies inside the triangle Opr, the new face does not intersect the two faces already present; that is, the new face does not appear on the crystal. Conversely, if Os lies outside the triangle Opr, the new face intersects the other two faces and it does appear on the crystal. When Os terminates on the line pr, then the new face just appears (or disappears).

FIG. 2

Since the index vector is inversely proportional to the growth velocity, it follows that *fast-growing faces are eliminated whereas slow-growing faces persist in a crystal*.

The relationship between the faces present on a crystal, called its *form* or *habit*, and the index vectors can be readily seen by extending the above construction to include other possible faces of the crystal. Figure 2 shows a cross section of an actual crystal and the index vectors of its faces. The polygon defined by the index vectors is called the *index polygon* and, as can be seen in Fig. 2, it is reciprocal to the crystal's form. The above deduction that fast-growing faces tend to eliminate themselves can be demonstrated by immersing a crystal that has been ground to the shape of a sphere into a saturated solution in which it can grow in size. At first, the disturbed regions near the sphere's surface dissolve, revealing a large number of different plane faces. As the crystal resumes its growth, however, the large number of small faces are rapidly replaced by a few larger ones. The successive development of faces seen on the sphere is diagrammatically shown by a cross-sectional view in Fig. 3.

The tendency of certain faces to grow more slowly and, hence, to predominate in the crystal's habit is related in a simple way to its structure. Certain planes in the crystal contain more atoms per unit area than do others. It is reasonable that these denser planes should take longer to complete a new layer than the less dense ones, so that it is possible to make a generalization that the *growth velocity of a face is inversely proportional to its atomic density.* This rule was first postulated by A. Bravais who based it on the assumption that the lattice planes having the largest reticular density are parallel to the slowest-growing crystal faces. Since the densest lattice planes have the largest interplanar spacings, the so-called *law of Bravais* states that *the relative importance of the faces of a crystal is directly proportional to the interplanar spacing of the parallel lattice planes.* Here, the term "importance" refers to both the frequency of occurrence and the size or area of the faces.

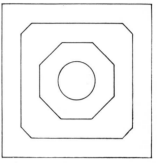

Fig. 3

The examination of the crystal habits of a large number of crystals shows that the law of Bravais is not always obeyed so that it is probably better to call it the *rule* of Bravais instead. Donnay and Harker have shown that a much larger number of crystals can be made to conform to this rule if the term interplanar spacing is interpreted to include subtranslations of the crystal such as are introduced by symmetry operations containing translation components, for example, screw axes. The combined *Bravais-Donnay-Harker rule* is a good generalization of the trend in form development for most crystals. It is only a generalization, however, because other factors, such as the conditions of crystallization, also influence the development of crystal faces.

Theories of growth. At the start of the twentieth century, the attention of many investigators turned to formulating the mechanism by which crystals actually grow in size. Early studies of crystal growth from saturated solutions indicated that a thin but rather dense layer adheres to the external surfaces of the crystal during growth. It was postulated that atoms or clusters of atoms can move laterally in the adsorbed layer until they become permanently fixed on the surface. The loss of atoms from this layer is then instantaneously replaced by other atoms from the surrounding solution. This leads to growth of crystals by diffusion through the relatively dense adsorbed layer, and the actual conditions of growth can be deduced directly from the laws of thermodynamics. It is interesting to note here that H. A. Miers discovered, in the course of his studies of the adsorbed layer, that the apparently plane low-index faces of a crystal actually can consist of several plane faces inclined by a few minutes of arc to the low-index plane. These so-called *vicinal faces* can be indexed only if very large indices are used. For example, the octahedral ((111)) faces of alum often consist of three planes whose respective indices are (251 251 250) and the necessary permutations.

Following the determination of crystal structures by means of x-ray diffraction procedures, it has become possible to study the atomistic nature of crystal growth. This approach differs from the earlier thermodynamic ones because it takes into account the forces existing between atoms on the crystal's surface and the atoms in the surrounding medium. Kossel and Stranski independently developed parallel theories in which it is assumed that the energy due to the unsaturated atomic bonds at the crystal's surface is lowered when an atom attaches itself to the surface.

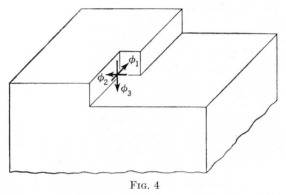

Fig. 4

The amount of energy released by such attachments is different in different parts of the crystal, being largest at a "step" on the surface. Consider such a step pictured in Fig. 4. The total energy released, ϕ, can then be resolved along three mutually orthogonal directions, as shown in Fig. 4, so that

$$\phi = \phi_1 + \phi_2 + \phi_3. \tag{5}$$

When a particle settles on the top face to begin a new layer it releases energy of amount ϕ_3. If it lands next to an atomic row on this surface it releases energy of amount $\phi_2 + \phi_3$, and if it attaches to a step on this surface the energy released is that given in (5). It is thus possible to compute the energy released at different parts of the crystal in terms of these three components. The calculations differ depending on the type of bonding that is assumed to exist in the crystal. It turns out that in an ionic crystal bounded by completed faces the energy of attachment is greatest at the corners, decreasing at its edges, and is least at the center of a face. Qualitatively this can be justified by realizing that the electrostatic attraction is greatest and the repulsion due to oppositely charged neighbors is least in the above sequence. Exactly the reverse is true for crystals in which the bonds are directed along lines joining adjacent atoms. In such cases, the energy of attachment decreases in the order midface > edge > corner. Although metallic crystals were not considered by Kossel or Stranski, it is reasonable to expect that the attachment energies are intermediate between these two but more similar to those of ionic crystals. This is so because the bonding in metal crystals does not have a strong directional tendency. The greater attraction of atoms to the corners of ionic and metallic crystals often leads to more rapid growth along these directions, with the result that the crystal grows with many branches called *dendrites* radiating from a common core. If the intervening regions are incompletely filled, the resulting crystal consists of large numbers of such dendrites, somewhat similar in appearance to a tree with many intermeshed branches. Dendritic growth is usually the result of very rapid growth such as occurs in highly saturated solutions. A common example of a dendritic ice crystal is a snowflake such as the one shown in Fig. 1 of Chapter 1. It should be emphasized, however, that under more normal growth conditions, once a new layer has begun to form, the affinity for an atom in the surrounding medium is greatest at a step in the new layer such as the one shown in Fig. 4.

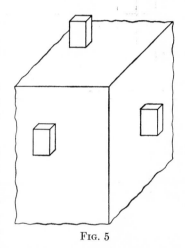

Fig. 5

M. J. Buerger has shown how the above theories can be related to the Bravais-Donnay-Harker rule by considering the growth of a nonionically bonded crystal as an accretion of chunks of atoms which for the sake of simplicity are assumed to be in the form of the unit cell of the crystal's lattice. The chunks of atoms can be pictured, therefore, as pinacoidal blocks which attach themselves to completed pinacoid faces by sharing faces of the block, as shown in Fig. 5. It follows that the frequency of attachment is proportional to the area of the contact face. Once a new face has started, all faces grow at nearly the same rate because the total contact surface becomes the same as soon as a step (Fig. 4) in the new layer develops. The growth rate of the different faces depends, however, on the frequency of attachment of the blocks. This leads to the empirically established relation that crystals having acicular unit cells develop platy habits whereas crystals having tabular unit cells grow with a needlelike habit (Fig. 6*A* and *B*). The above statements can be rephrased by observing that when several sites are available to an atomic cluster it prefers the one that produces the largest decrease in its surface energy.

Consider a crystal composed of parallelepipedon cells as shown in

Fig. 7.   When a new unit (the stippled unit a) attaches itself to the surface it projects above the level of the plane by an amount equal to the interplanar spacing d_{hkl} of that plane.   The amount of this excrescence is roughly proportional to the residual energy of the unit starting the new

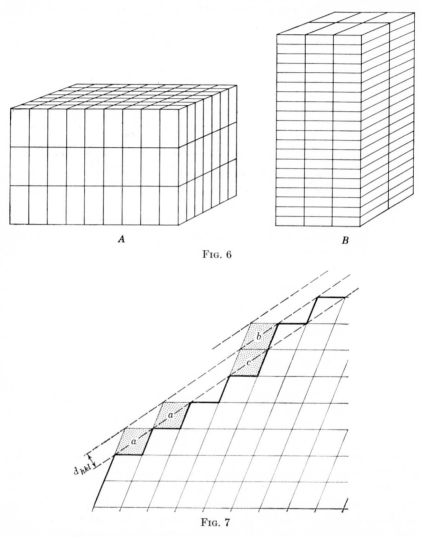

A   B

FIG. 6

FIG. 7

layer.   As can be seen in Fig. 7, the excrescence is least for deposition on high-index planes so that the planes having small interplanar spacings grow more rapidly and are not "important" in the Bravais sense.   Similar arguments are used by Buerger to show that the slope (indices) of a growing face does not change.   Although the addition of two units side by side tends to alter the slope of a growing face, it also doubles the excrescence, as shown by units b and c in Fig. 7, so that such additions increase the surface energy. Thus a plane, once started, tends to avoid any changes in its slope because of the opposition to an increase in the surface energy. This dependence of the stability of a crystal face on its surface energy means that, if a crystal can be grown in a medium having the same surface tension as the crystal, no real faces can develop. This is actually the case for many metal crystals which do not normally exhibit prominent face developments.

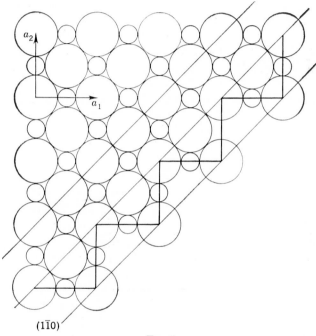

Fig. 8

The energy calculations of Stranski and Kossel have another interesting consequence. In the case of sodium chloride, for example, they show that only (100) faces are physically possible. This means that faces parallel to other crystallographic planes are never quite completed, in the sense that they consist of steps formed by mutually orthogonal ((100)) faces. These steps need be only a few atoms large, as shown for the $(1\bar{1}0)$ plane of NaCl in Fig. 8, so that they are not visible even with the aid of the most powerful microscopes. Recently, much larger steps have been observed by B. Chalmers and his students on the surfaces of metal crystals extracted from the melt in which they were growing. Careful investigation has shown that the crystallographic planes forming these steps are parallel to the closest-packed planes in the structures of the metals investigated. It was also found that the size of the planes was related to the speed of advance of the crystal-melt interface. The reentrant angles formed by these steps, in turn, constitute favored sites for continued attachment of atoms from the melt. The speed with which metal crystals grow from the melt depends on the way the heat liberated by the crystallization (heat of fusion) is dissipated. If the heat must be conducted away through the solid, growth proceeds slowly. On the other hand, if the crystal grows in a *supercooled* melt, that is, if the temperature of the melt is much lower than the true melting point of the metal, then the heat of crystallization can be absorbed by the melt and growth proceeds much more rapidly. When growth proceeds slowly and several crystal nuclei start to grow at once, only the ones favorably oriented attain an appreciable size. Consequently, several columnar crystals grow side by side separated by liquid inclusions between them. This is the reason, for example, why most castings consist of columnar crystals growing inward from the sides of the vessel containing the melt.

Mechanisms of growth. The influence of surface tension on crystal growth was first recognized by Gibbs who showed that below certain crystal dimensions the surface tension dominates the crystallization process. These ideas were extended by Balarev who assumed that surface tension was important in limiting the size of a crystal so that large crystals actually are composed of intimate accretions of colloidal-size crystallites. Using a somewhat different approach, Zwicky argued that a large crystal cannot grow as a perfect continuum because such an arrangement is thermodynamically unstable. He therefore postulated that crystals consist of blocks, 100 to 10,000 Å on a side, which are separated from each other by cracks, with the result that a regular secondary structure exists in a crystal. These hypotheses have been largely discredited in recent years because they are not necessary to explain the growth of crystals. A more satisfactory description of the ideally imperfect crystals known to exist in nature has been given by Buerger who has based his conclusions on the direct observation of a large number of crystals. According to Buerger, a crystal starts from an ideally perfect seed which may be limited in size by the surface tension, as suggested by Gibbs. The crystal grows by developing *lineages* which are branchlike extensions of the structure of the seed. The array in such a crystal is diagrammatically represented in Fig. 9. It can be seen that the lattices of each lineage are basically the same as that of the seed at the center; however, they have become slightly tilted with respect to each other. The picture shown in Fig. 9 can be considered to be a cross-sectional view of a three-dimensional crystal although the structure of actual crystals may be further complicated by having each lineage split into two or more sublineages. Figure 10 shows a photograph of a CdS crystal specially illuminated to show the lineages terminating on the surface. The existence of such crystal lineages also can be seen in crystals by examining successive sections of the same crystal.

The above mechanism describes how a crystal grows but does not explain why it grows; that is, it simply shows that imperfections occurring

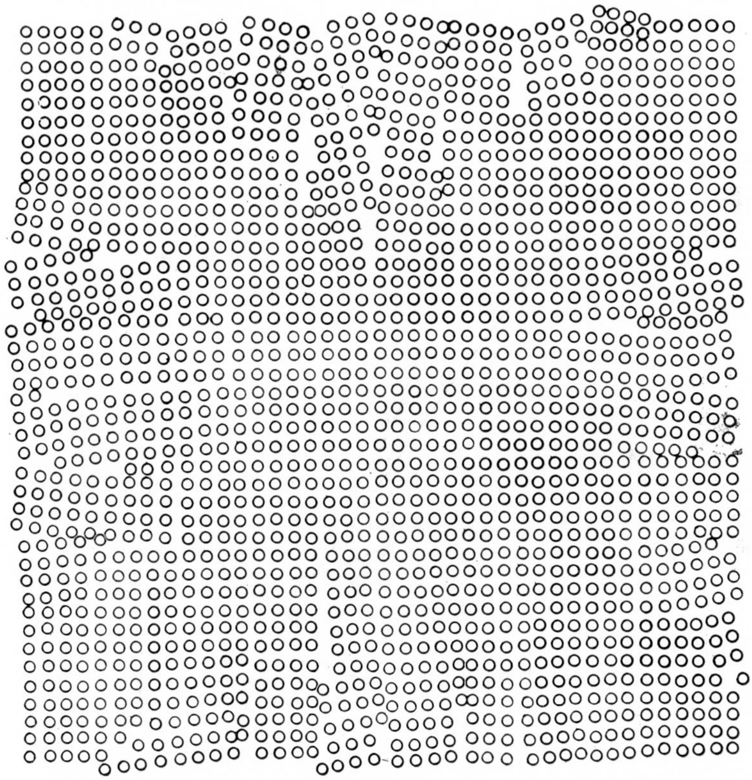

FIG. 9

in the initial seed produce lineages in the growing crystal. Implicit in this is the assumption that the crystal grows because the solid or crystalline state is thermodynamically more stable than the liquid state under the conditions at which growth occurs, for example, when a liquid is supersaturated or when a melt is supercooled. Recently it has been shown, however, that a crystal can grow even when these favorable growth conditions are not fulfilled. As described in the next paragraph, it is believed that growth proceeds in such a case because of the presence of screw dislocations in the crystal. It is reasonable to conclude, therefore, that the imperfections presumed to produce lineages actually cause screw dislocations to form in the seed crystal. The axes, or Burgers vectors, of the screw dislocations need not be parallel to each other so that neighboring regions in the crystal are caused to grow along slightly different directions. This is probably the way that lineages developed in the CdS crystal shown in Fig. 10, since this crystal grew by deposition from the cadmium and sulfur vapors contained in a sealed tube.

Recently, a mechanism of crystal growth has been proposed by Frank who postulated that crystals grow by means of dislocations that produce

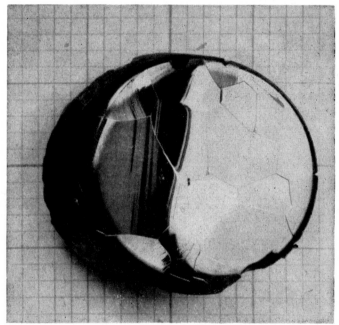

FIG. 10. Lineages in a crystal of cadmium sulfide. (Photographed by D. R. Boyd and Y. T. Sihvonen.)

steps in the crystal's surface. His views have been extended by others who have gathered large amounts of observational evidence to support them. A typical growth step resulting from a screw dislocation is shown in Fig. 11. As already discussed, the atoms or chunks of atoms prefer to attach themselves to this step in order to decrease their surface energy. Growth proceeds, therefore, by a continuous growth of the *same* layer in the form of a continuous spiral. The formation of these so-called *growth spirals* is shown in Fig. 12. The higher region *a* grows with a uniform speed along its entire front. Since it is anchored at one end at the screw dislocation, the angular velocity is greatest near the dislocation line and decreases outward from it. As the layer grows, therefore, it

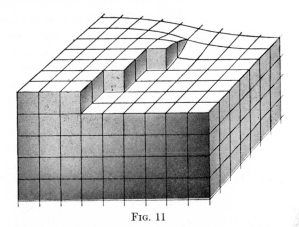

FIG. 11

develops a curvature near the dislocation line as shown in steps b, c, d, and e until finally it reaches an equilibrium with the solution and assumes the form of a perfect spiral in step f. This spiral then continues to sweep around the crystal's surface. A growth spiral can also form in another way. If an advancing layer encounters an obstacle, say a dirt particle embedded on the crystal's surface, it tends to grow around it. Before the layer can close upon itself, the strains produced in the vicinity of the occlusion may raise one side of the layer relative to the other. Growth then proceeds by the forming of a spiral layer, as shown in Fig. 13.

It is possible that more than one screw dislocation intersects a crystal surface. If the sense of the two resulting growth spirals is the same, they are said to have the same sign, whereas if they are not the same

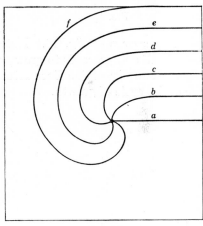

FIG. 12

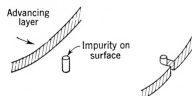

Advancing layer

Impurity on surface

FIG. 13

they are said to be of opposite sign. When two parallel growth spirals have the same sign they tend to reinforce each other. Consequently, when two parallel growth spirals have opposite signs, they tend to annihilate each other whenever they are very close together. On the

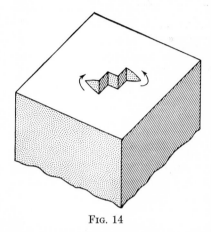

other hand, when the separation between two dislocations of opposite sign is large compared with the size of the atomic chunks by means of which growth proceeds, an irregular ledge arises between the two dislocation lines, as shown in Fig. 14. This ledge provides energetically attractive sites for atomic deposition so that growth proceeds by the formation of an ever-increasing loop which is anchored at the two dislocation lines. Figure 15 shows several such loops as they appear on a crystal's surface.

FIG. 14

The actual growth directions are indicated by arrows in Fig. 15. Note that the outermost loop has closed upon itself and proceeds to grow as a plane layer whereas the ledge joining the two dislocation lines returns to its initial stage ready to repeat the entire cycle of growth.

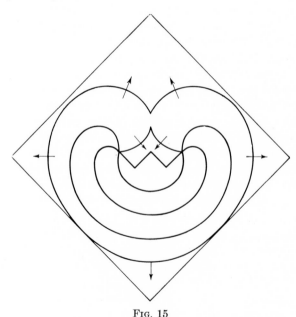

FIG. 15

The occurrence of a screw dislocation in a crystal can come about in different ways. When a crystal seed lies at the bottom of a vessel containing a somewhat supersaturated solution, the convection currents produced in the liquid favor growth along a plane parallel to the vessel's bottom. The crystal grows in the form of a flat platelet whose area increases much more rapidly than its thickness. It has been shown that when such a platelet is slightly raised or "tickled" by a sharp needle the induced strains produce a screw dislocation, as indicated diagrammatically in Fig. 16*A*. Since the bottom of the platelet lies on the bottom of the containing vessel, growth proceeds on the top face by the formation of a continuing growth spiral, as shown in Fig. 16*B*. After growth ceases, the unequally supported weight on the two sides of the growth step may cause the crystal to "collapse" along this step so that the final appearance of the crystal is as indicated in Fig. 16*C*. If growth is again resumed, the individual layers can continue to spread until all the layers have the same area. Thus it is possible for a crystal to grow by means of a growth spiral while not showing the presence of the screw dislocation in its final development.

The dislocation theory of crystal growth is supported by a very large number of direct observations of some of the growth features discussed above. A question frequently raised in this connection is how does one actually observe the minute steps produced by unit dislocations? One of the most powerful instruments for direct observation of these growth features is the electron microscope which has recently been developed to the point where it is possible to resolve separations of only a few tens of Ångstroms. Since the molecules of many organic compounds exceed these dimensions, it is possible to observe directly such molecules and the growth features of the crystals formed by them. In the case of other small features, it is also possible to observe them indirectly by the use of multiple-beam interferometry. In this technique, monochromatic visible light is first reflected by the crystal surface and next by a suitably parallel optical flat. If the crystal's surface is not perfectly flat, the different pathlengths of light rays reflected by different parts of the crystal surface produce interference effects which are readily observable.

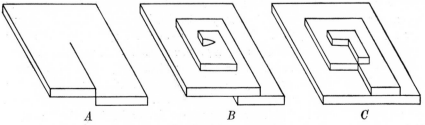

A   B   C

Fig. 16

It is then possible to deduce both the step height and the location of the step on the surface by direct measurement of these interference fringes. It is possible to measure step heights of approximately 15 Å in this way.

Twinning

It is possible for two or more identical single crystals to be joined together in a symmetrical manner to form a single entity called a *twinned crystal*. The symmetry element relating the two crystals can be a reflection plane or rotation axis or symmetry center not present in the crystal structure. The boundary separating the two crystals is called the *twin junction* and is usually exactly or very nearly parallel to a common lattice plane of the two crystals. In order for twinning to occur, it is necessary that the energy of the twinned crystal be very nearly the same as that of an untwinned crystal; otherwise the twin is unstable, and an untwinned crystal forms instead. Thus the structure of the twin must be such that the immediate coordination of the atoms lying at the twin junction is the same as that of similar atoms lying elsewhere in the twinned crystal. The coordination of the atoms lying at the junction by more distant neighbors can be different since the interactions between distant atoms make a very small contribution to the energy of a crystal. As an example of a twinned crystal, consider the c-axis projection of the twin structure of aragonite, the orthorhombic polymorph of calcium carbonate, shown in Fig. 17. The directions of the a and b axes of the two individual crystals are indicated by small arrows and the (110) plane, which is the twin plane, is indicated by a dashed line in Fig. 17. As can be seen in this figure, the two elements of the twin are related to each other by a glide plane lying in the twin junction.

The first observations of twinned crystals were made long before their structures had been determined. It was natural, therefore, for the early investigators to assume that the laws governing twinning were related to the lattices of the crystals. Thus Haüy postulated in 1801 that a twin must have a lattice that is either the same as the crystal lattice or some multiple thereof. Bravais and Mallard verified this postulate by studying numerous twinned crystals and concluded that twinning can occur whenever the symmetry of the crystal lattice is greater than the actual symmetry of the crystal. One of the additional symmetry elements present in the lattice but not in the crystal can then become the symmetry operator that relates the individuals forming the twin. Friedel extended this empirical rule to include the case when a multiple cell of the lattice has a pseudosymmetry which is greater than that of the individual crystals. Because the lattice of a crystal is determined by its structure, it is not surprising that these empirical rules are supported by observations of actual twins. In this connection it should be noted that a twinned crystal can consist of two juxtaposed individuals in twin orientation or of a larger number of individuals, usually present in the form of thin lamellae.

In view of modern concepts of crystal structure, it is necessary to consider other symmetry elements in the formation of twins, for example, glide planes. The twin plane can then be considered as a two-sided plane group. (See paper by Holser, listed at end of this chapter.) It is also possible to discuss the formation of twins by comparing the relative energies of crystals in the twinned and untwinned states. To do this

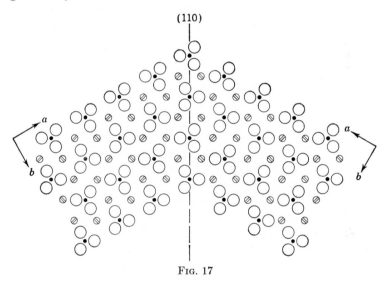

Fig. 17

it is convenient to take into account the processes by which twins can form. There are three distinct mechanisms possible.

1. Twin formation during the growth of the crystal. Such twins are called *growth twins*.

2. Twinning produced in an untwinned crystal by mechanical deformation of the crystal. This mechanism produces *deformation twins*.

3. Twinning that arises during the transformation of a high-temperature modification of a crystal to the low-temperature form. These so-called *transformation twins* include those produced during the annealing of metal crystals.

Growth twins. It has been shown in a previous section of this chapter that crystal growth proceeds by the addition of atoms or chunks of atoms to the external surfaces of a crystal. It is possible that there are several crystallographically distinct sites having similar energies where the newly arriving atoms can land. This situation is schematically depicted in Fig. 18 which shows the surface energy along some direction on a crystal face prior to the deposition of an atom on this surface. An atom that lands on site a is more stable than one that lands on site b because the energy required to displace it (move it over the energy barrier separating a from b) is greater. It can be inferred from Fig. 18 that the occupation of the a sites leads to a lower energy for the crystal and, hence, to the more stable structure. The situation changes somewhat if immediately following the landing of an atom on site b other atoms also land on b sites. R. E. Peierls has shown that the forces that dictate the crystal structure are short-range forces between atoms which do not extend their influence much beyond nearest neighbors. It is thus necessary to do a considerable amount of work to move many atoms from incorrect b sites

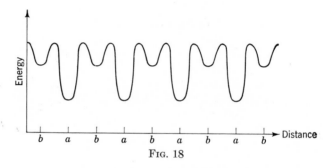

FIG. 18

into their correct a sites. Given enough time, however, this rearrangement is bound to occur because the energy of the crystal favors the occupation of the a sites. On the other hand, if the crystal is growing very rapidly, it is possible that new layers will be added to the crystal before these atoms can rearrange themselves. The consequence of this is that a *growth twin* having a slightly higher energy is produced.

Consider the growth of a crystal having the structure of a cubic closest packing. The normal sequence for the addition of closest-packed layers is ...ABC.... Suppose that at some point in the crystal's growth an error in the stacking or a stacking fault occurs so that the sequence at that point is ...$ABCABCB$. If the energy of the crystal favors the cubic closest packing, the next layer should be an A layer so that the crystal then proceeds to grow with an actual sequence ...$ABCABCBACBAC$..., resulting in a twin. This process is particularly likely to occur if the growing crystal is very small, that is, during the nucleation stages, and if the solution in which it grows is supersaturated. The smaller the size of the crystal is, the weaker are the forces that influence the stacking sequence, although it should be borne in mind that the energy of a crystal containing a stacking fault is greater than that of one having the correct sequence. This means that such twinned crystals will redissolve if the growth conditions return to equilibrium. On the other hand, if the twin continues to grow in a supersaturated solution until it reaches an appreciable size, the extra energy localized at the twin junction is no longer able to influence the surface energy which governs the crystal's growth and the twin structure is retained by the crystal. The presence of foreign atoms also tends to stabilize the twins formed, as is often the case in closest packings of metals. For example, twinning is quite common for the α solid solution of silicon in copper for which it has been shown by C. S. Barrett that the faulting tendency increases with increasing silicon content.

Deformation twins. When a crystal is deformed by applying a shear couple to the crystal, the deformation takes place by a movement of

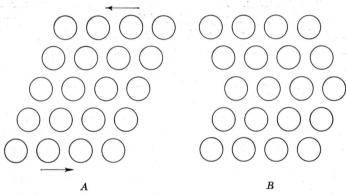

A   B

Fig. 19

atoms lying in certain planes past each other. The result of the atomic displacements depends on the amount by which the atoms have moved. If all the displaced atoms move into adjacent crystallographically equivalent positions, the deformed crystal has the same structure after deformation as it had before deformation. It is possible, however, that the movement of atoms in one plane is arrested after the atoms have moved into adjacent but unequivalent positions, similar to the *b*-site occupation in the case of growth twins discussed above. This produces a *deformation twin*, as shown in Fig. 19*A* and *B*. Note that the atoms lying farther away from the twin junction must be displaced by larger amounts than those lying close to the junction. In order for twinning to occur, the energy barriers separating the adjacent sites must be relatively small, lest the deformation stresses cause the crystal to rupture. It follows from this that deformation twinning can occur only parallel to energetically favored planes in the crystal. These planes need not be the same as the planes at which twinning can occur during growth, because the twin junctions of a growth twin are usually parallel to the more slowly growing faces of the crystal.

The increased energy of the twin is localized near the twin junction. Whereas in a growth twin this comes about as an accident of growth, in the case of deformation twins the additional energy is supplied by part of the work done in deforming the crystal. When a crystal deforms by twinning, it does so in a sequence of distinct steps which can be observed by examining sections of the crystal normal to the twin boundary. It is observed that twinning occurs in thin lamellae having nearly plane boundaries although the twinned domains may be somewhat lenticular in shape when further slip is stopped by some obstacle such as a grain boundary. Under continued deformation, these lamellae are observed to widen, and closely adjacent twin lamellae, having the same orientation, frequently merge. Although the twin lamellae appear almost immediately following the application of the stress, they usually proceed to grow in width rather slowly. The reasons why the twins form in this manner can be explained as follows: When a stress having a shear component parallel to certain planes is applied to the crystal, the same stress acts on all the parallel atom planes. For reasons discussed in the previous chapter, the resistance to the stress is smaller in certain planes than in others. Consequently, the crystal yields in these planes, and thin lamellae bounded by two twin junctions appear. The energy in these twin boundaries is higher than elsewhere in the crystal so that further atomic displacements can take place most easily in planes adjacent to the boundary. Each twin lamella thus proceeds to widen under continued stressing until it encounters some obstacle which prevents further atomic displacements. It frequently happens that the energy required to overcome this obstacle is greater than that required to start twinning in other parts of the crystal so that new twin lamellae are formed instead. Consequently, the deformed crystal contains several parallel twin lamellae. Occasionally, the twinning produced by mechanical deformation is accompanied by sharp audible noises indicating that the process takes place in abrupt steps.

The deformation twinning of metals is similar to the process of slip already described. The twin junction in body-centered cubic metals is parallel to one of the $((112))$ planes in the crystal. In face-centered cubic crystals it is parallel to $((111))$, and in metals having the structure of a hexagonal closest packing it is parallel to $((10\bar{1}2))$ planes. The atoms move past each other in parallel planes in a simple homogeneous shear, the amount of displacement increasing with distance from the twin boundary. An example of this type of displacement is shown for the (111) plane of a face-centered cubic crystal in Fig. 20. Two adjacent (111) planes are distinguished in this figure by shading all the circles

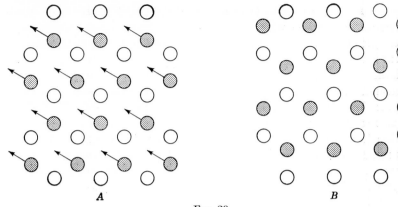

A   B

FIG. 20

representing atoms lying in one of the two planes. The atomic arrangement before deformation is shown in Fig. 20*A*, the arrows indicating the displacement, and the twin structure is shown in Fig. 20*B*. The twinning of body-centered cubic metals takes place most commonly by atomic displacements parallel to the ((112)) planes in the [[111]] directions. Defining the *shear plane* as the plane normal to the displacement plane and containing the displacement direction, a body-centered cubic structure is shown projected on the shear plane in Fig. 21. The displacements of the atoms along $[1\bar{1}\bar{1}]$ on one side of the twin boundary are indicated by arrows. Note that the amount of the displacement increases with distance from the boundary in steps of one-third of the translation distance parallel to $[1\bar{1}\bar{1}]$.

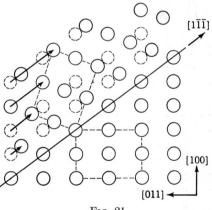

FIG. 21

In face-centered cubic metals twinning takes place parallel to the closest-packed ((111)) planes. Since there are two positions in which atoms of adjacent closest-packed layers have the same coordination, the energy difference between them is very small. The forces favoring the continuation of the twin arrangement are similarly small so that the twin is unlikely to become very thick under prolonged deformation. Instead, it is more likely that many twins, only a few atom layers in thickness, are formed. This produces stacking faults between the twins and explains why deformation twins of appreciable thickness do not occur in face-centered cubic metals. In the case of hexagonal closest-packed metals, however, the twinning takes place parallel to $((10\bar{1}2))$ so that the nearest-neighbor bonds must be strained to form a twin junction. As explained above, this leads to a widening of existing twin lamellae under a continued stress rather than to the formation of new ones.

Transformation twins. In certain crystals, it is possible that the structure at a twin junction is the same as the structure of a polymorphous modification of the crystal. That this is reasonable becomes clear when it is remembered that the immediate coordination of the atoms in two polymorphs is the same; only the next-nearest-neighbor coordination is different. Thus a twin junction is an example of two-dimensional

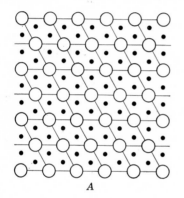
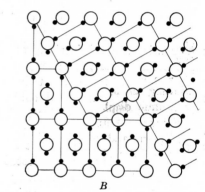

A   B

Fig. 22

polymorphism. It is not surprising, therefore, that high-low transformations are frequently accompanied by twinning. The structure of the low-temperature form is usually a derivative structure of the high-temperature form, obtained by suppressing certain symmetry operations of the latter. One of the suppressed symmetry operations can then become the symmetry element relating the twinned individuals.

When a high-temperature polymorph is cooled below the transition temperature, the low-temperature structure is assumed by different parts of the crystal simultaneously. As these regions grow in size they meet at boundaries which disappear if two adjacent regions have parallel orientations but become twin junctions if they are not parallel. If the suppressed symmetry element of the high-temperature form brings that form into self-coincidence m times, the low-temperature form can nucleate during the transformation in m different orientations. This means that the probability that two adjacent regions shall assume parallel orientations is $1/m$. For example, consider the hexagonal structure shown in Fig. 22*A*, consisting of mutually 3-fold coordinated white and black circles. Following the transformation, the black circles are shifted from the centers of their coordination triangles toward one of the corners. The consequence of these shifts is that the 6-fold rotation axes are suppressed. The resulting orthorhombic structure is shown in Fig. 22B in two out of the six orientations possible in this crystal. The boundary between two such regions is usually, though not necessarily, irregular.

When the high-temperature form of a crystal has a structure in which the different atoms are distributed at random among equivalent sites, then the low-temperature form may have a similar structure in which the different atoms assume an ordered arrangement. These so-called order-disorder transitions are frequently encountered in certain alloys. When such alloys are annealed below the transition temperature, the ordered regions may encounter stacking faults during their growth, with the result that twins are formed. Such twins are called *annealing twins* and sometimes occur during the *recrystallization* of polycrystalline metals discussed further below.

Growth in the solid state

Recrystallization. In the first part of this chapter, crystal growth was described for the case of growth from a vapor or solution or a liquid melt. As indicated above for the case of transformation twinning, it is also possible for new crystals to form in the solid state. In fact, new crystals can form under conditions such that a change from one distinct crystal phase to another does not take place. Such growth usually occurs when a previously strained polycrystalline solid is maintained at an elevated temperature for a prolonged period of time, a procedure called *annealing*. The annealing process normally consists of two stages: *recovery* and *recrystallization*. Of these, recovery is the name given to that relatively short period of time during which any strains present in the matrix are relieved without visible changes in the microstructure. This is the stage when the greater mobility of the atoms (due to interactions with the increased density of phonons present) allows the atoms to return to the lower-energy unstrained array. Such an atomic rearrangement may result in the migration of dislocations to subgrain boundaries, a process called *polygonization*. Alternatively, the rearrangement of the atoms leads to the formation of small strain-free regions or *nuclei*. This then becomes the initial stage in the recrystallization process and is called *nucleation*. The strain-free nuclei continue to grow in size, at the expense of their strained neighbors, until the recrystallization process is completed. The driving force for this process is due to the difference in the free energies of the strained and unstrained regions. The maximum annealing temperature for recrystallization is inversely related to the amount of prior deformation, although higher temperatures can be used to shorten the time required to complete the recrystallization process. The degree of deformation can also affect the ultimate grain size; the greater the prior deformation, the smaller is the average grain size.

When a completely recrystallized polycrystalline solid is annealed, further *grain growth* is possible. This process may occur, therefore, in any polycrystalline material, regardless of its prior history. It is quite easy to observe this growth on the surface of a polished metal. Such observations have shown that growth proceeds in an irregular fashion; for example, certain grains suddenly start to grow at the expense of their neighbors. Because this process involves larger displacements of atoms in the transforming region than the recrystallization process described above, the driving force in this case depends on the ease with which the atoms can diffuse in the various grains. Although all the reasons why certain grains appear to be favored in the grain-growth process are not as yet established, it appears that the surface tension at the grain boundaries is one of the principal factors. Some other factors are the activation energy for diffusion, initial relative grain size, and the impurity content of the grains.

Martensite transformation. The recrystallization process discussed above may take place at a constant temperature. Another kind of transformation, called a *martensitic transformation*, usually takes place in solids only while the temperature of the solid is changing. Unlike most structural changes that occur in solids, the martensitic transformation does not involve the diffusion of atoms to or from the transforming region. In this sense, it represents one extreme of the diverse mechanisms whereby transformations can occur. Another distinguishing feature of this transformation is that it is accompanied by a mechanical distortion of the transforming regions of the crystal. The distortion is produced by the small atomic displacements (less than an atomic radius) involved in the transformations. It is named after the transformation from face-centered cubic austenite to body-centered tetragonal martensite in steels. Phase changes occurring in nonferrous alloys are also called martensitic transformations if the small atomic displacements during the transformation cause a distortion of the transformed regions. In fact, this name is frequently given to any diffusionless solid-state transformation accompanied by a mechanical distortion.

It is natural that most of the studies of the martensite transformation have been carried out using steels. The structure of austenite consists of a cubic closest packing of iron atoms (γ-Fe) in which the carbon atoms are distributed among the equipoints $\frac{1}{2}00$, $0\frac{1}{2}0$, $00\frac{1}{2}$, $\frac{1}{2}\frac{1}{2}\frac{1}{2}$ in an interstitial solid solution.   If a body-centered tetragonal cell is chosen

$$\left(a_{\text{tetr}} = \frac{1}{\sqrt{2}} \, a_{\text{cubic}} \right)$$

in austenite, the martensite structure can be simply derived from it by a slight compression of the c axis and a dilation of the two a axes.   (The actual c/a ratio is a linear function of the carbon content.)   Since all the octahedral voids in gamma iron are statistically occupied by carbon atoms in the austenite structure, it is natural to ask why every cell in austenite should distort in the same way to produce the tetragonal martensite.   A possible explanation was suggested by Zener who proposed that the energy of the ordered array of carbon atoms required was actually lower than the disordered array that would leave the face-centered cubic structure of austenite intact.   Thus the transformation to martensite involves relatively small atomic displacements, without changing the coordination numbers of the atoms, but a relatively large distortion of the unit cell, up to 5 per cent increase in a when 6 per cent carbon is present.   The well-coordinated atom movements involved in the transformation change the shape of the transforming regions.   These changes can be observed particularly well when the martensite crystals form at the surface of a specimen being examined.

E. C. Bain was the first to suggest, in 1924, that the transformation can be explained simply as a compression of the c axis and an expansion of the a axis of the tetragonal cell, as outlined above.   Since then, a number of different investigators have suggested various shear mechanisms whereby the atoms undergo the required displacements consistent with the observed orientation relationships between the martensite crystals and the austenite matrix.   The details of these mechanisms are discussed in some of the references given at the end of this chapter.   Essentially they consist of displacements of whole planes of atoms, sometimes by two successive shear displacements, with the aid of slip dislocations.   This suggests that the martensite transformation can be initiated by plastic deformation, which is indeed the case.   It should be noted that probably the simplest example of a martensitic transformation is the one from a cubic to a hexagonal closest packing.   This transformation is most frequently encountered in cobalt where it involves displacements of parallel (111) planes and produces stacking faults, as discussed in the previous chapter.

Suggestions for supplementary reading

Charles S. Barrett, *Structure of metals*, 2d ed. (McGraw-Hill Book Company, Inc., New York, 1952), pp. 376–383; 562–576.

J. S. Bowles and C. S. Barrett, Crystallography of transformations, in *Progress in metal physics*, vol. 3 (Pergamon Press Ltd., London, 1952), pp. 1–41.

H. E. Buckley, *Crystal growth* (John Wiley & Sons, Inc., New York, 1951).

M. J. Buerger, The genesis of twin crystals, *Am. Mineralogist*, vol. 30 (1945), pp. 469–482.

J. E. Burke and D. Turnbull, Recrystallization and grain growth, in *Progress in metal physics*, vol. 3 (Pergamon Press, Ltd., London, 1952), pp. 220–292.

R. Clark and G. B. Craig, Twinning, in *Progress in metal physics*, vol. 3 (Pergamon Press Ltd., London, 1950), pp. 115–139.

R. H. Doremus, B. W. Roberts, and David Turnbull, *Growth and perfection of crystals* (John Wiley & Sons, Inc., New York, 1958).

Eric O. Hall, *Twinning and diffusionless transformations in metals* (Butterworths Publications Ltd., London, 1954).

William T. Holser, Relation of symmetry to structure in twinning, *Zeit f. Krist.*, vol. 110 (1958), pp. 249–265.

Ursula M. Martins, Solidification of metals, in *Progress in metal physics*, vol. 5 (Pergamon Press Ltd., London, 1954), pp. 279–310.

Ajit Ram Verma, *Crystal growth and dislocations* (Butterworths Publications Ltd., London, 1953).

Exercises

1. Make a scale drawing of the c-axis projection of a tetragonal crystal bounded by $((100))$ and $((110))$ faces of equal area. If the distance separating opposite faces initially is 1 mm and the growth rate of $((100))$ is 1 mm/hr and of $((110))$ is 0.5 mm/hr, show this crystal after it has grown for 1.5 hr and again after 3 hr.

2. Draw the index polygons for the crystals described in Exercise 1 after 0 hr, 1.5 hr, and 3 hr of growth.

3. The crystallographic axes for an orthorhombic crystal are chosen so that $b > a > c$. Thus, according to the Bravais rule, the most important faces should be the (010) pinacoids. Show that in a C-centered orthorhombic crystal this is not the most important face. Which is the most important face in this crystal?

4. The grain boundaries between grains in a polycrystalline metal can be considered to be made up of a large accumulation of edge dislocations. Describe a simple mechanism whereby a grain can grow in size when the metal is annealed at an elevated temperature for a prolonged period of time.

5. By means of a sketch, show that a dendritic crystal is a manifestation of lineage structure for a crystal grown in a highly supersaturated solution.

6. What conditions of growth, that is, vapor deposition, growth in solution, or growth from a melt, do you think are best suited for the production of visible growth spirals? State the reasons for your choice.

7. A crystal consisting of many parallel lamellae in twin orientation is called a *polysynthetic twin*. Suggest two possible methods for detecting the presence of polysynthetic twins in noncubic insulator crystals such as certain silicates, for example. Repeat for cubic metal crystals.

8. Consider the surface-energy distribution depicted in Fig. 18. Suppose that the landing of an atom on site b is immediately followed by the approach of another atom to the vicinity of this site. Is this atom more likely to occupy an adjacent a or b site? Why?

9. In calculating the surface energy of a crystal, the influence of all the atoms below the surface must be summed. If the contribution to this sum is inversely proportional to distance from the surface, why is twinning more likely to occur when the crystal is very small? Why do you think that the deposition of two successive layers in twin orientation on the surface of a large growing crystal is less likely to persist than a similar deposition on a small seed crystal?

10. Most cubic crystals of cobalt contain many stacking faults so that the crystals are twins. Do you think that these are growth or deformation twins? What is the reason for the greater frequency of twinning of cobalt than copper?

11. The high-temperature form of β brass has a body-centered cubic structure. When a single crystal of β brass is cooled below the transition point, the Cu and Zn atoms order to form the CsCl arrangement. Usually different parts of the crystal adopt different orientations so that the room-temperature crystal is composed of several so-called *antiphase* domains. By sketching the structure of such a crystal, show that these domains are in twin orientation.

12. It is possible to purify a metal by placing it in a cylinder and then melting a narrow cross-sectional area of the cylinder and moving the molten zone slowly from one end of the cylinder to the other. Suggest why this so-called *zone-refining* procedure should free the solid of impurities. Can one grow single crystals from a polycrystalline mass by this means? If so, what are the restricting conditions on the size of the cylinder, if any?

13. When an as-cast material is annealed, grain growth but not recrystallization occurs. Explain why this is the case. How can recrystallization be induced in such a material?

14. Look up some of the mechanisms whereby the martensite transformation is presumed to proceed. Show that the individual atomic displacements required are indeed small as compared with atomic dimensions.

8

Transformations in crystals

Elements of thermodynamics

Introduction. The exact treatment of most solid-state problems usually requires the application of *quantum mechanics* to their solution because, as indicated in Chapter 4, the different energies that an atom can have are quantized and cannot be handled by theories based on classical mechanics. The complexity of the attendant calculations, however, has limited detailed applications of quantum mechanics to relatively simple problems. It is shown in the next chapter that the cohesive energy of crystals can be calculated only approximately and only for very simple structures. Consequently, accurate theories describing the large number of different transformations possible in solids simply do not exist. There is, however, a wealth of experimental data which relate the transformations that occur within a system with similar transformations in other systems. It is possible to express these relations by the use of thermodynamics, or, more accurately, statistical thermodynamics. Because the reader of this book is not expected to be intimately familiar with the principles of statistical thermodynamics, the discussion of transformations is limited to a description of the most important transformations that occur in solids. Wherever they are needed to elucidate the transformation mechanisms, thermodynamic relations are presented and explained. However, a complete discussion of their various interrelationships is not attempted.

Several different kinds of transformations can occur in solids. The polymorphic or allotropic transformation, consisting of a change in the crystal's structure but not in its composition, already has been encountered in Chapter 4. Similarly, the martensitic transformation, which is accompanied by a mechanical deformation of parts of the crystal, has been described in the preceding chapter. Some of the many factors that

166

control these and other kinds of transformations are discussed below. The factors that are discussed at length have been selected in order to illustrate the basic principles involved in relatively simple transformations. Additional examples of actual transformations in the solid state can be found in later chapters.

A system can exist in an equilibrium state as a single homogeneous phase or as a heterogeneous mixture of several homogeneous phases, each of which has its characteristic temperature, energy, and entropy. The relationship between these quantities and the atoms comprising the system is statistical in nature and is difficult if not impossible to describe in detail. Nevertheless, it is possible to use the principles of statistical thermodynamics to describe certain phase transformations in solids in terms of the energies of these phases.

The first to analyze transformations on this basis was J. Willard Gibbs who obtained the relation

$$G = E - TS + PV \tag{1}$$

where G is called the *Gibbs free energy*
E is the internal energy of system
S is the entropy
T is the temperature (on the absolute scale)
P is the pressure
V is the volume.

At a fixed temperature and pressure, two phases having free energies G_1 and G_2 are in equilibrium if

$$G_1 - G_2 = 0 = (E - TS)_1 + PV - (E - TS)_2 - PV$$
$$= F_1 - F_2 \tag{2}$$

where $\qquad\qquad F = E - TS \tag{3}$

is the *Helmholtz free energy*. It is possible, therefore, to discuss transformations in solids in terms of the Helmholtz free energy, although it should be kept in mind that such a discussion is only approximately correct since small changes in V do occur in most transformations.

In general, a system tends to be in the state that has the minimum free energy. This follows directly from (3) and the first and second laws of thermodynamics. At low temperatures, the second term in (3) is small and the atoms attempt to form a structure that has the lowest possible internal energy. As discussed below, the internal energy is inversely proportional to the coordination number of the constituent atoms. This is consistent with the tendency of atoms in ionic and metallic compounds to surround themselves with as large a number of other atoms as possible. As the temperature increases, however, the second term in (3) becomes more important. The entropy of a crystal is determined by the Boltzmann relation

$$S = k \ln W \qquad (4)$$

where W is the total number of different ways in which the atoms can arrange themselves. The condition of minimum free energy at any temperature, therefore, becomes a sort of tug of war between a tendency toward a maximum entropy by an increase in the number of atomic arrays possible and a corresponding increase in the internal energy produced by changes in the coordination of the atoms. Note that this tendency of the entropy to increase is responsible for the formation of atomic imperfections or point defects in a crystal. As can be seen in (3), the tendency of the entropy to increase means that the Helmholtz free energy tends to a minimum.

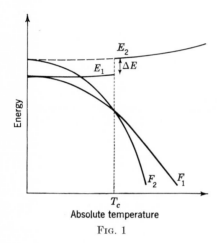

In order to see how this can be possible, consider a chemical compound that can adopt either of two structures whose internal energies are E_1 and E_2. (This is the case when allotropic or polymorphic transformations can occur.) The free energies are shown plotted as a function of temperature in Fig. 1. In order that a transformation from one polymorphic modification to another can occur, it is necessary that the two free-energy curves cross at some temperature T_C, called the *critical temperature*. If initially $F_1 < F_2$, then for temperatures greater than the critical temperature $F_1 > F_2$, and the more stable structure has the larger internal energy E_2. At the critical temperature, the free energies must equal

$$F_1 = F_2$$
$$E_1 - T_C S_1 = E_2 - T_C S_2. \qquad (5)$$

The change in the internal energy ΔE can be determined by rearranging the terms in (5):

$$\Delta E = E_2 - E_1$$
$$= T_C (S_2 - S_1). \qquad (6)$$

Since entropy is defined as the amount of energy (thermal) absorbed per unit increase in temperature, $S = dF/dT$ and it follows that above the critical temperature $S_2 > S_1$ and ΔE is positive. Consequently (6) states that energy must be supplied to the system, usually in the form of heat, in order for the transformation from one structure to the other to take place.

Similar considerations apply in the investigation of the stability of a crystal structure as a function of composition. Suppose that the two curves in Fig. 2 represent the free-energy curves of two possible structures α and β as a function of composition in a binary alloy. Here α is a solid solution of B in A and β is a solid solution of A in B. In the composition range 0 per cent B to X_1 per cent B, the α structure has the lower free energy and hence it is the stable phase. Similarly, in the composition range X_2 per cent B to 100 per cent B, the stable phase is β. At first glance, it would appear that in the region between the compositions X_1 and X_0 the stable phase is α, and between X_0 and X_2, the stable phase is β. It can be shown quite easily, however, that actually the

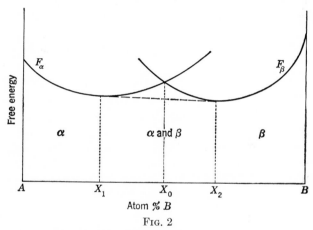

FIG. 2

heterogeneous alloy consisting of a mixture of α and β is more stable in this composition range than either phase alone. This is always the case when the two free-energy curves cross and possess a common tangent. The lowest free energy for each alloy in this system, therefore, lies on the α curve from pure A to X_1, on the tangent line from X_1 to X_2, and on the β curve from X_2 to pure B. This is the case when complete solid solubility between two elements A and B is not possible, for example, when the structures of α and β are different. In such systems, a mechanical mixture of the two phases is more stable, at certain compositions, than either phase alone.

Free-energy calculation. It is instructive to consider how the internal energy and entropy of a crystal can be calculated. Because the free energy of a binary solid solution can be calculated quite easily assuming that nearest-neighbor interactions only are important, this calculation is carried out below by first determining the internal energy and then the entropy of such a system. Suppose that the fraction of A atoms present is f_A; then the fraction of B atoms present is $f_B = 1 - f_A$. Let the coordination number of the atoms be z, so that $z = 8$ for a body-centered cubic structure and $z = 12$ for a closest packing. The number of nearest-neighbor pairs of the type AA, BB, and AB in a completely random solid solution then is given by

$$\frac{zf_A^2 N}{2} \qquad \text{pairs with an energy of interaction } E_{AA}$$

$$\frac{z(1 - f_A)^2 N}{2} \qquad \text{pairs with an energy of interaction } E_{BB} \qquad (7)$$

$$zf_A(1 - f_A)N \qquad \text{pairs with an energy of interaction } E_{AB}$$

where N is the total number of atoms present. The number of pairs of each kind in (7) is determined by counting the number of atoms of each type surrounding any atom in the solid solution. In this process, each pair AA and BB is counted twice; hence the number of such pairs counted is divided by 2.

The internal energy of a crystal at absolute zero, E_0, is the sum of the energies of interaction of all the atoms plus any strain energy present in the crystal. The strain energy may be due to differences in atomic sizes, electrochemical factors, etc. Because it is nearly impossible to express these strain energies exactly, the internal energy is calculated below on the assumption that the solid solution has been thoroughly annealed in order to minimize any remaining strain energy and that, in any case, it is sufficiently small to be neglected. With this assumption, the internal energy of the crystal is

$$
\begin{aligned}
E_0 &= \frac{zf_A^2 N}{2} E_{AA} + \frac{z(1 - f_A)^2 N}{2} E_{BB} + zf_A(1 - f_A)N E_{AB} \\
&= \frac{zN}{2} [f_A^2 E_{AA} + (1 - f_A)^2 E_{BB} + 2f_A(1 - f_A)E_{AB}] \\
&= \frac{zN}{2} \left[f_A E_{AA} + (1 - f_A)E_{BB} + 2f_A(1 - f_A)\left(E_{AB} - \frac{E_{AA} + E_{BB}}{2} \right) \right].
\end{aligned}
$$
$$(8)$$

The first two terms in (8) are the internal energies of two homogeneous phases containing $f_A N$ atoms A and $(1 - f_A)N$ atoms B, respectively. Thus it is necessary to consider the third term in order to determine whether the internal energy and, hence, the free energy of the crystal are decreased by the formation of a solid solution or not. Since $f_A \leq 1.0$, the term $f_A(1 - f_A)$ is always positive, reaching a maximum value when $f_A = \frac{1}{2}$. If the energy of interaction between two unlike atoms, E_{AB}, is less than the arithmetic average of the interaction energies of the two like atoms, then the third term is negative and the crystal's energy is decreased. Physically, this means that more energy is required to form an AA and BB bond than an AB bond, so that each atom will tend to surround itself with as many unlike atoms as possible. Conversely, if $E_{AB} > \frac{1}{2}(E_{AA} + E_{BB})$, the crystal's energy is lowered if the two phases segregate at temperatures other than absolute zero. The total internal energy of the crystal must also include a term relating the specific heat so that the internal energy at any temperature is

$$E = \frac{zN}{2}\left[f_A E_{AA} + (1 - f_A)E_{BB} + 2f_A(1 - f_{AA})\left(E_{AB} - \frac{E_{AA} + E_{BB}}{2}\right)\right]$$
$$+ \int_0^T C_P \, dT. \quad (9)$$

The entropy of the solid solution is determined by the specific-heat terms of the two components and a third term which expresses the entropy of mixing, or *configurational entropy*, given by the Boltzmann relation (4). The maximum number of ways possible to arrange the N atoms occurs in a random solid solution for which

$$W = \frac{N!}{(f_A N)![(1 - f_A)N]!} \quad (10)$$

so that the configurational entropy is

$$S_{\text{conf}} = k \ln \frac{N!}{(f_A N)![(1 - f_A)N]!}$$
$$\simeq -Nk[f_A \ln f_A + (1 - f_A) \ln (1 - f_A)] \quad (11)$$

if Stirling's formula $\ln x! \simeq x \ln x$ is applied. The total entropy of the crystal is

$$S = S_{\text{conf}} + \int_0^T \frac{C_P}{T} \, dT \quad (12)$$

and the Helmholtz free energy is

$$F = E - TS$$
$$= E - TS_{\text{conf}} - T \int_0^T \frac{C_P}{T} \, dT \quad (13)$$

where E and S_{conf} are given by (9) and (11), respectively. Note that when a solid solution is formed the free energy is decreased from what it would be in an ordered arrangement by an amount S_{conf} and also by the third term in (9), which is negative in this case.

The meaning of these thermodynamic relations can be seen by plotting the free energy as a function of composition for several cases. Suppose that $E_{AA} > E_{BB}$; then Fig. 3 shows the free-energy curves for the three

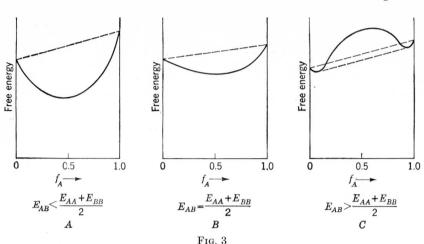

$$E_{AB} < \frac{E_{AA}+E_{BB}}{2}$$

$$A$$

$$E_{AB} = \frac{E_{AA}+E_{BB}}{2}$$

$$B$$

$$E_{AB} > \frac{E_{AA}+E_{BB}}{2}$$

$$C$$

Fig. 3

possible cases: when the energy of forming like pairs is greater than that of unlike pairs (Fig. 3*A*), when the two energies are equal (Fig. 3*B*), and for the reverse of the first case (Fig. 3*C*). The free energy of a simple mixture of A and B is also indicated by the broken line drawn in each figure. Note that the free energy starts to decrease sharply in all three cases because of the configurational-entropy term in (13). In the first two cases, it reaches a minimum when $f_A = \frac{1}{2}$; the free energy decreases as the difference between E_{AB} and $\frac{1}{2}(E_{AA} + E_{BB})$ increases. On the other hand, when the energy of forming like pairs is less than the energy of forming unlike pairs, the decrease in the free energy due to the entropy of mixing is rapidly overcome by the increase in the internal energy, and the curve rises above the broken line. This means that, except for compositions near the two extremes of the diagram, a mechanical mixture of two phases has a lower free energy than either phase alone. This lower free energy is indicated by the lower dashed line in Fig. 3*C* and is similar to the energy relations illustrated in Fig. 2.

Equilibrium transformations

First- and second-order transformations. It is convenient to classify the different transformations that can occur according to the way that the entropy changes during the transformation. Returning to the Gibbs relation (1), the entropy can be determined by differentiating G with respect to T:

$$S = - \left(\frac{\partial G}{\partial T}\right)_P \tag{14}$$

where the subscript P denotes that the pressure is held constant. If the change in entropy is discontinuous at the critical temperature, the transformation is called a *first-order* transformation. This type of transformation occurs in a single-component system, for example, when a solid melts or undergoes a polymorphic transformation. The relation between the internal energies, entropies, and free energies for a typical first-order transformation is shown in Fig. 4.

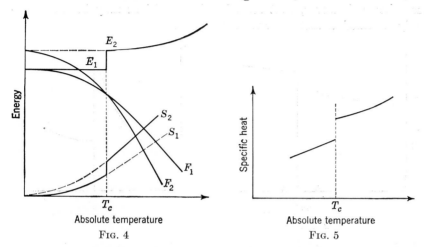

Fig. 4   Fig. 5

Another quantity which changes discontinuously at the critical temperature is the specific heat. The specific heat at constant pressure C_P is given by the first derivative of the *enthalpy,* $H = E + PV$,

$$C_P = \left(\frac{\partial H}{\partial T}\right)_P. \tag{15}$$

In a first-order transformation, the change in enthalpy is discontinuous, since E changes discontinuously, so that the specific-heat curve looks like the one shown in Fig. 5. At the critical temperature, heat is absorbed without further change in the temperature (latent heat of transformation) so that the specific heat is actually infinitely large at that point.

Suppose that the internal energy of a crystal changes gradually as the critical temperature is approached. Such a change is shown in Fig. 6 as a series of small discontinuous increments, which is probably the way that the change actually occurs. The specific heat, which measures this change in the internal energy, increases as shown in Fig. 7. Such transformations are frequently called *second-order* or *lambda transformations,* because of the characteristic shape of this curve. As the temperature range during which the second-order transformation takes place becomes narrower, the height of the specific-heat curve increases. Finally, in the limit of an infinitesimally narrow temperature range, the specific heat becomes infinitely high and the phase change becomes a first-order transformation. Several second-order transformations are described in later chapters. For example, transformations not involving changes in the crystal structure occur in ferromagnetic transitions discussed in Chapter 10, whereas the similar ferroelectric transitions discussed in Chapter 14 are accompanied by structural changes. Recently it has been shown, however, that ferroelectric transitions may be more correctly classified as first-order transformations.

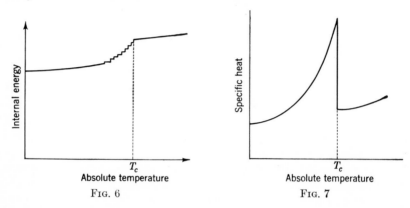

<table>
<tr><td>F<small>IG</small>. 6</td><td>F<small>IG</small>. 7</td></tr>
</table>

F<small>IG</small>. 6   F<small>IG</small>. 7

Order–disorder transitions. The chief limitation of transformation theories developed to date is that they are unable to take proper account of all the physical factors involved in a transformation. Nevertheless, the predictions of some of the theories are in very good agreement with experimental observations. This is particularly true of so-called *order-disorder transitions* described below. (A number of actual examples are discussed in Chapter 11.) When a random solid solution formed at an elevated temperature is slowly cooled, there may exist a tendency for the atoms to order; that is, each atom tends to surround itself with predominantly unlike atoms. If the ordering forces are weak, each atom may succeed in surrounding itself with unlike atoms for short periods of time so that, on an average, it is surrounded by more unlike atoms than it would be in a completely random arrangement. This is called *short-range* order. On the other hand, if the ordering forces are large, the atoms arrange themselves in specific lattice arrays leading to *long-range* order until, in the limiting case of complete order, the change in the crystal structure is completed. Experimental evidence shows that the predominant ordering in most metal systems is that of short-range order. It is nevertheless instructive to consider the long-range-order theory first, particularly since it is mathematically quite simple.

The approximate theory presented below is based on the classical Bragg and Williams long-range-order theory and is given for the simple case of a binary alloy containing equal numbers of A and B atoms. In the completely ordered structure, the A atoms are said to occupy a set of equipoints called α sites and the B atoms are in β sites. For the case of disorder, it is convenient to define an order parameter $\mathcal{S}$ such that $\mathcal{S} = 1$ when there is complete order and $\mathcal{S} = 0$ when there is complete disorder. If the total number of atoms in the crystal is N, then it is possible to define $\mathcal{S}$ as a linear function of composition by assuming that

$$\text{Number of } A \text{ atoms in } \alpha \text{ sites} = \frac{(1 + \mathcal{S})}{4} N,$$

$$\text{Number of } A \text{ atoms in } \beta \text{ sites} = \frac{(1 - \mathcal{S})}{4} N,$$

$$\text{Number of } B \text{ atoms in } \alpha \text{ sites} = \frac{(1 - \mathcal{S})}{4} N,$$

$$\text{Number of } B \text{ atoms in } \beta \text{ sites} = \frac{(1 + \mathcal{S})}{4} N. \tag{16}$$

It is easy to show that the above relations reduce to the proper values of $\mathcal{S}$ in the limiting cases of complete order and disorder.

The free energy can now be calculated similarly to the procedures used in the previous section. As before, it is assumed that only nearest-neighbor interactions contribute to the internal energy. Since there are $N/2$ α sites and β sites in the crystal, the total number of pairs AA formed is equal to the number of A atoms in α sites times $z/(N/2)$ times the number of A's on β sites, where z is the coordination number determined by the structure. For simplicity, assume that the disordered structure is body-centered cubic and that the atoms are arranged at random (no short-range order). The coordination number z is then equal to 8 and

$$\text{Number of pairs } AA = \frac{(1 + \mathcal{S})}{4} N \frac{8}{N/2} \frac{(1 - \mathcal{S})N}{4} = (1 - \mathcal{S}^2)N$$

$$\text{Number of pairs } BB = \frac{(1 + \mathcal{S})}{4} N \frac{8}{N/2} \frac{(1 - \mathcal{S})N}{4} = (1 - \mathcal{S}^2)N. \tag{17}$$

The number of pairs AB is the number of A atoms on α sites times the number of B's on β sites, plus the number of A's on β sites times the number of B's on α sites; the sum multiplied by $8/(N/2)$. Thus

$$\text{Number of pairs } AB = \left[\frac{(1 + \mathcal{S})^2 N^2}{16} + \frac{(1 - \mathcal{S})^2 N^2}{16} \right] \frac{8}{N/2}$$
$$= (1 + \mathcal{S})^2 N + (1 - \mathcal{S})^2 N$$
$$= 2(1 + \mathcal{S}^2)N. \tag{18}$$

The internal energy then is given by (9):

$$E = N(1 - \mathcal{S}^2)(E_{AA} + E_{BB}) + 2N(1 + \mathcal{S}^2)E_{AB} + \int_0^T C_P \, dT. \tag{19}$$

For the general case, when the fraction of A and B atoms is not exactly equal,

$$
E_0 = E - \int_0^T C_P \, dT
$$
$$
= 4N \left[f_A E_{AA} + (1 - f_A) E_{BB} + 2 f_A (1 - f_A) \left(E_{AB} - \frac{E_{AA} + E_{BB}}{2} \right) \right]
$$
$$
+ 8N f_A^2 \mathcal{S}^2 \left(E_{AB} - \frac{E_{AA} + E_{BB}}{2} \right) \quad (20)
$$

which reduces to the form of (19) when $f_A = \frac{1}{2}$. Also note that at complete disorder ($\mathcal{S} = 0$) the expression in (20) reduces to that in (8).

Similarly, the configurational entropy can be determined by considering all the possible ways of arranging the A and B atoms on α and β sites. Using relations (11) and (16),

$$
S_{\text{conf}} = k \ln \frac{(N/2)!}{\left[\frac{(1 + \mathcal{S})}{4} N \right]! \left[\frac{(1 - \mathcal{S})}{4} N \right]!}
$$
$$
= -kN \left[\frac{(1 + \mathcal{S})}{2} \ln \frac{(1 + \mathcal{S})}{2} + \frac{(1 - \mathcal{S})}{2} \ln \frac{(1 - \mathcal{S})}{2} \right]
$$
$$
= kN \ln 2 - \frac{kN}{2} [(1 + \mathcal{S}) \ln (1 + \mathcal{S}) + (1 - \mathcal{S}) \ln (1 - \mathcal{S})]. \quad (21)
$$

This relation has an interesting meaning. At complete disorder ($\mathcal{S} = 0$) it reduces to $kN \ln 2$ which is the value of (11) for $f_A = \frac{1}{2}$. On the other hand, at complete order ($\mathcal{S} = 1$) the configurational entropy is zero. This is so because there is only one way to arrange the atoms in the correct ordered array ($W = 1$) so that $\ln 1 = 0$.

It is now possible to determine the free energy by subtracting the quantity T times (21) plus $T \int (C_P/T) \, dT$ from (20). If ordering is to occur, of course, $E_{AB} < \frac{1}{2}(E_{AA} + E_{BB})$; otherwise the two components prefer to segregate. This is illustrated by a plot of the free energy against the order parameter $\mathcal{S}$ for several temperatures shown in Fig. 8. Observe that below the critical temperature the minimum in the curve lies near $\mathcal{S} = 1$ but does not occur at $\mathcal{S} = 1$ unless the absolute temperature is zero. This indicates that perfect order is never achieved in such alloys at ordinary temperatures. At the critical temperature T_C the curve is flat over a certain region near $\mathcal{S}' = 0$ so that, although some order is still present, long-range order has disappeared. Above T_C there is a single minimum in the free-energy curve at $\mathcal{S} = 0$, and the stable system is completely disordered.

Order-disorder transformations in solids are accompanied by characteristic changes in the crystal's structure. Suppose that the ordered structure of a crystal can be represented by alternating black and white circles as shown in Fig. 9A. The completely disordered structure then consists of "statistical" circles which are half black and half white, as shown in Fig. 9B, since the probability that a given site is occupied by a black or white circle is exactly the same. It is evident in Fig. 9 that the

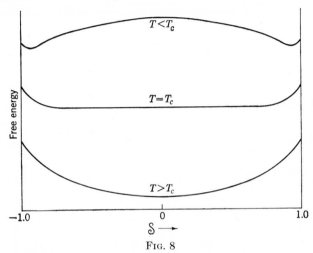

FIG. 8

effect of disordering the structure in Fig. 9A is to halve the translations a_1 and a_2 in the ordered structure. Conversely, when the disordered structure (Fig. 9B) orders, the translations a'_1 and a'_2, defining the unit cell of the disordered structure, are doubled. The point-group symmetry is not affected by this transition and remains 4mm for both structures

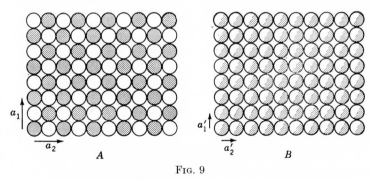

FIG. 9

although the density of symmetry operators is reduced on ordering. The lattice of the ordered crystal, however, is a *superlattice* of the disordered crystal's lattice. As shown in Chapter 3, the position of x-ray reflections, that is, their Bragg angle, is determined by the lattice spacings. The ordering of a crystal structure, therefore, can frequently be detected in an x-ray diffraction photograph by observing the appearance of so-called *superlattice reflections* of the ordered structure in addition to the *fundamental reflections* of the disordered crystal. It should be realized that superlattices can form in fully ordered state only when the atomic ratio in a solid solution can be expressed very closely by small integers. Superlattice formation has been observed to occur most commonly in alloys whose constituents are present in the ratios 1:1 or 3:1 although it also occurs in other alloys when the ratio is 1:2, 2:3, 4:1, etc.

The long-range-order parameter is shown plotted against temperature in Fig. 10. It is constant at low temperatures and decreases gradually with increasing temperature until, near the critical temperature, it drops off very rapidly to zero. The critical temperature is related to the energy and, for the 50-50 composition discussed above, $T_C = (1/4k)$ $(2E_{AB} + E_{AA} + E_{BB})$, as can be shown by appropriate manipulation of

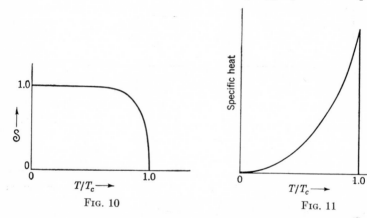

Fɪɢ. 10   Fɪɢ. 11

the above equations. Similarly, the specific-heat curve shown in Fig. 11 rises slowly until, at the critical temperature, it drops abruptly to zero. The shape of this curve can be determined directly from the above theory by assuming that the volume does not change during the transformation so that (15) reduces to $C_P = (dE/dT)_P$.

Actual determinations of the specific heat show that the curve does not fall quite to zero at or above the critical temperature but instead levels off at some small value. This discrepancy with the theory is largely due to the simple assumptions made in deriving it, specifically, that below the critical temperature $E_{AB} < \frac{1}{2}(E_{AA} + E_{BB})$ and the structure tends to order completely, whereas above T_C, $E_{AB} = \frac{1}{2}(E_{AA} + E_{BB})$ and the structure can disorder at random. Experimental evidence indicates, however, that in solid solutions the energy of interaction in unlike pairs is usually less than that in like pairs, at all temperatures. Thus disorder is produced primarily by the thermally increased freedom of motion of the atoms so that long-range order gradually gives way to short-range order. The simplest model of short-range order is that of small ordered blocks or *domains* whose size varies with temperature. The boundary between two such blocks is shown schematically in Fig. 12. The adjacent blocks have the same ordered structure except that, if a set of α and β sites are defined for the entire crystal, the atomic positions are exactly reversed in each block. These blocks are popularly called *antiphase* domains although it should be realized that actually they are in twin orientation relative to each other. This is the origin of the annealing twins discussed in the previous chapter. The formation of such domains is not inconsistent with the requirement that $E_{AB} < \frac{1}{2}(E_{AA} + E_{BB})$ because the number of AA and BB pairs formed is minimized by restricting such pair formation to the domain walls only. At low temperatures, the presence of these walls increases the internal energy of the crystal so that they are unstable and the walls are absorbed in the growth of one domain at the expense of its neighbors until long-range order sets in. At higher temperatures, however, the entropy term in the free-energy expression becomes dominant and the presence of domain walls lowers the free energy by increasing the configurational entropy.

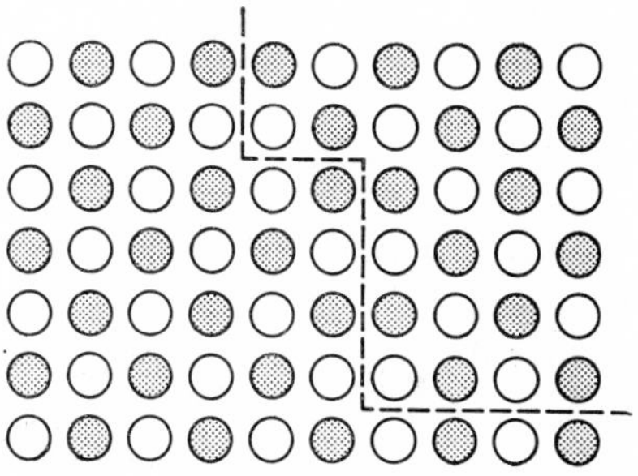

FIG. 12

The first to develop a successful theory of short-range order, which subsequently has been modified slightly by several investigators, Bethe explicitly considered the interaction energy between pairs of unlike atoms. He then computed the energy required to convert two AB pairs into an AA and a BB pair. If the fraction of AB pairs present at a specific temperature is f_{AB}, it is possible to define a short-range-order parameter in terms of this fraction:

$$\sigma = 2f_{AB} - 1. \tag{22}$$

$\sigma = +1$ at complete order and goes to zero at complete disorder since, on an average, the number of A and B atoms coordinating any atom in the crystal is the same. At a specific temperature, the fraction of unlike atom pairs present is $\frac{1}{2}(1 + \sigma)$ and the fraction of like atom pairs is $\frac{1}{2}(1 - \sigma)$. The ratio of the two kinds of pairs present when equilibrium is established can then be determined from the Boltzmann relation

$$\frac{\frac{1}{2}(1 + \sigma)}{\frac{1}{2}(1 - \sigma)} = e^{-\varepsilon/kT} \tag{23}$$

where $\varepsilon = E_{AB} - \frac{1}{2}(E_{AA} + E_{BB})$. The dependence of the short-range-order parameter on temperature is indicated in Fig. 13. It does not drop to zero at the critical temperature but approaches it asymptotically at higher temperatures.

In his first calculation, Bethe considered the interactions of an atom on a central site with its immediate neighbors only and expressed its interaction with all the other atoms by a single term. It turns out that this term can then be eliminated by the physically reasonable assumption that it should make no difference to the calculation whether the central site chosen is an α or β site. (In a second and better calculation, Bethe also took into account the second-nearest-neighbor interactions.) Because of their relative complexity, the expressions for the internal energy and entropy are not reproduced here; however, it can be shown that they predict the formation of long-range order below the critical temperature. Above the critical temperature, the short-range-order parameter is given in terms of the coordination number of the atoms, z, by

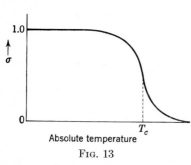

FIG. 13

$$\sigma = \frac{z^{Tc/T} - (z - 2)^{Tc/T}}{z^{Tc/T} + (z - 2)^{Tc/T}} \tag{24}$$

which reduces to

$$\sigma_C = \frac{z - (z - 2)}{z + (z - 2)}$$
$$= \frac{1}{z - 1} \tag{25}$$

at the critical temperature.

Transformations in complex structures. Suppose that the random solid solution whose structure is shown in Fig. 14A transforms upon ordering to the structure shown in Fig. 14B. The effect of ordering in this case is to change not the lattice but the symmetry from $6mm$ to $3mm$. Thus, the structure of an ordered phase is invariably a derivative structure of the disordered phase and its symmetry is a subgroup of the ordered crystal's point group. It is possible, therefore, to classify transformations on the basis of the symmetry changes produced. However, this leads to a somewhat artificial classification scheme since, although the symmetry of a crystal is reflected in its properties, factors not related to symmetry may play a dominant role. It is much more meaningful to base the classification on what happens to the bonding of the atoms during

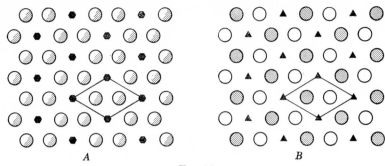

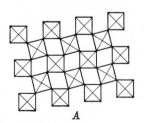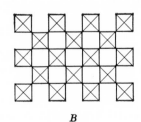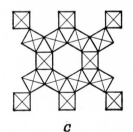

Fig. 14

the transformation. Such a classification applicable primarily to polymorphic transformations in nonmetals has been proposed by Buerger and is reproduced in Table 1. The relative speeds at which the various transformations usually occur are noted in parentheses in this table following each transformation type.

Table 1
Types of transformation

1. Transformations of secondary coordination:
    1. Displacive (rapid)
    2. Reconstructive (sluggish)
2. Transformations of first coordination:
    1. Dilatational (rapid)
    2. Reconstructive (sluggish)
3. Transformations of disorder:
    1. Rotational (rapid)
    2. Substitutional (sluggish)
4. Transformations of bond type:
    (These are usually sluggish.)

Suppose that a crystal's structure consists of atomic polyhedra sharing corners, as represented diagrammatically in Fig. 15A. It is possible for the structure to transform to either of the two types shown in Fig. 15B and C without changing the coordination of the atoms within each

A   B   C

Fig. 15

polyhedron. Since only the arrangement of the polyhedra is changed, such changes are described as a transformation of the secondary coordination of the atoms located at the centers of each polyhedron. Obviously, it is easier to make the transition to the structure shown in Fig. 15B because none of the bonds between atoms are actually disrupted. It is easily shown that the structure in Fig. 15B is an average of the structure shown in Fig. 15A and its enantiomorphous equivalent which is skewed in the opposite direction. At high temperatures, the structure can alternate between these two equally stable configurations, giving the "open" structure in Fig. 15B. This so-called *displacive* or *high-low* transformation can proceed quite rapidly, therefore, and occurs at a characteristic transition temperature, for example, at 573°C in quartz. The reconstructive transformation leading to the structure shown in Fig. 15C, on the other hand, requires that the second-coordination bonds be broken and reformed anew so that it proceeds very sluggishly. For example, both of the two polymorphic modifications of lead azide, PbN_6, appear to be equally stable at room temperature if left in a dry state. When placed in a solution containing dissolved lead azide, however, the unstable β modification undergoes a reconstructive transformation to the apparently more stable α form, as shown by the time-lapse photographs in Fig. 16. Similarly, this is the reason why pure tridymite, a high-temperature polymorph of SiO_2, persists for indefinite periods at ordinary temperatures even though it is thermodynamically unstable at these temperatures.

The simplest way that a transformation involving changes in the first coordination of atoms can proceed is for the coordination to change from one state to the other without forming any intermediate states. For example, when CsCl is heated above 460°C, the cubic coordination of the atoms is thermally dilated until the octahedral coordination of the NaCl structure results. Such *dilatational transformations*, therefore, proceed fairly rapidly. If the new phase requires a complete rearrangement of the atoms, then the transformation proceeds very sluggishly, if at all. Similarly, in the case of order-disorder transformations, the *substitutional transformation* discussed in the previous section proceeds relatively slowly. On the other hand, if disordering can occur merely by the rotation of groups of atoms, then a *rotational transformation* can proceed quite rapidly. This case is similar to the displacive transformation discussed above, except that some second-coordination bonds are temporarily broken during the rotation of an atomic group. The broken bonds are immediately reformed with other atoms when the rotation of the group is completed. Finally, it is possible that completely new types of bonds are formed as the result of the transformation. Such transitions are obviously more difficult to accomplish and usually require extremely

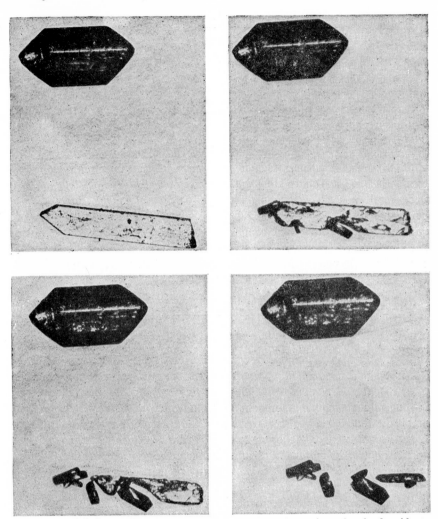

FIG. 16. Time-lapse photographs showing the transformation of β lead azide to small crystallites of α lead azide in an aqueous solution containing a large α crystal.

high temperatures and pressures. An example of such a transformation is the transformation of graphite to diamond discussed in Chapter 13.

Equilibrium diagrams

Despite the lack of rigorous theories to describe the transformations that can occur in solids, a wealth of experimental data is available that describes the different transformations that actually take place. The relations between the different phases or structures that are encountered are usually represented graphically in so-called *constitution diagrams* or *phase diagrams* or *equilibrium diagrams*. The latter name is derived from the fact that such diagrams usually show the most stable phases that occur under equilibrium conditions. Strictly speaking, equilibrium is attained after sufficient time has elapsed so that the reaction is completed, that is, when no further changes can occur. In practice, it is frequently not possible to control the reaction rate sufficiently to allow equilibrium to be reached at each stage in a transformation. The four principal variables in thermodynamic reactions are pressure, temperature, volume, and composition of the material. Most reactions are carried out at atmospheric pressure and, in the solid state, usually involve very small volume changes so that they can be ignored. For a two-component system, therefore, a two-coordinate diagram is sufficient to show what happens at different compositions as a function of temperature. On the other hand, in a three-component system, a three-dimensional figure is needed in order to represent all possible compositions of three components as a function of temperature. Since such figures are difficult to draw and to interpret, it is more usual to represent such information on a number of isothermal sections drawn for a series of different temperatures.

A typical equilibrium diagram for the iron-carbon system is shown in Fig. 17. The curves in this figure outline the regions in which the phases indicated within the boundaries are in stable equilibrium, as a function of temperature and composition. The term *phase* is defined as that part of the system which is macroscopically and microscopically homogeneous and is distinguished from its environment by distinct physical boundaries. A phase is considered to be in an equilibrium state at constant pressure and temperature when it does not undergo any further changes either in its structure or its composition. Many phases of practical importance are stable for extremely long time periods but may ultimately undergo a transformation. Such phases are said to be *metastable*. For example, in the iron-carbon system, the stable end phases are iron and graphite. However, in the temperature and composition range important for steels, shown in Fig. 17, the carbon phase is not pure graphite but rather the metastable iron carbide or *cementite*, Fe_3C. Since this phase is very persistent, it is more meaningful to consider the metastable equilibrium diagram between Fe and Fe_3C than the stable equilibrium diagram for iron and graphite. Note in Fig. 17 that two (or more) phases can coexist in equilibrium in certain regions of the diagram. Such regions are usually called *mixed-phase regions*.

The phase rule. It is possible to construct equilibrium diagrams for systems containing one, two, three, or more components. It is convenient for this discussion to define the *components* of a system as *the mini-*

mum number of chemical entities that are sufficient to specify completely the composition of the system. In the simplest case, the components are the elements present; however, it may be more meaningful, as discussed above for the iron-carbon system, to select a compound as one of the components. Latin roots are used to designate the number of independent components in a system so that a one-component system is

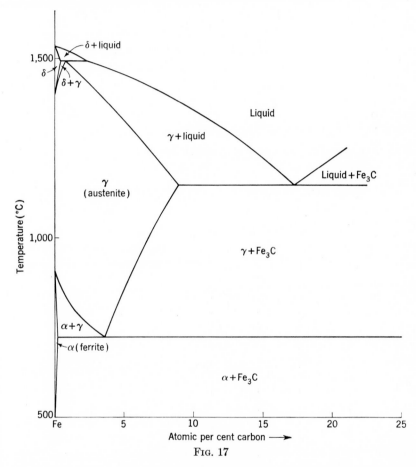

FIG. 17

called a *unary* system, a two-component system is called a *binary* system, a three-component system is called a *ternary* system, and so forth. It should be noted that when two components combine to form a single phase a new component is added to the system. Actually this new component is not independent of the other two since it is related to them by a chemical equation. For example,

$$3Fe + C = Fe_3C. \tag{26}$$

It was pointed out by Gibbs in 1876 that the number of components C and phases P present in a system is related to the degrees of freedom of the system by the so-called *phase rule*

$$F = C - P + 2 \qquad (27)$$

where the *degrees of freedom* F are all those conditions influencing the system that are independently variable, specifically, the temperature, pressure, and composition. If $F = 0$, there are no degrees of freedom; that is, the phase is stable only for a fixed temperature, pressure, and composition. When $F = 1$, either one of these parameters may be varied without affecting the stability of the phase. When $F = 2$, two of these parameters may be arbitrarily specified, etc.

As stated above, the pressure is usually assumed to be constant and equal to 1 atm in most cases. This means that one of the degrees of freedom in (27) is fixed so that there remain

$$F' = F - 1 = C - P + 1 \qquad (28)$$

degrees of freedom.

Solid solutions. Solid solutions can form between two or more components provided that their atomic radii, electronic structures, and

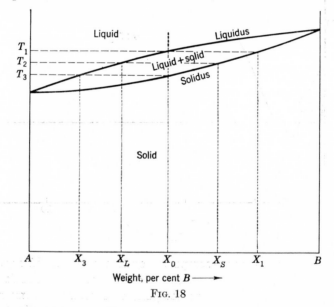

Fig. 18

crystal structures are similar. Although these are necessary conditions they are not sufficient conditions for complete miscibility at all compositions. Consider first the completely miscible binary solid solution whose equilibrium diagram is shown in Fig. 18. The meaning of such a diagram can be understood best by considering what happens to the melt as it is gradually cooled, say, by following the dashed vertical line at X_0 downward. At the composition X_0, the alloy is a liquid for all temperatures $T > T_1$. If it is cooled sufficiently slowly to allow equilibrium to be attained at each temperature, it remains a liquid until the uppermost curve in the diagram, called the *liquidus* line, is reached. At this temperature, T_1, part of the liquid solidifies with a composition X_1. This composition is determined by the intersection of the $T_1 = \text{const}$ line with the so-called *solidus* line. Upon further cooling, say to temperature T_2, the solidification continues, but the composition of the solid formed is different, namely, X_S. The composition of the liquid at this temperature, therefore, is X_L. Note that if this were a single-component system, that is, if it consisted of element A only,

$$F' = C - P + 1$$
$$= 1 - 2 + 1$$
$$= 0$$

and solidification could occur only at one temperature. Since this is a two-component system

$$F' = 2 - 2 + 1 = 1$$

and solidification can occur over a range of temperatures. Finally, when the alloy is cooled to a temperature $T \leq T_3$, solidification is completed, and a solid solution with composition X_0 is formed. In practice, the solid formed at this temperature is an intimate mixture of phases ranging in composition from X_1, which is relatively rich in component B, to an almost pure A phase, since the last drop to freeze has the composition X_3. This is so because solidification normally proceeds too rapidly for equilibrium conditions to prevail. It is necessary, therefore, to maintain the solid at a temperature just below T_3 for some time, that is, to anneal it, in order to form a homogeneous phase.

Between the temperatures T_1 and T_3, the alloy consists of two phases, one liquid and one solid phase. The relative amounts of the two phases present in a two-phase region can be determined by the so-called *lever rule*. Consider the dashed horizontal line at the temperature T_2 in Fig. 18, sometimes called a *tie line*. If the weights of the phases at each end of the tie line are assumed to balance a mechanical lever whose fulcrum is at the alloy's composition, the condition of mechanical equilibrium requires that

$$w_L(X_L - X_0) = w_S(X_0 - X_S) \tag{29}$$

where w_L and w_S are the weight fractions of the liquid and solid phases,

respectively.   The same rule also holds for two solid phases in equilibrium with each other.

When the two components in a binary alloy are completely miscible in
the liquid but only partially miscible in the solid, then the equilibrium
diagram has the appearance shown in Fig. 19.   Starting on the left side
of the diagram, liquid alloys having compositions ranging from 100 per
cent A to X_A solidify on slow cooling by the same process as that described
for completely miscible solid solutions above.   In the composition
range X_A to X_E, however, solidification proceeds as follows: When the
temperature of the alloy is dropped below the liquidus line for that composition, the solidified material is pure α, which is the solid-solution

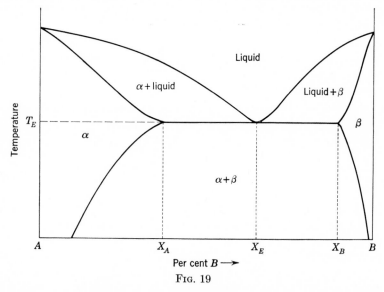

Fig. 19

phase rich in A.   Upon further cooling, the liquid is continually depleted
of A atoms until at T_E its composition is X_E.   At this point, called the
eutectic point, three phases are in equilibrium with each other, namely, a
liquid phase saturated with A and B atoms, and the two solid phases
α and β which have different crystal structures.   Thus, according to (28),

$$F' = C - P + 1$$
$$= 2 - 3 + 1$$
$$= 0$$

at this point and solidification can occur at only one temperature.   Note
that this is the lowest temperature at which an alloy in this system can
be in the liquid state.   The solid formed at this point is an intimate
mixture of both solid phases, giving a characteristic eutectic structure.

To the right of the eutectic composition, solidification proceeds in an analogous manner.   Between X_E and X_B the solid contains crystals of β in the eutectic mixture.   Between X_B and 100 per cent B, solidification again proceeds as in a completely miscible solid solution.   Note that the two lines separating the single-phase regions, α and β, from the two-phase region are slanted.   Thus, as the temperature of a heterogeneous solid consisting of a mixture of α and β is lowered, the relative amounts of the two phases present change according to the lever rule (29).

The form of the equilibrium diagram in Fig. 19 is determined by the relative free energies of the different phases.   Below the eutectic temperature the free energies of the α and β phases are similar to the curves

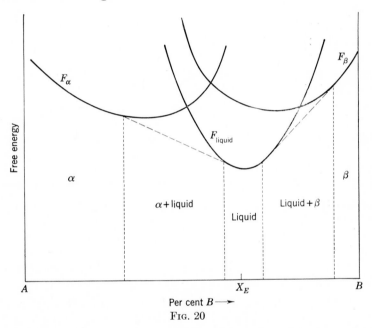

FIG. 20

shown in Fig. 2.   Since the free energy is a function of temperature, this plot is correct for only one particular temperature.   Usually, in such systems, the minima in the free-energy curves of each phase move toward each other as the temperature increases.   This is the explanation of the changing slopes of the two lines marking the boundaries of the two-phase region in Fig. 19.   Above the eutectic temperature, the free energy of the liquid phase must also be considered.   The relative free energies of α, β, and liquid at some temperature above T_E are shown in Fig. 20.   As can be seen in this figure, the eutectic composition X_E is approximately determined by the intersection of the two dashed lines marking the common tangents of the α and liquid free-energy curves and the β and liquid curves. Since the dashed line marking the common tangent of the α and β free-energy curves lies above the α-liquid and β-liquid lines, equilibrium between solid α and β phases is not possible at this temperature. Instead, just to the left of X_E equilibrium exists between a mixture of solid α and liquid, while to the right a mixture of solid β and liquid is stable. At the more extreme ends of the diagram, the respective solid phases are the stable forms of this system. When the temperature is increased still further, the free energies of the solid phases relative to the liquid increase until only the liquid is stable for all compositions.

The minima of the free-energy curves of α, β, and liquid need not be in the order (as a function of composition) indicated in Fig. 20. For example, consider the equilibrium diagram shown in Fig. 21B. The relative free-energy curves of the three phases at temperature T_1 are shown in Fig. 21A. Since, at this temperature, the free energy of β is everywhere greater than the free energies of the other two phases, the equilibrium conditions for different compositions are not unlike those encountered in Fig. 2, namely, at the two extremes, either the α or the liquid phase is stable alone, while the stable phase in between is a heterogeneous mixture of both. At another temperature, say T_2, the free-energy curves of all three phases cross each other in pairs; that is, for certain compositions the minimum free energy is that of one of the three single phases. Probably the simplest way to understand the relations in Fig. 21C is to consider the left- and right-hand portions of the diagram separately, since each side shows the interactions of only two phases. The composite equilibrium of these three phases at all temperatures is shown in the equilibrium diagram in Fig. 21B. This diagram can be interpreted as follows: Starting at the left side of the diagram, solidification proceeds for all compositions up to X_A as in a completely miscible solid solution. (In this range, of course, complete miscibility does exist.) In the composition range X_A to X_P, however, a notable change occurs when the isothermal line at $T = T_P$ is reached. At this temperature, a reaction takes place wherein the solid α reacts with the liquid to form β crystals. That this must be so can be seen from the phase rule. At the isothermal, which is called the *peritectic temperature*, there are three phases in equilibrium with each other, namely, liquid, α, and β, so that according to (28)

$$F' = 2 - 3 + 1 = 0$$

and there are no degrees of freedom available. Thus, the equilibrium composition of the β phase must be that of the *peritectic point* at X_P. Since the liquid is depleted of A atoms by the time it reaches this temperature, some of the α phase must redissolve at this point. Consequently, all the alloys in the range X_A to X_P must consist of two phases.

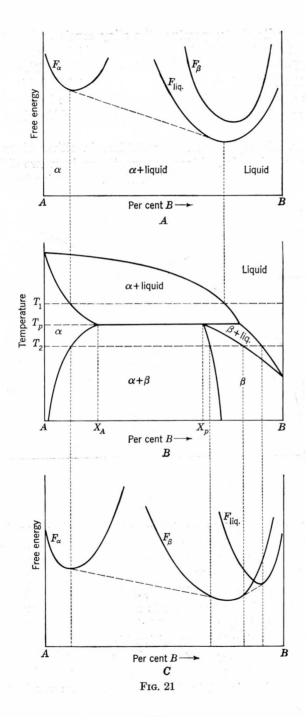

Fig. 21

Below the peritectic temperature the alloy consists of α and β, while above T_P it consists of liquid plus α only. At the composition of the *peritectic* X_P, on the other hand, the liquid solidifies with a single phase, β, below the peritectic temperature. To the right of this composition, the alloys contain excess liquid below the peritectic temperature so that on further cooling the composition of the β phase shifts along the solidus line.

When an allotropic element crystallizes in either of two different structures as a function of temperature, it can form two different solid solutions. The resulting equilibrium diagram contains two isothermals

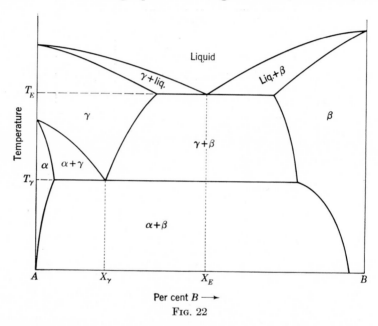

FIG. 22

and two singularity points, as shown in Fig. 22. Suppose that the two solid solutions rich in A can crystallize with an α or γ structure. Then for temperatures above T_γ the diagram is similar to the eutectic reaction shown in Fig. 19. Below this temperature, a singularity point called the *eutectoid* occurs at the composition X_γ and at the *eutectoid temperature* T_γ. This point is similar to the eutectic at X_E and T_E, except that at the eutectoid the three phases in equilibrium with each other are all solid. When an alloy having the composition X_γ is cooled below the eutectoid temperature, the solid γ phase transforms into an intimate mixture of α and β. The construction of the free-energy plots for the different temperature regions is left to the reader. (See the exercises at the end of this chapter.)

Complex diagrams. As already indicated in the equilibrium diagram shown in Fig. 22, it is possible for several different reactions to occur in the same system. One possible feature of such diagrams not mentioned thus far is the formation of *intermediate phases*. An intermediate phase is the name given to any new phase whose composition and stability range are limited to intermediate regions of the equilibrium diagram. When the intermediate phase has an ordered structure, it usually differs from ordinary compounds because its structure may be stable over a

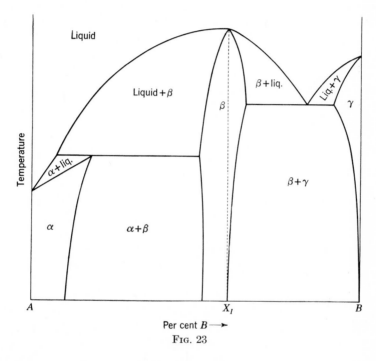

Per cent $B \longrightarrow$

Fig. 23

range of compositions whereas most compounds must be very nearly stoichiometric in order to exist at all.

There are two ways in which intermediate phases can form. The simplest way is for the intermediate phase to form directly from the liquid at the composition X_I, as shown in Fig. 23. A notable feature of all such diagrams is that the liquidus and solidus lines come to a common maximum at X_I. Alternatively, an intermediate phase may be formed by a peritectic reaction, as shown in Fig. 24. Actual equilibrium diagrams may be even more complicated than the examples cited so far; however, they will usually consist of the reactions described above so that they can be broken up into parts containing one reaction type only. For example, if Fig. 23 is divided into two parts by a vertical line at X_I,

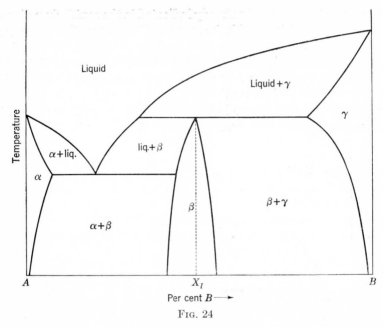

Fig. 24

the left side contains only a peritectic reaction while the right side contains only a eutectic reaction.

Kinetics of transformations

Transformation rates. The speed with which a transformation can proceed is related to the stabilities of the different atomic configurations of the two phases. A certain energy, called the *activation energy*, is required for a group of atoms to assume a new configuration. Only when the group of atoms is supplied with this energy does the transformation actually occur. Another way of stating this is to observe that, when the internal energy of the two states is separated by an energy barrier, the transformation from one to the other can proceed as soon as sufficient energy to surmount the barrier is supplied. The nature of the barrier, therefore, plays an important role in determining the rate at which the transformation can proceed. If the barrier has the shape shown in Fig. 25*A*, then the transformation to the higher-energy configuration can proceed virtually instantaneously upon absorption of the activation energy. It is possible that local phonon-atom interactions can displace an atom from an α to a β site even below the critical temperature. The relatively small energy barrier impeding its return to the α site, however, precludes the occupancy of β sites for long periods of time. On the other hand, above a critical temperature, the free energy may be lower for a structure composed of atoms on β sites so that the minima in the free-energy curve for these sites are the reverse of the internal-energy curve shown in Fig. 25A.

When the internal-energy curve has a large hump separating the two states, then the transformation proceeds more sluggishly. (This is the reason why the dilatational transformation can proceed rapidly because intermediate coordinations are not involved.) The internal-energy curve for this, the more usual case, is shown in Fig. 25B. Locally, an atom or group of atoms can absorb sufficient thermal energy to overcome the barrier at any temperature above absolute zero. The relative height of the barrier then prevents their immediate return to the lower-energy state. As the temperature is increased, successively more and more local transitions can occur until, above the critical temperature, the entire structure has transformed. Note that above the critical temperature,

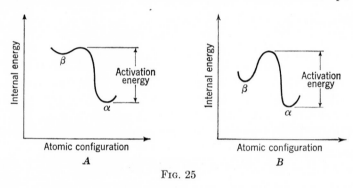

FIG. 25

transitions in the opposite sense also can occur. Since the free energy favors the high-temperature configuration β, however, local transitions to α sites are relatively infrequent.

Because the free energy of the high-temperature structure is lower, the entire crystal should undergo a transformation at the critical temperature, according to thermodynamics. In most cases, this is extremely unlikely to occur because it requires that a very large number of atoms simultaneously take up the positions of the new structure. This means that all the atoms must absorb sufficient energy to overcome the energy barrier, a process which is much more likely to occur gradually. Consequently, transformations tend to proceed by the formation of *nuclei* having the stable structure and by the growth of these nuclei at the expense of the untransformed regions. Thus the rate of transformation is determined by two distinct processes, nucleation and growth, each having characteristic activation energies that are usually different. The growth of nuclei has been briefly described in the preceding chapter; some nucleation processes are described below.

Homogeneous nucleation. Nucleation can occur in a crystal in two ways. A local imperfection in the crystal, say a point or line defect, produces strains in its vicinity so that the total energy required for the transition to a new configuration is lowered by the strain energy at the site of the imperfection. The reduction in the activation energy means that such sites may become preferred nucleation centers and so-called *heterogeneous nucleation* takes place. The presence of imperfections is not imperative, and *homogeneous nucleation* can occur in the absence of such defects in the crystal. The formation of a nucleus having a different structure than the matrix, however, produces an imperfection in the host crystal's structure, and it can be shown, similarly to the discussion of the formation of vacancies, that the number of nuclei formed, n, at any temperature is given by

$$n = Ne^{-\Delta G/kT} \tag{30}$$

where N is the total number of nucleation sites and ΔG is the free energy of formation of a nucleus. In a large region, ΔG simply equals the difference in the *chemical* or *bulk free energies*, ΔG_B, of the two different phases. In a region so small that the transformation can proceed back and forth due to local fluctuations in the thermal energy, two other factors must be considered, namely, the *surface free energy* of the nucleus-parent crystal interface, ΔG_S, and the *elastic energy*, ΔG_E, due to the strains produced in changing the structure. Therefore, the change in the free energy when a nucleus is formed is

$$\Delta G = -\Delta G_B + \Delta G_S + \Delta G_E \tag{31}$$

where ΔG_B is negative because the transformation proceeds from an unstable to a stable state.

In principle, the nucleation process can be described in terms of interatomic forces by an appropriate kinetic theory. Because of the complexity of the problem, such a description is not possible at present. It is possible, however, to describe nucleation by a phenomenological theory, particularly if the formation of a solid nucleus from a liquid is considered. If the composition of a liquid is the same as that of the solid, then the small changes in the elastic energy upon freezing can be neglected. Thus, the only factors that need be considered in (31) are the difference in the bulk free energy and the surface energy of the solid-liquid interface. Now, the bulk free energy is obviously proportional to the volume of the nucleus or l^3, whereas the surface free energy is proportional to l^2. By analogy to (31), the change in the free energy due to the formation of a nucleus can thus be expressed by a relation

$$\Delta G = -k_1 l^3 + k_2 l^2 \tag{32}$$

where the proportionality constant k_1, expressing the bulk free energy of a unit volume, is smaller than k_2, which is determined by the surface tension at the nucleus-liquid interface. The meaning of (32) is best seen by plotting the change in the free energy as a function of l. As can be seen in Fig. 26, the free energy increases as l increases until a maximum value G_0 is reached at some critical size indicated by l_0. Below this critical size the nucleus is unstable, because any increase in its size increases the total free energy. On the other hand, when the size of the nucleus exceeds the critical size, further growth decreases the free energy. A nucleus having the critical size determined by l_0 is in a metastable equilibrium, since a small variation in its size produces conditions that favor either its dissolution or an increase in its size. The energy of forming this metastable nucleus G_0 depends on temperature in the same way that ΔG_B does. This is so because the surface free energy does not vary appreciably with changes in temperature and the energy of formation is very nearly the difference between the free energies of the two phases. If the nucleation from the liquid proceeds in accordance with (32), this means that, approximately, the free energy of nucleus formation depends only on

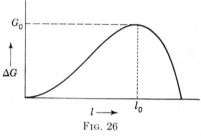

FIG. 26

the difference between the free energies of the nucleated and liquid phases. Above the critical temperature, ΔG is positive so that according to (30) the number of nuclei formed decreases very rapidly with increasing temperature. Below the critical temperature, ΔG is negative and the exponential term is positive. As the temperature is lowered, therefore, the number of nuclei formed must increase exponentially according to (30). As the *undercooling* increases, however, the decreased thermal activity actually tends to slow down nucleation. Thus, in silicates, for example, rapid undercooling leads to the formation of glasses. In most other inorganic substances, including all metals, however, it is not possible to undercool the liquid phase without forming a large number of crystal nuclei. This is caused by the presence of large numbers of impurities which act as nucleation sites.

Heterogeneous nucleation. The rate of a transformation in poly-crystalline solids usually increases when there are imperfections, especially impurity inclusions, present in the solid. The formation of nuclei in *heterogeneous nucleation* is influenced by the relative interfacial tensions between the nucleus and the imperfections σ_{ni} and between the parent phase and imperfection σ_{pi}.

$$\Delta G_i = \sigma_{ni} - \sigma_{pi} \tag{33}$$

where ΔG_i is the change in the free energy due to the formation of a unit area of interface between the nucleus and the imperfection. Heterogeneous nucleation will be preferred to homogeneous nucleation if ΔG_i is less than the interfacial tension between the nucleus and the parent phase. According to (33), the free energy decreases (the change is negative) when $\sigma_{pi} > \sigma_{ni}$, meaning that the interatomic forces of attraction between the nucleating phase and the imperfection are greater than those between the parent phase and the imperfection. In the case of nucleation at the surfaces of impurity inclusions, this means that the relation of the crystal structure of the impurity to that of the nucleating phase is an important factor. For example, when particles of the nucleating phase are present as inclusions in the parent phase because of a previous heat treatment, such inclusions may form preferential sites for nucleation.

Since the interfacial tension between the nucleus and the matrix phase and, hence, the free energy in (33) are reduced when the interatomic forces of attraction crossing the interface are large, there is a tendency for the nucleating phase to have certain planes of its structure parallel to similar planes in the host phase. The formation of such *precipitates* usually is characterized, therefore, by a definite *orientation relationship* and by certain *habit planes* that the precipitate develops in an alloy. For example, the atomic arrangement and interatomic spacings are very nearly the same for the (110) planes of β brass and the (111) planes of α brass if the planes are mutually oriented so that [111] in β is parallel to [110] in α. Consequently, β brass tends to precipitate in α brass with the foregoing orientation relationship. In addition to this orientation, the precipitating β brass tends to form needlelike crystals. More commonly, a precipitate adopts a platelike habit. Such lamellae frequently form regular networks, called *Widmanstätten structures*, which can be seen in many alloys and in most meteorites, in which they were first described.

Grain boundaries also form suitable sites for heterogeneous nucleation. It can be shown that the grain-boundary energy decreases the free energy of nucleation. This is so because any stresses formed during nucleation are more readily relieved at grain boundaries. Moreover, strains already present in the boundary may actually aid in the formation of a nucleus. Depending on the nucleating structure, either compressive or tensile stresses can aid in its formation. Recalling that both types of stresses are present at an edge dislocation, it is easy to see that the presence of such dislocations at a grain boundary also aids the nucleation there. The presence of other imperfections, notably inclusions, at grain boundaries means that, provided that the energy conditions expressed by (33) are met, these inclusions can become nucleation sites. Consequently, the frequency of nuclei formation at a grain boundary proceeds in this order: point of intersection of four grains > line of intersection of three grains > plane of intersection of two grains.

Precipitation from solid solutions. Quantitative measurements of the rate of nucleation in general precipitation are not available. Published results indicate, however, that the nuclei tend to form at grain boundaries or other imperfections such as subboundaries or slip planes. This is supported by evidence that plastic deformation, such as cold-working a metal, greatly increases the nucleation rate. At the beginning,

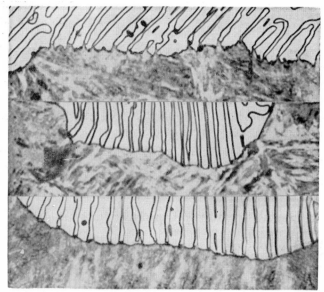

Fig. 27. Three stages of pearlite:austenite interface magnified 2000 times. The pearlite region consists of alternating lamellae of ferrite and cementite. (Photographed by Robert F. Mehl and William C. Hagel.)

the precipitate formed along such imperfections is too small to be seen with an ordinary microscope. These so-called *Guinier-Preston* zones attain thicknesses of about 100 to 200 Å and can be detected usually by changes in the physical properties of the alloy, with the aid of an electron microscope, or by special x-ray diffraction effects. It is believed that such zones can form only when the densely packed planes of the equilibrium precipitate and the solid-solution structure are very nearly parallel although there is considerable evidence that indicates that Guinier-Preston zones are initially formed in most precipitates.

An important factor affecting precipitation in a solid solution is the possibility of *impingement* of two adjacent nuclei. As the nuclei grow in size, they deplete the solution surrounding them so that, when the region separating two nuclei becomes small, their further growth along a common direction is impeded. It follows from this that the rate of growth depends on the rate of diffusion of the solute atoms in the solid solution. Assuming that the rate of diffusion is the only limiting factor on the growth rate, it follows that a spherical particle will grow most slowly. This is so because each growing spherical nucleus is surrounded by a sphere depleted of solute atoms. As neighboring spheres grow in size, these depleted regions approach each other and the growth rate is slowed down. On the other hand, diffusion tends to aid rod-, plate-, or disk-shaped particles to grow much more rapidly. This is particularly true if the growth velocities of their external habit planes are favorable. This phenomenon is observed in steels having a composition near the eutectoid (Fig. 17). Ferrite and cementite form thin parallel lamellae (the complex is called *pearlite*), which advance into the austenite region by increasing the length (or width) of the plates without an appreciable change in their thickness, as illustrated in Fig. 27 which shows several stages in the advance of the interface. The rate of advance of the pearlite:austenite interface depends on the rate of diffusion of carbon in the austenite region. Since the carbon concentrates in cementite (Fe_3C) and not in ferrite (α-Fe), the thickness of the lamellae is limited by the ability of carbon to diffuse to the appropriate regions of the interface.

Suggestions for supplementary reading

A. H. Cottrell, *Theoretical structural metallurgy*, 2d ed. (St. Martin's Press, Inc., New York, 1957), pp. 94–203.

Frederick N. Rhines, *Phase diagrams in metallurgy* (McGraw-Hill Book Company, Inc., New York, 1956).

J. C. Slater, *Introduction to chemical physics* (McGraw-Hill Book Company, Inc., New York, 1939).

R. Smoluchowski, J. E. Mayer, and W. A. Weyl, *Phase transformation in solids* (John Wiley & Sons, Inc., New York, 1951).

Exercises

1. Calculate the free energy of a random solid solution having the composition A_3B. Do this by calculating separately the internal energy and the entropy. Plot the free energy as a function of the long-range-order parameter at T_C.

2. Determine the free energy of a random solution having the composition AB_2. Plot the free energy as a function of $E_{AB} - \frac{1}{2}(E_{AA} + E_{BB})$ for this solid solution.

3. In considering the transition from short-range order to long-range order below the critical temperature, it appears, at first sight, that the antiphase domains should be stable down to absolute zero. Yet x-ray evidence clearly shows the formation of a superlattice. How do you explain this?

4. In the SiO_2 system, the high-temperature or β form of quartz becomes unstable relative to another polymorph, cristobalite, above 1000°C, yet the transition does not proceed directly. β quartz first melts and then devitrifies from the silica glass to form cristobalite. If the glass is also unstable relative to cristobalite at this temperature, explain the above transformation. Using the classification scheme in Table 1, what type of transformation is this?

5. In steels, the formation of ferrite and cementite from austenite often proceeds only after the formation of the metastable martensite (see Chapter 11). Explain and classify this transformation.

6. Apply the phase rule at each singularity point in Fig. 17, that is, at each point where two or more lines meet. Repeat for any other point along the two isothermal lines. Why are the degrees of freedom determined by the phase rule different for the points and lines?

7. Consider the composition X_0 of an alloy in Fig. 18. Suppose that it is cooled rapidly to a temperature slightly below T_3 and maintained at that temperature for sufficient time to form a homogeneous solid solution. What is the atomic mechanism by which annealing occurs? Why does it occur at all?

8. In a binary alloy, it is possible that the two components are only partially miscible in the liquid and in the solid. Such an alloy is characterized by a two-phase region in the equilibrium diagram in which the two liquids coexist as separate phases. At a given temperature the *monotectic* reaction *liquid α = liquid β + solid α* takes place. Construct a hypothetical equilibrium diagram showing this reaction.

9. A *peritectoid* reaction bears the same relation to a peritectic that a eutectoid bears to a eutectic. Construct a fictitious equilibrium diagram showing a peritectoid reaction.

10. Similarly to Fig. 21 in the text, prepare two diagrams showing the relations of the free-energy curves as a function of composition of the three phases forming a eutectoid reaction. *Hint:* Do this by selecting one temperature slightly above and one slightly below T_γ.

11. Derive the expression (30) relating the number of nuclei formed, n, to the free energy of formation ΔG, if there are N nucleation sites in a crystal.

12. It is sometimes possible to *quench* a phase that is unstable relative to its matrix by cooling an alloy very rapidly. If this phase is unstable at room temperature, what prevents the stable phase from nucleating after quenching? Why is it not possible to quench certain phases no matter how rapidly they are cooled?

13. It is possible to grow a crystal, from its solution, on the surface of a different kind of crystal when the latter is placed into the solution. Explain this process of *epitaxy* in terms of nucleation energy and list the factors that determine the suitability of a crystal placed in the solution.

14. When the cooling of an alloy is accompanied by the precipitation of a new phase, its hardness usually increases. This is called *age hardening* since the size of the precipitate increases with time or age. When such an alloy is reheated, it again becomes softer, a process which is called *retrogression*. Explain both processes by first noting the structural changes that take place on cooling and heating and then by considering the plasticity of the alloy in each case.

15. When a steel containing 0.9 per cent carbon is cooled below the eutectoid temperature (Fig. 17) it is observed that pearlite grows from nuclei formed at grain boundaries or on particles of undissolved carbides. Discuss the reasons why such nucleation sites should be preferred.

9

The bonding of atoms

Elements of quantum mechanics

Principles of wave mechanics. In order to understand how atoms are joined in solids it is necessary to gain a more quantitative insight into the makeup of an individual atom. It has been stated in Chapter 4 that an atom consists of a positively charged nucleus about which revolve a number of negatively charged electrons. In 1924, De Broglie postulated that electrons, although particles of finite mass, behave as if they had associated with them waves of wavelength

$$\lambda = \frac{h}{mv} \tag{1}$$

where h is Planck's constant ($h = 6.628 \times 10^{-27}$ erg-sec)

m is the mass of an electron ($m = 9.115 \times 10^{-28}$ g)

v is the velocity of the wave.

This postulate, a logical extension of Einstein's earlier theories showing that electromagnetic radiation simultaneously has the properties of particles (photons) and of waves, initiated a branch of mathematical physics called *quantum mechanics* or *wave mechanics*, depending on the mathematical formulation used, as distinct from Newton's classical mechanics.

The principles of wave mechanics are best illustrated by considering the *wave equation* of a vibrating string of length L, clamped at both ends. If the string is set into motion, say by plucking it, its displacement u as a function of distance along the string x, for every instant of time t, is given by

$$\frac{\partial^2 u}{\partial x^2} = \frac{1}{\omega^2} \frac{\partial u}{\partial t} \tag{2}$$

where ω is its angular frequency. If, however, the string is vibrated in such a manner that the nodes of the string are stationary in space and

202

the maximum displacement at any point does not vary with time, that is, when *standing waves* are set up, then the equation giving the displacement u as a function of x is

$$\frac{d^2u}{dx^2} + \omega^2 u = 0. \tag{3}$$

This is the well-known equation for a harmonic oscillator and has a general solution of the form

$$u = A \cos \omega x + B \sin \omega x \tag{4}$$

as can be verified by direct substitution in (3).

Now, the total period of the string is $2L$, which, if divided into n parts by the vibrating string, corresponds to a frequency of $n/2L$, or

$$\omega = 2\pi \frac{n}{2L} \tag{5}$$

and (3) and (4) become

$$\frac{d^2u}{dx^2} + \left(\frac{\pi n}{L}\right)^2 u = 0 \tag{6}$$

and

$$u = A \cos \pi \frac{n}{L} x + B \sin \pi \frac{n}{L} x. \tag{7}$$

Since the string is clamped at both ends, the displacement u is zero when $x = 0$ and when $x = L$. These so-called *boundary conditions* must be satisfied by (7), and it is possible to use them to determine the values of A, B, and n.

When $x = 0$ $\quad u = 0 = A \cos (0) + B \sin (0)$

$$= A. \tag{8}$$

When $x = L$ $\quad u = 0 = B \sin \pi \frac{n}{L} L$

$$= B \sin \pi n. \tag{9}$$

According to (8), A is zero; therefore, excluding the trivial solution when B is also zero, the only way that the right side of (9) can be zero is for $\sin \pi n$ to equal zero. This is the case when n is equal to an integer. Several possible solutions of (6) are plotted in Fig. 1 for $n = 1$, 2, and 3. These are the familiar fundamental and higher-order harmonics. Note that B is an arbitrary constant determining the amplitude and is not fixed by the boundary conditions.

Schrödinger's theory. An important conclusion to be drawn from the above example is that the solutions of boundary-condition problems expressed by wave equations like (6) are *quantized*; that is, they are different from zero only for a definite set of values of n and are equal to zero for any other value of n. Following De Broglie's postulate of the wave nature of electrons,† Schrödinger showed in 1926 that the wave equation can be used to describe the motion of electrons in atoms in agreement with the quantization requirements of Bohr's earlier postulates. In fact, whenever the results of the Bohr theory agree with experimental observations, Schrödinger's theory gives an identical result. Moreover, Schrödinger's theory agrees with experiment even where Bohr's theory does not. It should be noted that the Schrödinger theory is not an exact theory since it involves certain approximations. This is also true of the other theories of solids. Nevertheless, these theories give a physically meaningful description of phenomena whose truth can be verified experimentally.

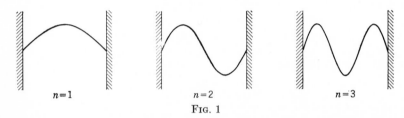

$n=1$ $n=2$ $n=3$

FIG. 1

The wavelengths of the vibrating string determined by the standing-wave solutions in (9) are $\lambda = 2L/n$. Substituting for n/L in (6),

$$\frac{d^2u}{dx^2} + \frac{4\pi^2}{\lambda^2} u = 0. \tag{10}$$

Substituting for λ De Broglie's postulate (1),

$$\frac{d^2u}{dx^2} + \frac{4\pi^2 m^2 v^2}{h^2} u = 0. \tag{11}$$

The kinetic energy of an electron is, of course, the difference between its total energy E and its potential energy V.

$$\begin{aligned} \text{KE} &= \tfrac{1}{2}mv^2 \\ &= E - V \end{aligned} \tag{12}$$

and

$$v^2 = \frac{2(E - V)}{m}. \tag{13}$$

Substituting (13) for v^2 in (11) and representing the position of the electron by the so-called *wave function* ψ instead of the displacement u,

† It should be noted that De Broglie's postulate of the wave nature of electrons was subsequently confirmed by direct experiment. In 1927 Davisson and Germer in the United States and Thomson in England demonstrated that electrons are diffracted by crystals similarly to x-rays.

the one-dimensional, time-independent form of Schrödinger's equation results:

$$\frac{d^2\psi}{dx^2} + \frac{8\pi^2 m}{h^2}(E - V)\psi = 0. \tag{14}$$

In three dimensions, $d^2\psi/dx^2$ must be replaced by partial derivatives with respect to the x, y, and z axes so that the three-dimensional Schrödinger equation is

$$\left(\frac{\partial^2}{\partial x^2} + \frac{\partial^2}{\partial y^2} + \frac{\partial^2}{\partial z^2}\right)\psi + \frac{8\pi^2 m(E - V)}{h^2}\psi = 0. \tag{15}$$

The solutions of (15) are not unlike the solutions of (6) except that the wave function ψ is a function of three space coordinates x, y, z. In this sense, the wave function describes the position of an electron. There is one very important distinction, however. The displacement of a vibrating string can be readily observed, and it is meaningful, therefore, to describe its displacement precisely. The displacement or position of an electron, on the other hand, cannot be observed. The reason for this becomes obvious when the "tools" of observation are considered. In order to observe an electron, either light photons, or x-ray photons, or other electrons have to be used. These particles interact with the electron, changing its position immediately as the signal describing its previous position reaches the observer. Thus, the information obtained from the experiment no longer correctly describes the state of the electron. It is not meaningful, therefore, to seek an equation that accurately describes the position of an electron because the correctness of such an equation could not be verified.

Although it is not meaningful to predict the exact position of an electron at a particular instant of time, it is possible to determine the most probable place where the electron will be. Max Born showed in 1926 that the quantity $|\psi|^2$ tells the probability of the presence of an electron at a particular point in space at the time at which the wave function ψ is being considered. When a large number of identical experiments are performed, this so-called *probability density* accurately predicts what the spatial distribution of electrons will be. Since the wave function is a function of space coordinates, the probability density has different values as a function of space coordinates also. Moreover, it predicts quite accurately the most probable locations of an electron for each possible value of the energy E in (15). (These energy values are quantized just like the energy values assumed by Bohr.) In fact, the most probable values of the distance from the nucleus for an electron predicted by the probability density agree quite well with the radii of the Bohr orbits. Because the electrons are not limited to the occupation of prescribed positions in space according to quantum mechanics, an electron is said to occupy an *orbital* described by its orbital wave function. It is then convenient to express the probability of finding the electron by

$$\int_{-\infty}^{\infty} |\psi|^2 \, dv = 1 \tag{16}$$

which states that the probability of finding the electron somewhere in space is equal to unity.

In addition to being unable to predict the exact location of an electron at every instant of time, it turns out that it similarly is not possible to specify the exact velocity of an electron when it occupies a particular point in space, nor its energy at a particular instant of time, and so forth. This limitation was expressed by Heisenberg in the *uncertainty principle* which states that the product of the uncertainties in specifying two such conjugate characteristics can never be less than a constant value. This can be expressed analytically by relations such as

$$\Delta x \times \Delta p \geq \frac{h}{2\pi}$$

or

$$\Delta E \times \Delta t \geq \frac{h}{2\pi} \tag{17}$$

where x is a position coordinate and $p = mv$ is the momentum of an electron, while E and t are, respectively, energy and time, and h is Planck's constant. It follows from this that most quantum-mechanical calculations yield a description of the most probable situation rather than the exact picture one obtains from classical mechanics. The transition to the case when classical mechanics applies, that is, when the bodies considered are much larger than the size of electrons, can be determined with the aid of (17). For example, if both sides of the first relation in (17) are divided by the mass m, it turns out that the smallest value that the product $\Delta x \, \Delta v$ can have is $h/2\pi m$. It follows that, as m becomes larger, the uncertainties become smaller, until in the limiting case of macroscopic bodies, the uncertainty has virtually disappeared and both the position and velocity can be predicted exactly.

Hydrogen atom.   The application of Schrödinger's equation to actual atoms is illustrated by the simplest atom, hydrogen. In this atom, an electron of charge $-e$ moves in the central field of force caused by the positive charge of the nucleus. The attractive force of the nucleus produces a potential energy

$$V = -\frac{Ze^2}{r} \tag{18}$$

where $Z = 1$ for hydrogen, and $r^2 = x^2 + y^2 + z^2$. Substituting this value for V in (15) and abbreviating the partial differential operator in the parentheses by ∇^2 (pronounced *del-squared*),

$$\nabla^2\psi + \frac{8\pi^2 m}{h^2}\left(E + \frac{Ze^2}{r}\right)\psi = 0. \tag{19}$$

Relation (19) is the Schrödinger equation for a central force field. It can be solved most easily by introducing spherical coordinates and separating the variables; however, this solution is not carried out here although some of the results are described below. The reason for deriving (19) is simply to indicate its similarity to (3), whose solutions turned out to be quantized. Quite similarly, the energy values corresponding to nonzero solutions of (19) are quantized also; in fact, they are the same as the energy levels of the Bohr atom.

$$
\begin{aligned}
E_n &= -\frac{2\pi^2 m e^4}{h^2}\frac{Z^2}{n^2} \\
&= -\frac{2\pi^2(9.1 \times 10^{-28}g)(4.8 \times 10^{-10}\text{ esu})^4}{(6.63 \times 10^{-27}\text{ erg-sec})^2}\frac{Z^2}{n^2} \\
&= -(13.6\text{ eV})\frac{Z^2}{n^2}.
\end{aligned}
\tag{20}
$$

By analogy to the Bohr atom, the *principal* quantum number n determines the energy level of the hydrogen atom. Since hydrogen has only one electron, the lowest energy level that it can have, the so-called *ground state*, corresponds to $n = 1$, and according to (20) $E_1 = -13.6$ eV. If $n = 2$, then $E_2 = -3.4$ eV, indicating that 10.2 eV of energy is needed to raise a hydrogen atom from the ground state to this first *excited state*. Now, although E_2 is a higher energy level than E_1, the absolute magnitude of E_2 is less than E_1, which means that the attractive force binding the electron to the nucleus is less. Since the binding energy is inversely proportional to distance, this, in turn, means that the electron is farther removed from the nucleus in such excited states.† One must remember that the uncertainty principle does not allow the exact distance at which an electron is found to be specified. Nevertheless, it is possible to calculate the radius at which the probability density for a given state has a maximum. To a close approximation,

$$r_n = (0.53 \times 10^{-8}\text{ cm})\frac{n^2}{Z} \tag{21}$$

for a single electron moving about a nucleus of charge Z.

---

† It should be noted that nonnegative values of E also give solutions to (19). When $E > 0$, however, the electron is no longer bound to the nucleus. Whereas there exists a discrete spectrum of negative E_n values for the case of the bound electron, the free electron can have all positive energy values, forming a continuous spectrum.

The above discussion applies to solutions (wave functions) of (19) that depend only on r and are therefore spherically symmetrical. Such wave functions describe electron orbitals called s orbitals. It is also possible to obtain solutions that depend on x, y, z separately. Such solutions contain two constants l and m. It can be shown that l, the *azimuthal* quantum number, measures the orbital angular momentum, and m, the *magnetic* quantum number, specifies the direction of the angular-momentum vector in space. The numerical values of the three quantum numbers are interdependent; specifically, n can equal any positive integer (excluding 0), l can have all integer values from $l = 0$ to $l = n - 1$, and m can have all negative and positive integer values from $m = -l$ to $m = l$, including zero. The shapes of such wave functions are shown in Fig. 2 for several different values of l and m. The three orbitals corresponding to $l = 1$ are called p orbitals; the five orbitals corresponding to $l = 2$ are called d orbitals.

The total number of permissible values that m can have is $2l + 1$, corresponding to the total number of ways that the magnetic vector due to the angular momentum of the electron can differ in its orientation. If an atom is placed in a strong magnetic field, therefore, there are an odd number of ways that the magnetic vectors of the electrons can align themselves with respect to the external field. Each different way of aligning in the magnetic field produces a small but finite change in the energy. This effect was first reported by Zeeman and bears his name. For certain atoms, notably alkali metals, however, even numbers of energy levels were observed. To explain this effect, an additional magnetic moment had to be postulated. It is assumed that the charge of an electron is not stationary but spins about an axis passing through the electron. The electron can spin only in essentially two unique directions, say clockwise and counterclockwise. Thus the total number of ways to orient the magnetic vector of the spin momentum is equal to 2. Now the spin momentum, like the angular momentum due to the orbital motion of the electron, can give rise to $2m_s + 1$ levels. In order to limit the total number to 2, the magnitude of the so-called *spin* quantum number m_s must be equal to $\frac{1}{2}$. The direction of the electron spin vector is indicated by letting m_s equal $+\frac{1}{2}$ or $-\frac{1}{2}$, depending on whether the spin vector is parallel to the orbital momentum or not.

Pauli exclusion principle. It is more convenient to speak of electronic orbitals in terms of the four quantum numbers than in terms of the wave-function solutions of Schrödinger's equation. An electron described by four such numbers has a definite energy and travels with a predictable average velocity in a predictable orbital. A complete picture of the atom can be given, therefore, by specifying the four quantum numbers of each electron and by listing the number of electrons of each

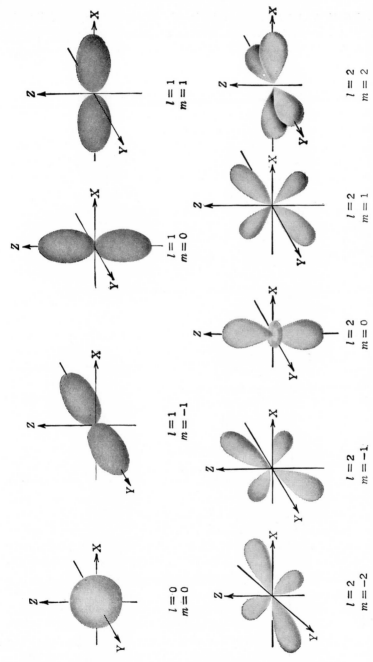

FIG. 2. Spherical s and spheroidal p and d orbitals. Note that when $l = 2$ and $m = -2$ the orbitals are inclined by 45° to X and Y, when $l = 2$ and $m = -1$ the orbitals are inclined by 45° to Y and Z, and when $l = 2$ and $m = 1$ the orbitals are inclined by 45° to X and Z.

kind. A systematic procedure for doing this was made possible by Wolfgang Pauli in 1925 when he proposed the principle that *no two electrons in an atom can have exactly the same set of four quantum numbers.* According to this so-called *Pauli exclusion principle,* there can be two electrons for each combination of n, l, and m, provided that each has a different value for m_s. Thus hydrogen can have one s electron with either positive or negative spin, whereas helium can have two s electrons only if their spins are oppositely directed.

Periodic table. Some of the values of the three quantum numbers specifying solutions of the Schrödinger equation and their spectrographic designations are listed in Table 1. Each such solution predicts the

Table 1
The quantum numbers describing solutions of Schrödinger's equation

Bohr atom designation of shell	Principal quantum number n	Azimuthal quantum number l	Magnetic quantum number m	Spectrographic designation
K	1	0	0	1s (for "sharp")
L	2	0	0	2s
		1	0, ±1	2p (for "principal")
M	3	0	0	3s
		1	0, ±1	3p
		2	0, ±1, ±2	3d (for "diffuse")
N	4	0	0	4s
		1	0, ±1	4p
		2	0, ±1, ±2	4d
		3	0, ±1, ±2, ±3	4f (for "further")

orbital of an electron, from which it follows that a combination of solutions, one for each electron in the atom, can be used to describe the most probable locations of all the electrons. It should be realized, however, that the direct solution of Schrödinger's equation (15) is possible only for the hydrogen atom which has only one electron. Like the three-body problem of classical mechanics, no simple solutions of (15) are possible for atoms having more than one electron. Approximate solutions are possible if it is assumed that the electrons are affected only by a central field force due to the nucleus, like (18), with Z taking on different values for different atoms. The energy levels for such a central field model are given by

$$E_n = -(13.6 \text{ eV})\frac{(Z - Z_0)^2}{n^2} \tag{22}$$

for $n \leq 3$. Z_0 in (22) is a *shielding* constant that expresses the decrease in the nuclear attraction for a given electron due to the shielding effect of the other electrons present. In a given atom, the numerical value of Z_0 depends not only on n but also on l and varies from practically zero for $n = 1$ to almost Z for the highest quantum state possible. The consequence of this is that for hydrogen, which has only one electron, all the wave functions corresponding to a single value of n have the same energy given by (20). For atoms which have two or more electrons, wave functions having the same n values may have different energies, depending on the value of l. It is more convenient, therefore, to use the spectrographic designation given in the last column of Table 1 as a shorthand notation for discussing the energy levels of electrons. Approximate relative energy levels of different quantum states are shown in Fig. 3.

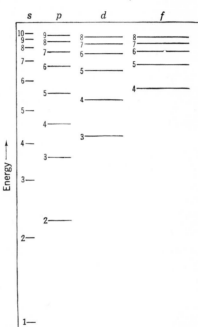

It is now possible to attempt a systematic classification of the elements. According to Table 1, for $n = 1$ there is only one energy level, the 1s state, which can contain two electrons having opposite spins. For $n = 2$, the 2s state can contain two electrons of opposite spin and three 2p states (corresponding to $m = 0$, $m = +1$, $m = -1$), each of which can contain two electrons of opposite spin for a total of six electrons, and so forth,

FIG. 3. Relative energy levels of atomic orbitals. The levels are labeled with appropriate values of n.

for larger values of n. This can be represented diagrammatically by drawing a box for each pair of electrons having opposite spins. According to this representation, the s state consists of one box containing one or two arrows, the senses of the arrows indicating the spin directions. The p state can be represented by three such boxes, and so forth. Using this notation, the lowest quantum state or *ground state* of hydrogen can be represented

$$1s \;\boxed{\uparrow} \qquad \text{or} \qquad 1s \;\boxed{\downarrow}. \tag{23}$$

The next atom in the periodic table, helium, has two electrons. In the ground state of helium, these two electrons are 1s electrons. This is usually represented by the symbol $1s^2$, where the superscript indicates the number of electrons occupying the same state. (For example, $3p^4$ means that four electrons are occupying the $3p$ state.) If it were not for the Pauli exclusion principle, the two electrons of helium could have their spins parallel or antiparallel since, in the absence of an external magnetic field, the energies of both possibilities are the same. In the presence of an external magnetic field, however, these two cases can be distinguished because the parallel spins give rise to a net magnetic moment which can be measured experimentally. No such magnetic moment has ever been observed for helium, from which it is concluded that the two spins cannot be parallel; that is, the parallel state is statistically an unlikely or a *forbidden state* for helium. The antiparallel state, therefore, is the only *allowed state*, in complete agreement with the Pauli exclusion principle. Accordingly, the ground state of a helium atom can be represented by

$$1s^2 \; \boxed{\uparrow\downarrow}. \tag{24}$$

The next atom, lithium, has three electrons. According to Fig. 3, the lowest energy available to these electrons is the $1s$ state. According to the Pauli exclusion principle, however, only two electrons can occupy this orbital. Consequently, the third electron in lithium must occupy the next highest energy state, which is $2s$. Consequently, the ground state of lithium can be represented diagrammatically as follows:

$$1s^2 \; \boxed{\uparrow\downarrow}$$
$$2s^1 \; \boxed{\uparrow} \qquad 2p^0 \; \boxed{\,|\,\,|\,} \tag{25}$$

The Bohr concept of electronic shells can now be given a new interpretation. The K shell can contain two electrons having opposite spins. These two electrons complete the K shell and are both equally tightly bound to the nucleus. The L shell can contain two $2s$ electrons and six $2p$ electrons. Since the $2s$ electrons have lower energies than the $2p$ electrons, the third electron in Li goes into the $2s$ shell, as shown in (25). Furthermore, this electron is not as tightly bound as the $1s$ electrons, as can be seen from the fact that the first ionization potential for Li is 5.37 eV, compared with the second ionization potential of 75.26 eV.

The M shell can contain two s electrons, six p electrons, and ten d electrons, or a total of eighteen electrons. In filling this shell, however, it should be noted in Fig. 3 that the energy of the $3d$ state is slightly higher than that of the $4s$ state. Thus, in the ground state, potassium, having a total of nineteen electrons, fills the $3p$ states but places the nineteenth electron in the $4s$ state of the N shell. This can be represented by the formula $1s^22s^22p^63s^23p^64s^1$, or diagrammatically by

$1s^2$ ↑↓

$2s^2$ ↑↓ $2p^6$ ↑↓↑↓↑↓

$3s^2$ ↑↓ $3p^6$ ↑↓↑↓↑↓ $3d^0$ ⬜⬜⬜⬜⬜ (26)

$4s^1$ ↑

Following this outline, it is possible to determine the electronic configurations of each atom in the periodic table. To do this, place the electrons into successively higher states, being careful to fill the lowest available energy states first and to obey the Pauli exclusion principle. As an example, consider the filling of the $3d$ and $4s$ states of the *transition metals* shown in Table 2.

Table 2
Electronic structure of transition elements

Element†	K	Ca	Sc	Ti	V	Cr	Mn	Fe	Co	Ni	Cu	Zn
Number of electrons in 3d	0	0	1	2	3	5	5	6	7	8	10	10
Number of electrons in 4s	1	2	2	2	2	1	2	2	2	2	1	2

† The alkali metal potassium and the alkaline earth calcium are included along with copper and zinc, which are not transition metals, in order to show the sequence of filling the $3d$ and $4s$ shells. The next elements in this row, Ga, Ge, As, Se, Br, and Kr, proceed to fill the $4p$ states.

It is easy to see with the aid of the above theory why the particular periods found in the periodic table (Fig. 4) arise and why certain sequences of elements have closely similar properties. The periods simply reflect the filling of a particular shell. Thus, the first period reflects the filling of the K shell first by one electron in H and finally by two electrons in He. Similarly, the second period reflects the filling of the L shell, and so forth. The third period stops with argon ($Z = 18$) because the M shell is now complete except for the $3d$ levels whose energies are too high to be filled next. The fourth period marks the beginning of the filling of the N shell even though the M shell is not quite full, and so forth.

Within each period, certain elements have similar outer electron structures. These elements are connected by dotted lines in Fig. 4. Thus, H, Li, Na, . . . have one s electron in the outer shell; O, S, Se, . . . each have two p electrons missing; while He, Ne, A, . . . have the outer shells complete. These parallelisms express themselves in the properties of the atoms. Accordingly, Li, Na, K, . . . have low

H 1	He 2

Li 3	Be 4	B 5	C 6	N 7	O 8	F 9	Ne 10
Na 11	Mg 12	Al 13	Si 14	P 15	S 16	Cl 17	A 18

K 19	Ca 20	Sc 21	Ti 22	V 23	Cr 24	Mn 25	Fe 26	Co 27	Ni 28	Cu 29	Zn 30	Ga 31	Ge 32	As 33	Se 34	Br 35	Kr 36
Rb 37	Sr 38	Y 39	Zr 40	Nb 41	Mo 42	Tc 43	Ru 44	Rh 45	Pd 46	Ag 47	Cd 48	In 49	Sn 50	Sb 51	Te 52	I 53	Xe 54
Cs 55	Ba 56	La 57 †	Hf 72	Ta 73	W 74	Re 75	Os 76	Ir 77	Pt 78	Au 79	Hg 80	Tl 81	Pb 82	Bi 83	Po 84	At 85	Ry 86
Fr 87	Ra 88	Ac 89	Th 90	Pa 91	U 92	Np 93	Pu 94	Am 95	Cm 96	Bk 97	Cf 98						

† Rare earth metals	Ce 58	Pr 59	Nd 60	Pm 61	Sm 62	Eu 63	Gd 64	Tb 65	Dy 66	Ho 67	Er 68	Tm 69	Yb 70	Lu 71

Fig. 4

first ionization potentials, 5.36, 5.12, and 4.32 eV, respectively, whereas those of He, Ne, A, . . . are very high, 24.46, 21.47, 15.68 eV, respectively. The other similarities that exist between atoms are discussed in later chapters.

Atomic bonds

Forces between atoms. In order to see what happens when two atoms are brought together in close proximity, consider first two atoms in their ground states, infinitely far apart. The potential energy of interaction at the beginning, therefore, is zero, since potential energy is inversely proportional to some power of the distance of separation. Assuming that the atoms consist of moving electrical charges, one of two things can happen as the atoms approach each other. Either they attract each other or they repel each other. The potential energy due to the attraction is negative, since the atoms do the work of attraction. The repulsive energy is positive because external work must be done to bring two such atoms together and it is also inversely proportional to some power of the separation. The total potential energy then must be the sum of two such terms,

$$V = -\frac{\alpha}{r^n} + \frac{\beta}{r^m} \tag{27}$$

where α is the proportionality constant for attraction and β for repulsion. Figure 5A shows a plot of (27). The dashed lines show the repulsive and attractive terms and the solid curve the total potential energy.

The forces of interaction can be derived directly from (27), remembering that the force is the derivative of the potential energy.

$$F = -\frac{dV}{dr} = -\frac{n\alpha}{r^{n+1}} + \frac{m\beta}{r^{m+1}}. \tag{28}$$

The form of (28) is similar to (27) and so is the resultant plot of force as a function of separation shown in Fig. 5B.

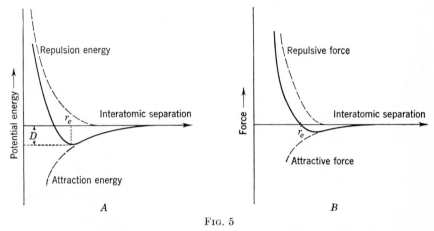

FIG. 5

At large distances, the two atoms are attracted by weak electrostatic forces. As they approach each other, the attractive forces increase, starting to become appreciable when the atoms are separated by only a few atomic diameters. These forces are essentially due to the attraction of negative and positive charges in the two atoms. At this same separation, the repulsive forces between the like charges of the nuclei, however, start to assert themselves although somewhat more slowly. At some separation, called the *equilibrium separation*, r_e, the forces of attraction just equal the forces of repulsion, and the potential energy is at a minimum. As the atoms try to move more closely together than this, the repulsive force increases more rapidly than the attractive force and a great deal of work must be done to accomplish such motion, as can be seen from the rapid increase in the potential energy. This is the reason why two atoms cannot interpenetrate each other, a reassertion of an old maxim in physics that two objects cannot occupy the same space at the same time.

The above discussion is quite general and does not take into account the detailed nature of the charge distribution in the two different atoms.

If the two atoms are inert gases, that is, if they have completely filled outer electron shells, then any electrostatic forces of attraction are due primarily to nonuniformities in the electrostatic charge distribution caused by momentary shifts of the electrons and nuclei toward opposite ends of the atoms, producing so-called *dipoles*. These weak forces are called *van der Waals* forces and in the case of inert gases are insufficient to hold two such atoms together for any length of time at room temperature and atmospheric pressure. It is for this reason, of course, that inert gases are monatomic gases under standard conditions.

For two atoms which are respectively electropositive and electronegative, the weak van der Waals forces operating at relatively large separations are replaced by much stronger electrostatic forces at smaller separations as the electropositive atom loses its valence electron to the electronegative atom. The force of attraction in this case is due to the electrostatic attraction of two oppositely charged ions and is called an *ionic bond*.

The attractive forces between all other atoms come about as follows: As two atoms, having incomplete outer electronic shells, come closely together, the unpaired electrons of each atom that have opposite spins tend to pair up with similarly unpaired electrons in the other atom. The number of such *electron-pair bonds* that can be formed are limited by the Pauli exclusion principle. If the atom has a virtually complete outer shell, that is, if it has only a few unpaired electrons, quantum mechanics shows that it can form one electron-pair bond with as many atoms as there are unpaired electrons available. The resulting bond is also called a covalent bond or *homopolar bond*, because the atoms must all have the same polarity. If the number of electrons in the outer shell is much smaller than the number of states available in the shell, then the atom tends to surround itself with as many similar atoms as it can. This number is usually greater than the number of unpaired electrons so that each atom can form electron-pair bonds with its neighbors in a statistical sense only; that is, it forms such a bond with each neighbor for only part of the time. The result is an incomplete covalent bond, also called an *unsaturated* covalent bond. This bond is found to occur only between metal atoms and is, therefore, popularly called the *metallic bond*. It is, of course, implicit in the above discussion that the pairing of two electrons can occur only if the two electrons have opposite spins.

Ionic bonds. Some of the properties of ionic crystals have already been discussed in previous chapters. An ion can be thought of as a positively or negatively charged atom which has the same outer electron configuration as the nearest inert gas. It has attained this stable configuration by the loss or by the addition of one or more electrons. Consequently, the ionic bond is entirely due to Coulomb-type attraction between two essentially spherically distributed charges of opposite sign. Because of the spherical symmetry, such a bond is nondirectional, and ions have a tendency to surround themselves with as many ions of opposite sign as can possibly fit around the central ion. The surrounding ions, being of like sign, tend to repel each other, and some type of compromise is reached in actual structures. Each ion tends to surround itself in the same way, with the result that a continuous network of ions builds up to form the crystal instead of forming small discrete molecules. The ionic bond is relatively strong, and ionic crystals are characterized by their strength, hardness, and high melting points.

Several types of ionic bonds are of special interest because they differ somewhat from the above picture of simple spherical ions in that they have a directional character. These are as follows:

1. The *hydrogen bond* between two negative ions, which was first postulated to explain the abnormally short F-F distance in $NaHF_2$. This was done by postulating that the two negative fluorine ions are drawn together by a positive hydrogen ion halfway between them. Since hydrogen has only one electron, it readily loses it to another ion having a high electron affinity. On the other hand, since it can lose only one electron, it can lose it to either of the two adjoining ions, with the result that there is an equal probability of finding the electron on either ion. This leads to a type of *resonance* of the electron between the two atoms, drawing them more nearly together. Although it may appear, at first glance, that the position of lowest energy for the H^{+1} ion is halfway between the two negative ions, it turns out that there are two equivalent positions having even lower energy, each respectively one-third of the way along the separation distance between two negative ions.

2. The *hydroxyl bond* is a special case of the hydrogen bond. Since oxygen has a high electron affinity, it has a tendency to attract one hydrogen atom. The result is the complex ion OH^{-1} having nearly cylindrical symmetry. In many respects, this complex ion is quite similar to the readily polarizable fluorine ion and behaves like it in many structures. Most common hydroxides are of the $A(OH)_2$ type, where A can be Ca, Hg, Zn, Co, Ni, Fe, or Cd. In these structures the hydroxyl ions are bonded on one side to metal ions and on the other side to other hydroxyl ions. The hydroxyl ion is pictured as containing four charges, each of magnitude $\frac{1}{2}e$, disposed at the corners of a tetrahedron. Three of the charges are negative and one of them is positive, leaving the over-all charge at $-1e$. The positive half-charge of one hydroxyl aligns itself opposite a negative half-charge of an adjacent hydroxyl, etc. The hydroxyls thus form a sort of continuous chain, while the remaining two negative half-charges are neutralized by the positive charge of

adjacent cations. The hydroxyl bond, therefore, is a directed bond that can exist only between two hydroxyl ions. It can be distinguished from the hydrogen bond by the difference in the resulting 0-0 separation. These distances are compared for the three possible cases of a hydrogen bond, a hydroxyl bond, and a van der Waals bond below.

	Hydrogen bond	Hydroxyl bond	Van der Waals bond
0-0 separation	2.54 Å	2.70 Å	3.20 Å (29)

3. The *ion-dipole bond* is found to occur in certain complex ions, such as $Fe(H_2O)_6^{+3}$, for example. In this ion, the excess charge on the central positive ion causes an unbalance in the charge distribution of the electrically neutral water molecules, producing an electrostatic field of force similar to a dipole field. This type of bond is interesting because it shows that water can play a part in the bonding in ionic crystals. Although a water molecule is electrically neutral, it can be pictured as consisting of four tetrahedrally arranged half-charges, not unlike the hydroxyl ion, with the difference that two of the half-charges are positive and two are negative. It follows, therefore, that the water molecule can transmit the charge of an adjacent positive ion by aligning its negative charges next to it and its positive charges away from it. In this way, water molecules actually take part in the bonding, serving primarily to increase the effective size of the cation which they surround. This so-called *water of hydration* or *water of crystallization* can be distinguished from interstitially absorbed water by heating the crystal. The interstitial water is readily driven off whereas the structurally bound water can be released only when the crystal is melted.

Covalent bonds. Following the postulation of the Bohr picture of the electronic structure of an atom, Lewis and Kossel independently suggested similar mechanisms for the formation of bonds between atoms by pairing the unpaired electrons of two atoms. For example, chlorine, having one unpaired electron in its outer shell, can pair up with another chlorine atom to form the Cl_2 molecule. The resulting electron-pair bond can be pictured like this:

$$: \overset{..}{Cl} \cdot + \cdot \overset{..}{Cl} : \rightarrow : \overset{..}{\underset{..}{Cl}} : \overset{..}{\underset{..}{Cl}} :$$

The two electrons lying between the two chlorine atoms belong equally to both and provide each atom with the stable inert-gas configuration. The total number of such bonds that an atom can form depends on how many unpaired electrons it has. This number is given by the so-called $8 - N$ *rule*, where N is the number of the column in the periodic table containing the atom.   Thus, chlorine can form one electron-pair bond, sulfur can form two, phosphorus three, and so forth.

The above rule was proposed before quantum mechanics had been developed and it was not able, therefore, to explain why only two and not some other number of electrons can take part in the bonding.   Following the postulation of the Pauli exclusion principle, it is easy to see that only two electrons, each having the same quantum numbers except for the sense of the spin vector, can effectively "pair up."   A third electron would have to have one of the spins of these two electrons and, hence, would be repelled.   In order to explain why two or more unpaired electrons do not form pairs with each other, it is necessary to invoke *Hund's rule*.   This rule is derived from quantum mechanics and states that, for equivalent orbitals, electrons tend not to share the same orbitals and the electrons occupying different but equivalent orbitals tend to have their spins parallel.   Consequently, nitrogen has three unpaired electrons and forms three electron-pair bonds with another nitrogen atom in the N_2 molecule.   It should be noted that the covalent bond is pictured as an *overlap* of the electron orbitals of the two atoms.

The Lewis-Kossel theory also failed to explain why carbon should be able to form four bonds.   According to quantum mechanics, the electron configuration of carbon is $1s^2 2s^2 2p^2$ and the two $2p$ electrons are unpaired according to Hund's rule.   The reason why carbon does form four bonds can be understood when the energies of the $2s$ and $2p$ states are considered.   It turns out that the energy difference between them is very small, so that a carbon atom can distribute its electrons as follows:

$$1s^2 \; \boxed{\uparrow\downarrow}$$
$$2s \; \boxed{\uparrow} \qquad 2p^3 \; \boxed{\uparrow \mid \uparrow \mid \uparrow} \qquad\qquad (30)$$

and the resulting four unpaired electrons have elliptical orbitals which are disposed toward the four corners of a tetrahedron.   The slightly higher energy of the atom is then compensated by the extra energy lost when four instead of two bonds are formed.

This type of rearrangement in the ground-state electron configuration of an atom is called *hybridization*.   The resulting state for carbon is called the sp^3 hybrid for short.   Other hybrid bonds can also be formed, notably the dsp^2 hybrid formed by nickel in $Ni(CN_4)^{-2}$, or by copper in CuO, in which the four bonds are coplanar and directed toward the corners of a square.   Hybrids containing five bonds can also be formed, for example, sp^3d and spd^3 hybrids found in $MoCl_5$, $NbCl_5$ and $NbBr_5$, in which the five bonds are directed toward the corners of a trigonal bipyramid.

Metallic bonds.   The first attempt to explain the nature of metal crystals as a distinct group was made by Drude and Lorentz at the turn of this century. Before that time, metals and alloys had been treated similarly to other chemical compounds without any successful attempt to explain the rather distinctive properties that metals possess, such as their high thermal and electrical conductivity, ductility, metallic luster, opaqueness, etc. In modern-day terms, Drude assumed that a metal consisted of atoms which gave up their valence electrons to a common electron "gas" which permeated the whole crystal. The crystal was believed to be held together by the electrostatic attraction between the negative electron gas and the positive metal ions. This *free-electron theory* was extremely successful in explaining most of the metallic properties. For example, it is easy to explain high conductivity if it is postulated that the electrons are perfectly free to migrate through the crystal. Similarly, the reasons for the high ductility and malleability of metals become apparent if it is assumed that the electron gas "lubricates" the atoms as they are forced to glide past each other under external force. One of the properties of metals that this theory failed to explain was the observed specific heat of metals. The values predicted by the theory were 100 times as large as the observed values. This difficulty was resolved with the advent of quantum mechanics through the application of the Pauli exclusion principle, as discussed in the next chapter.

The modern picture of the metallic bond assumes that the metallic bond is more closely related to the covalent or electron-pair bond than to an ionic-type bond. Consider the approach of two sodium atoms $(Z = 11)$ toward each other. Each atom has a complete K and L shell and one unpaired $3s$ electron in its outer shell. If the electron spins of the two $3s$ electrons are of opposite sense, then an electron-pair bond forms between the two atoms. As a third sodium atom approaches this pair, it also has an unpaired $3s$ electron, which according to the Pauli exclusion principle must be repelled because the two available $3s$ states are already occupied. It turns out, however, that the energy of the unoccupied $3p$ states is very nearly the same as the energy of a $3s$ state. Consequently, the third electron can go over into this state without violating the Pauli exclusion principle. In fact, it turns out that a very large number of atoms can thus surround a single sodium atom. Since the central sodium atom has only one unpaired electron, this electron must "take turns" forming electron-pair bonds with each of the surrounding atoms. Consequently, it forms less than a whole electron-pair bond with each neighbor. Solid sodium has the body-centered cubic structure in which each sodium atom is surrounded by eight other atoms. On an average, therefore, each sodium atom can form one-eighth of an electron-pair bond, or one-quarter of an *electron bond*, with each of its nearest neighbors.

It is clear from this discussion that, in a metal, each atom can surround itself with more atoms than it has unpaired electrons, in clear violation of the $8 - N$ rule. The valence electrons of each atom spend only part of the time between any two atoms, forming bonds with other atoms during the rest of the time. In a crystal composed of many atoms, the electrons form these essentially covalent bonds but can migrate from atom to atom throughout the crystal. Thus it can be seen that the modern picture of the metallic bond in metal crystals leads to a situation that is not very different from that prescribed by the earlier free-electron theory.

The reason why metal atoms can form such bonds is the much weaker forces that bind the valence electrons. Table 3 lists the first ionization potentials of a series of elements. It is evident from this list that the force required to remove one valence electron from the alkali metal K and the other metals is much less than that required for a nonmetal such as chlorine. The slight discontinuity following zinc in this listing is due

Table 3
Properties of valence electrons

Element	First ionization potential, eV	Radius of electron orbital, Å
H	13.53	.53
Al	5.96	1.21
Si	8.12	1.06
P	8.75	.92
S	10.30	.82
Cl	12.95	.75
A	15.68	.67
K	4.32	2.20
Ca	6.09	2.03
Sc	6.70	1.80
Ti	6.81	1.66
V	6.71	1.52
Cr	6.74	1.41
Mn	7.41	1.31
Fe	7.83	1.22
Co	7.81	1.14
Ni	7.61	1.07
Cu	7.68	1.03
Zn	9.36	.97
Ga	5.97	1.13
Ge	8.09	1.06
As	10.50	1.01
Se	8.70	.95
Br	11.80	.90
Kr	13.93	.86

to the completion of the filling of the 3*d* and 4*s* states and the beginning of the filling of the 4*p* state with gallium. Note how rapidly the ionization potentials rise as the elements become increasingly less metallic in their nature. Also note, in Table 3, the radii of the orbitals of these outer electrons. As expected, these orbitals are largest when the binding forces are weakest. These larger orbitals in metals cause the electron orbitals of adjacent atoms to overlap to a larger extent than in nonmetals. Consequently, it is easier for a number of neighbors to share in homopolar attraction for each other.

The features of the metallic bond can be summarized as follows:

1. The bond is essentially a covalent bond, without saturation, allowing a large number of atoms to be held together by a mutual sharing of valence electrons.

2. The density of electrons between the atoms is much lower than is allowed by the Pauli exclusion principle. This allows electrons to move fairly freely from point to point without a significant increase in their energy.

Van der Waals bonds. The van der Waals attraction was first explained for electrically neutral gas molecules by Debye, who assumed that neighboring molecules induced dipoles in each other because of their own changing electrical fields. This interaction produces a force that is inversely proportional to the seventh power of the separation. These ideas were not applied to solids until much later when it was found that the structures of ionic crystals could not be explained unless a small but finite van der Waals contribution was assumed. The van der Waals forces produce very weak bonds. In a solid they are due to residual fields between molecules or other electrically neutral atomic groups whose charge distribution is not uniform; however, since the van der Waals contribution to the over-all bonding in inorganic solids is relatively small, its further discussion in this book is not warranted.

Cohesion of crystals

Quantum-mechanical approach. The four ways of bonding atoms in crystals are described above. These forces explain the cohesion of crystals and such properties as elasticity, thermal expansion, melting points, etc. The cohesive forces in very few crystals, however, are exclusively of one type. It is far more usual that either the cohesive forces are of a mixed type, say having partially ionic and partially covalent character, or some of the atoms are bound in groups by bonds of one kind while the groups are bound by bonds of another kind.

The simplest case of cohesion is that of a diatomic molecule. Consider the case of two hydrogen atoms approaching each other from infinity, where their energy of interaction is assumed to be zero. As they approach each other, one of two things can happen. If the spins of their respective $1s$ electrons are parallel, the two atoms will repel each other, and if the spins are antiparallel, the atoms will attract each other. The potential energy of these two cases is diagrammatically represented in Fig. 6. Note that the potential energy of the attractive state of the two electrons exhibits a minimum at the interatomic separation r_e which is the equilibrium separation at which a stable molecule is formed.

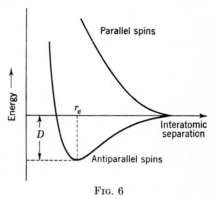

Fig. 6

The instantaneous position of an electron surrounding the nucleus in a hydrogen atom is predicted by $|\psi|^2$. If the two atoms above are called atom A and atom B, respectively, and the electron of atom A is called a and that belonging to atom B is called b, then it is possible to describe the state of the two electrons by the following wave functions:

ψ_{Aa} if the a electron is in an orbital about the nucleus of A
ψ_{Ab} if the b electron is in an orbital about the nucleus of A
ψ_{Bb} if the b electron is in an orbital about the nucleus of B
ψ_{Ba} if the a electron is in an orbital about the nucleus of B

The probability that the a electron is in an orbital around the nucleus of A and that the b electron is in an orbital around the nucleus B is given by $|\psi_{Aa}|^2 |\psi_{Bb}|^2$, while the probability of the reverse case is given by $|\psi_{Ab}|^2 |\psi_{Ba}|^2$. (The probability that both electrons are in orbitals about the same nucleus is finite but very small and is ignored in the following discussion.) The wave function describing both electrons in the molecule comprised of atoms A and B can thus have the form $\psi_{Aa}\psi_{Bb}$ or $\psi_{Ab}\psi_{Ba}$. This treatment of the hydrogen molecule was first proposed by Heitler and London.

As already stated in the first part of this chapter, any linear combination of solutions of the Schrödinger equation is also a solution of that equation. Hence, it is possible to construct two new wave functions

$$\psi_+ = \psi_{Aa}\psi_{Bb} + \psi_{Ab}\psi_{Ba}$$

and
$$\psi_- = \psi_{Aa}\psi_{Bb} - \psi_{Ab}\psi_{Ba}. \tag{31}$$

Note that the interchange of the subscripts a and b in the two equations in (31) does not alter the wave functions. This is because of the indistinguishability of the two electrons; that is, after the molecule is formed, there is no longer any way of distinguishing which is electron a and which is b.

The probabilities of finding the two electrons somewhere in space is given by either

$$|\psi_+|^2 = (\psi_{Aa}\psi_{Bb})^2 + (\psi_{Ab}\psi_{Ba})^2 + 2\psi_{Aa}\psi_{Bb}\psi_{Ab}\psi_{Ba}$$
$$|\psi_-|^2 = (\psi_{Aa}\psi_{Bb})^2 + (\psi_{Ab}\psi_{Ba})^2 - 2\psi_{Aa}\psi_{Bb}\psi_{Ab}\psi_{Ba}. \tag{32}$$

It turns out that the four kinds of wave functions on the right side in (31) all have very nearly the same value in the region halfway between atoms A and B. Consequently, $|\psi_+|^2$ has a large value at this point which can be explained physically to mean that the ψ_+ function represents the case of electron-pair bond formation with the electrons located between the two nuclei. On the other hand, $|\psi_-|^2$ has a small value when the electrons are located between the atoms and a large value when they are at opposite sides of the molecule; hence ψ_- is a state which opposes bonding, that is, a repulsive state.

A similar treatment is possible when infinitely large molecules such as crystals are considered. In this connection it should be emphasized that, because of the undirected nature of the ionic and metallic bonds, it is not possible to form molecules joined by such bonds in the solid state. Saturated covalent bonds can exist between groups of atoms in crystals, forming complex ions or molecules; however, these groups must then be joined in infinite three-dimensional arrays by other kinds of bonds. On the other hand, atoms can be joined by covalent bonds without forming discrete molecules so that the entire crystal is one big molecule. In principle, it is possible to calculate the energies of different kinds of crystal structures for each kind of binding. If the wave function corresponding to the most stable configuration based on one kind of bond is ψ_1 and that for another kind is ψ_2, then the linear combination of the two kinds of wave functions can be written

$$\psi = a\psi_1 + b\psi_2. \tag{33}$$

The ratio of the coefficients, a/b, which gives the wave functions in (33) corresponding to the lowest energy for a particular structure, determines the most stable configuration of the system. If a is either much larger or much smaller than b, one or the other type of bond predominates. On the other hand, if the coefficients have comparable magnitudes, then the structure is said to resonate between the two possible configurations. This postulate of resonance is, of course, a direct consequence of the statistical nature of the results of quantum-mechanical analysis. It should be understood that resonance does not imply that the system literally divides itself into the state described by ψ_1 for $a/(a + b)$ part of the time and into the state described by ψ_2 for the rest of the time, but rather that, on an average, the system behaves as if it were rapidly alternating between the two states, with the relative predominance of each determined by the relative magnitudes of a and b.

There is an alternative approach possible to the treatment of cohesive forces in molecules known as the *method of molecular orbitals*. In this treatment, it is assumed that each electron's behavior is primarily affected by the nucleus and the outer electrons of each atom. Therefore, the molecular orbitals are compounded from the individual atomic orbitals; that is, they are obtained from a linear combination of atomic orbitals. Pauling and Slater pointed out that the energy of an electron-pair bond is greatest when there is maximum overlapping between the two atomic orbitals, provided that the two orbitals correspond to very nearly the same quantum states. It is interesting to note that in the case of the hydrogen molecule, the only molecule for which exact calculation is possible, the method of molecular orbitals and the Heitler-London method give identical results. The calculations for more complex molecules require that certain assumptions be made, so that calculations for infinitely large molecules such as crystals can give only approximate results.

Ionic crystals. The simplest type of bond to consider is the ionic bond which can be very closely approximated by electrostatic forces between point charges of negative and positive electricity. The Coulomb attraction between two point charges z_1e and z_2e, separated by r, is $(z_1ez_2e)/r$. In a crystal, however, there are present repulsive forces which also are assumed to be inversely proportional to some power of the separation r. The potential energy of the crystal can be written, therefore,

$$V = -A\,\frac{z_1z_2e^2}{r} + B\,\frac{1}{r^n} \tag{34}$$

where A and B are constants to be determined. For the simplest case of the univalent alkali halides, (34) reduces to

$$V = -\frac{Ae^2}{r} + \frac{B}{r^n}. \tag{35}$$

At the equilibrium separation r_e, the potential energy must be a minimum and the first derivative of (35) must vanish.

$$\left(\frac{dV}{dr}\right)_{r=r_e} = 0 = +\frac{Ae^2}{r_e^2} - \frac{nB}{r_e^{n+1}}. \tag{36}$$

From this it follows that

$$B = \frac{Ae^2}{r_e^2} \frac{r_e^{n+1}}{n}$$
$$= A \frac{e^2 r_e^{n-1}}{n}. \tag{37}$$

Substituting (37) in (35),

$$V = -\frac{Ae^2}{r_e} + \frac{Ae^2 r_e^{n-1}}{n r_e^n}$$
$$= -\frac{Ae^2}{r_e}\left(1 - \frac{1}{n}\right). \tag{38}$$

This type of analysis was first applied to ionic crystals by Born and Landé. The constant A was first evaluated by Madelung and bears his name. It depends on the exact crystal structure and is very difficult to calculate exactly; however, it can be approximated quite easily for most simple structures. The value of n can be determined empirically from the compressibility of the crystal. It can be shown that the compressibility is given by the relation

$$\kappa = \frac{18 r_e^4}{Ae^2(n-1)} \tag{39}$$

in which κ is measured experimentally and all the other factors except n are known. It should be noted that the potential energy in (38) is not greatly affected by small errors in n.

One of the requirements of a good theory of cohesion is that it be able to predict the structural arrangements that a group of atoms will assume. This, the most stable of several possible crystal structures, is the structure having the lowest value for the potential energy in (38). It turns out that the form of (38) is not adequate for this purpose because the repulsive term is incorrectly formulated and the small but nevertheless finite van der Waals forces must be taken into account. These alterations of the theory were worked out by Born and Mayer, giving the following relation for the potential energy:

$$V = -\frac{Ae^2}{r} + Be^{-r/n} - \frac{C}{r^6} + \delta \tag{40}$$

in which A, B, C are constants, n is determined from compressibility data as before, and δ is a small contribution expressing the energy of the structure at the absolute zero of temperature. Notice that the attraction term is unaltered, the repulsion term is proportional to an exponential in r/n, and the third term expresses the van der Waals forces. Actual computations based on (40) give energy values not too different from those obtained using (38); however, the agreement with experimentally determined values is improved.

The application of quantum mechanics to the determination of cohesive forces in ionic crystals was carried out by Hylleraas for lithium hydride and by Landshoff for sodium chloride. Landshoff's calculations were based on the Heitler-London method in which the electronic wave functions used were those for Na^{+1} and Cl^{-1} ions. Instead of determining the absolute energy of the NaCl structure, he calculated the energy of the structure relative to the energy of the ions in a free state. The accuracy of his solutions cannot be estimated on a theoretically absolute basis; however, the cohesive energy of NaCl calculated by Landshoff turns out to be exactly equal to the experimental value.

Metallic crystals. The next simplest type of bonding to subject to theoretical analysis is the metallic bond. As in the case of ionic crystals, structures of monovalent metal atoms are mathematically simpler to treat than structures of metals having higher valencies. The earliest calculations were based on semi-empirical methods analogous to the Born theory for ionic crystals. Grüneisen combined such a formulation with the condition that his expression for energy give the observed values of atomic volume, cohesive energy, and compressibility of the solid at the absolute zero of

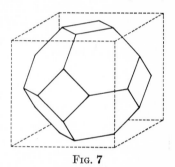

FIG. 7

temperature. Grüneisen applied his results to the calculation of elastic properties of several monatomic metals, and his results are in good agreement with experimental measurements. Grüneisen's methods have been extended by others and are quite valuable in the calculation of elastic properties such as thermal expansion and compressibility.

The cohesive energy predicted by the above method does not agree too well with experimental values, however. A much better agreement is obtained by using quantum mechanics. The method usually is based on a procedure first proposed by Wigner and Seitz and bears their names. The crystal volume is first divided into identical polyhedra surrounding each atom. Such an atomic polyhedron is constructed by bisecting the separation distances between an atom and its nearest neighbors by planes which are terminated at their mutual intersections. The atomic polyhedron for a monatomic metal in a body-centered cubic structure is shown in Fig. 7. The Wigner-Seitz approximation consists of the assumption that the valence electron of the atom inside such a polyhedron is influenced only by a spherically symmetrical potential field due, solely, to the positively charged ion at its center; that is, the fields of neighboring polyhedra do not extend past their boundaries. Consequently, it turns out that the polyhedra can be replaced by spheres without introducing appreciable errors. For alkali metals, the resulting electronic wave functions are constant over 90 per cent of the atomic volume (they have pronounced variations only in the immediate vicinity of the nucleus). This means that the electrons in alkali metals are free to move throughout this volume, not unlike the assumptions of the early Drude-Lorentz theories. In the case of heavier metals such as copper, silver, and gold, the wave functions are constant over very small ranges, indicating that the free-electron model is not applicable to the same degree.

It is possible to give this a simple physical interpretation. If an electron is really influenced only by the field of the positive metal ion, this field falls off as the electron moves farther away from the nucleus. Accordingly, when the ratio between the ionic radius and one-half the separation between atoms in the metal structure is small, then the electron is relatively more free than when this ratio is large. Some values of this ratio are given below.

	Li	Na	K	Cu	Ag	Au	
Ratio	0.39	0.51	0.58	0.78	0.88	0.95	(41)

It is clearly evident from this comparison that the naive picture of a metal consisting of positive ions imbedded in a "sea" of negative electrons is not too bad an approximation for the alkali metals but cannot be carried over in detail to the other metals.

Thus, in general, the potential energy of a metal crystal is the sum of the interaction energies of the charge within each atomic polyhedron plus the energy of interaction of the polyhedra with each other. In applying the Wigner-Seitz method to alkali metals, it is assumed that the potential field due to the cation is limited to the volume of one polyhedron which contains one valence electron and is therefore electrically neutral. The potential energy of the crystal is determined directly by the kinetic energy of each electron, E_0, and the potential energy of each electron, V_0, in the field of the positive ion. The cohesive energy E_c is then given by the expression

$$E_c = -(V_0 + \tfrac{3}{5}E_0 + V_1) \tag{42}$$

where V_1 is the first ionization potential of the atoms. Actually, this equation is an oversimplification since it does not include electron-electron interactions nor van der Waals interactions. Nevertheless, the approximate treatment is in fairly good agreement with experimental values, as shown by a comparison between calculated and observed values below.

	Li	Na	K
Calculated E_c	36.2	24.5	16.5 (kg-cal/mole)
Observed E_c	39	26	23 (kg-cal/mole).

$$(43)$$

Fuchs has attempted to extend the Wigner-Seitz approximation to the heavier metals. It turns out in these cases that the outermost filled shells extend outward from each atomic polyhedron and, hence, contribute to the binding almost as much as the valence electrons. The exact treatment of this situation becomes very complex; however, by means of several approximations, Fuchs was able to calculate the cohesive energy of copper and obtained a value of 33 kg-cal/mole. When this value is compared with the experimentally determined energy of 81 kg-cal/mole, it is evident that the Wigner-Seitz model is inadequate for these metals.

An alternative approach to cohesion in metal crystals was proposed by Pauling. It will be recalled from the discussion of the metallic bond that there exist in metals several unoccupied energy levels having very nearly the same energies. Pauling suggested that, because of this, the electrons resonate among several positions, where they can form electron-pair bonds. The greater this resonance, that is, the larger the coordination number of an atom, the lower the energy of the structure. This is in agreement with the observed tendency of metals to form closest-packed structures. If all the valence electrons are forming covalent bonds, however, it is not possible to explain the high electrical conductivity of metals. Pauling gets around this by postulating a nonuniform distribution of electrons in which some of the atoms become temporarily ionized. Although the ionization of an atom requires an increase in its energy, it turns out that the over-all energy of the crystal is lowest for this type of distribution.

It is possible to obtain a qualitative correlation between the cohesive properties of metal structures and the metallic valence obtained from Pauling's theory. Consider the elements of the first long period from potassium through germanium. In each of these metal atoms there are five $3d$ orbitals, one $4s$ orbital, and three $4p$ orbitals available for the outer electrons. According to Pauling, the electrons can occupy these hybridized nine available orbitals as follows: One orbital, which is set aside so that the electrons can resonate into it, is called the *metallic orbital*. The other orbitals are successively occupied by unpaired electrons, with the further restriction that the number of valence electrons can never exceed six. The resulting valences for these metal atoms are plotted in Fig. 8. The number of valence electrons increases gradually from one in potassium to six in chromium, then levels off at six until nickel, after which it decreases again. The reason for this decrease is seen by considering the copper atom whose eleven outer electrons are schematically distributed as follows:

$$3d \;\; \boxed{↑↓|↑↓|↑↓|↑ |↑\;} \qquad 4s \;\; \boxed{↑\;} \qquad 4p \;\; \boxed{↑ |↑ | \;} \qquad\qquad (44)$$

where the unoccupied $4p$ state is reserved for the metallic orbital. The elastic properties of the elements show a great similarity to the graph in Fig. 8; that is, the elastic properties, as evidenced by, say, critical-stress

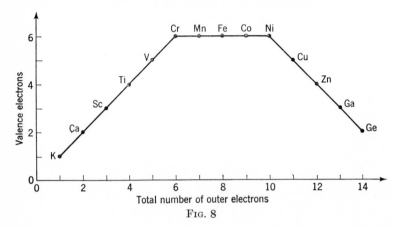

Fig. 8

values, increase from potassium to chromium, are similar for the transition metals, and decrease for Cu, Zn, Ga, and Ge, in that order.

Introductory band theory

There is a $1s$ state in hydrogen which its only electron can occupy. Actually, two electrons can occupy the $1s$ state of hydrogen provided that they have opposite spins. One concludes, therefore, that there are two possible $1s$ states in a hydrogen atom. When two hydrogen atoms combine to form the H_2 molecule, there are a total of four $1s$ states available in the molecule, two of which are occupied in the case when the two atoms attract each other, while the other two represent the case when the two atoms repel each other, as discussed earlier. To distinguish the two sets of $1s$ states, they are called attractive states and repulsive states, respectively. The energies of these two states depend on the separation between the atoms, being the same at large separations but differing or "splitting up" as the separation decreases. Ignoring the difference in the energies of these states, it follows that the total number of possible states in the molecule is equal to the sum of like states in each atom. In fact, it can be proved that *the joining of atoms to form a molecule does not alter the total number of quantum states with a particular quantum number* regardless of the size of the molecule.   Thus, if a crystal is thought of as an infinitely large molecule, the total number of quantum states of one kind that it contains is equal to the total number of atoms in the crystal.

The meaning of the above principle is quite simple.   If a crystal consists of n identical atoms each having two possible $1s$ states, then there exist $2n$ such states in the crystal.   The energies of these states or the so-called energy levels differ slightly, however; in a crystal weighing only 1 mg there are enough atoms to make the number of such levels approximately equal to 10^{19} and the energy separations between them of the order of 10^{-19} eV.   Since such small energy differences cannot

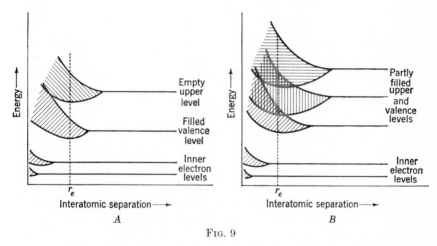

Fig. 9

be measured, it is convenient to use a model in which the distribution of energy levels is very nearly continuous and constitutes an energy *band*.

The way that the energy levels split up and the degree to which the number of states in a band are actually occupied determine the properties of a crystal.   A quantitative discussion of band theory can be found in the next chapter; nevertheless, several qualitative observations can be made here.   Figure 9A and B shows plots of energy versus interatomic separation for two hypothetical crystals.   Note that in Fig. 9A the energy bands at the equilibrium distance r_e are separated by forbidden regions of energy.   These forbidden regions arise from the fact that the energies of the electrons are quantized and must correspond to the values lying within the energy bands of each allowed energy state.   Note also that the inner electron levels, corresponding to orbitals which are confined more closely to the vicinity of the nucleus, do not split up until the interatomic separation is so small that these orbitals can overlap in adjacent atoms.

Suppose that the number of electrons in the hypothetical crystal in Fig. 9*A* is sufficiently large just to occupy all the available states in the inner and the valence bands, leaving the higher-energy bands unoccupied. Next, suppose that an electric field is applied to this crystal. The amount of energy that an electron can gain from even a strong field is very small when compared with the energy gap separating the filled and unfilled bands. If an electron is to absorb energy from the external electric field, it must be able to move into a correspondingly higher energy state. As long as the energy increment is smaller than the width of the forbidden-energy region, an electron occupying a state near the top of the filled band cannot absorb this energy. To do so would require it to occupy a forbidden state. Conversely, an electron whose energy corresponds to a state near the bottom of the filled band cannot absorb the energy increment even though the higher energy state lies within the allowed band, because that state is already occupied. This, of course, is because of the Pauli exclusion principle. It follows from this that an electron can transfer from a quantum state in a filled band only to one lying in an unfilled band. To do so it must absorb sufficient energy from the external field to bridge the energy gap separating the two bands. In the case pictured in Fig. 9*A*, the electron cannot bridge the forbidden-energy region and must stay in the filled or valence band. Such a crystal, therefore, cannot absorb energy from an external electric field and is called a nonconductor or an *insulator*. It is, of course, possible that the filled and unfilled bands are separated by a very narrow forbidden-energy gap. In this case, a limited number of electrons occupying quantum states lying near the top of the filled band can be excited to quantum states in the unfilled band after the absorption of a relatively small amount of energy, say by interacting with a phonon. Because the number of unfilled states is much larger than the number of filled states in this band, the electrons can move from one state to an adjacent state under the influence of an electric field. This leads to limited conductivity, and such a crystal is called a *semiconductor*. Finally, in a crystal whose energy-band model is represented in Fig. 9*B*, the valence band and the upper bands overlap at the equilibrium separation. The continuous range of unfilled quantum states available to the valence electrons of such a crystal accounts for its very high conductivity. Figure 9*B* represents, therefore, the case of a *conductor* or *metal* crystal.

The two hypothetical diagrams shown in Fig. 9 can be compared with the two diagrams shown in Fig. 10 for diamond and Fig. 11 for sodium metal. It is clearly seen that a very large gap separates the filled valence band from the empty band in diamond, making this form of carbon an insulator. Note also the dip in the valence band at the equilibrium

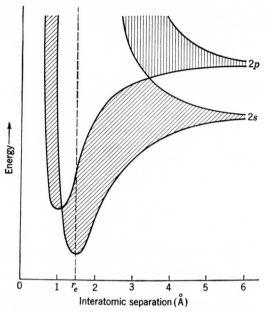

FIG. 10. Energy bands of diamond. The upper shaded band is empty while the lower one is completely filled. (After Slater.)

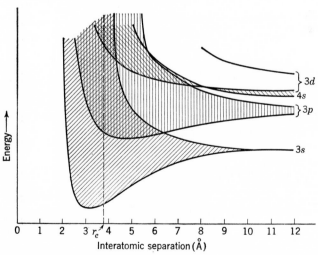

FIG. 11. Energy bands of sodium. Note how the bands overlap at the interatomic separation. (After Slater.)

separation, indicating that the covalent bond in diamond is a very strong one. On the other hand, it is clearly seen in Fig. 11 that the $3s$ and $3p$ bands overlap and that, at the equilibrium separation, sodium metal is a very good conductor.

Suggestions for supplementary reading

R. C. Evans, *An introduction to crystal chemistry* (Cambridge University Press, London, 1948), especially pp. 9–88.

Linus Pauling, *The nature of the chemical bond*, 2d ed. (Cornell University Press, Ithaca, N.Y., 1948).

John C. Slater, *Introduction to chemical physics* (McGraw-Hill Book Company, Inc., New York, 1939), especially pp. 352–376.

A. F. Wells, *Structural inorganic chemistry*, 2d ed. (Oxford University Press, London, 1950), especially pp. 7–27 and 684–685.

Suggestions for further reading

W. Heitler, *Elementary wave mechanics*, 2d ed. (Oxford University Press, London, 1956).

John C. Slater, *Quantum theory of matter* (McGraw-Hill Book Company, Inc., New York, 1951), especially pp. 1–255.

Exercises

1. The translational kinetic energy of a gas molecule is equal to $\frac{3}{2}kT$, where k is the Boltzmann constant and T is the temperature measured on the absolute scale. What is the De Broglie wavelength of a hydrogen atom at a room temperature of 20°C?

2. The usual operating voltage of an electron microscope is 50 kV. What is the De Broglie wavelength of an electron accelerated by such a potential field?

3. Equation (20) states that the energy of an electron in the first excited state of an atom ($n = 2$) has a magnitude equal to one-fourth the magnitude of the ground-state energy. How is this made compatible with the fact that the energy of the electron in an excited state is greater than its energy in the ground state?

4. Using equation (21), calculate the radii of the first two electronic orbitals of hydrogen. Compare these values with the results of Exercise 1 in Chapter 4.

5. Prepare a table showing the distribution of electrons in the allowed-energy states for the first eighteen atoms in the periodic table.

6. Using equations (27) and (28), derive an expression for the potential energy at the equilibrium separation involving only the constants α, n, and m.

7. Draw a schematic representation of the structure of $NaHF_2$. (Assume a CN for H^{+1} of 2 and for Na^{+1} of 6 and use the methods of distributing bonds developed in Chapter 4.)

8. Draw a schematic representation of the structure of $Al(OH)_3$, assuming octahedral coordination for Al^{+3} and that the aluminum octahedra form sheets which are joined to adjacent sheets by hydroxyl bonds.

9. How do you explain the formation of O_2 molecules in the gaseous state using the Lewis-Kossel theory? The quantum theory?

10. Look up the crystal structure of tenorite, CuO, and note the lengths of the six Cu-O bonds found in the crystal. Why are they different? What kinds of bonds exist between copper and oxygen atoms in this structure? Why are the four Cu-O distances in cuprite, Cu_2O, all of the same length?

11. Explain the statement that the free-electron theory of Drude and Lorentz was able to account for the optical properties of metals.

12. Describe briefly what happens when lithium atoms approach each other to form a body-centered crystal structure.

13. Bragg has shown that the Madelung constant for NaCl can be calculated as follows: Starting with any atom, it is surrounded by six nearest neighbors of opposite sign at a distance r, twelve next-nearest neighbors of like sign at a distance $\sqrt{2}r$, eight next-next-nearest neighbors of unlike sign at $\sqrt{3}r$, etc. The value of A is given by adding up such terms in a series of the form

$$A = \frac{6}{\sqrt{1}} - \frac{12}{\sqrt{2}} + \frac{8}{\sqrt{3}} - \frac{6}{\sqrt{4}} + \frac{24}{\sqrt{5}} - \cdots .$$

What is the potential energy of sodium chloride, at equilibrium, if the separation between sodium and chlorine atoms is 2.76 Å and the value of n from compressibility data is 9.1?

14. What is the potential energy of cesium chloride, at equilibrium, if the separation between cesium and chlorine atoms is 3.56 Å and n is 11.5? Compute the Madelung constant similarly to the procedure outlined in Exercise 13 for NaCl.

15. The potential energy of a valence electron within an atomic polyhedron in lithium can be approximated by $V_0 = \alpha e^2/r$, where $\alpha \sim 2$ and has the units of g-cm^3/(esu-sec)^2. Using the approximate equation (42), calculate the cohesive energy of lithium metal if $r = 3.21$ Å, $E_0 = 1.896$ eV, and $V_1 = 5.365$ eV. Compare it with the values in (43). (1 eV $= 23$ kg-cal/mole).

16. Pauling has shown that such physical properties as hardness, melting points, and others change in proportion to the interatomic separation in the structures of the elements. Specifically, this can be illustrated by computing a quantity which Pauling calls the *ideal density*. The ideal density for the elements from potassium through germanium is equal to 50/(gram-atomic volume) and is the density that these elements would have if they all had the same atomic weight, 50, and crystallized in a closest packing. Using the metal atom radii in Appendix 3, calculate the ideal density for the elements from K through Ge and plot the calculated values against the number of outer electrons in each atom. Compare this plot with Fig. 8.

17. Using Fig. 9A as a guide, make a schematic drawing showing the separation of the energy levels for a diamond crystal consisting of only one unit cell, that is, if there are only eight atoms in the crystal.

10

Properties of metals

Free-electron theory

Early theories. At the beginning of the twentieth century, a bold guess was made by Drude regarding the electronic structure of metals. The resulting *free-electron theory* was modified by Lorentz a few years later and has come to be known as the *Drude-Lorentz theory* of metals. The basic assumption of this theory is that a metal crystal consists of positive metal ions whose valence electrons are free to move between the ions as if they constituted an electron gas. The crystal is then pictured to be held together by electrostatic forces of attraction between the positively charged ions and the negatively charged electron gas. It is further assumed that the electrons are free to move throughout the entire crystal subject only to the laws of classical mechanics. In fact, Lorentz extended the postulates made by Drude to the point of applying the laws of the classical kinetic theory of gases to the electrons. The mutual repulsion between negative electrons is ignored in this theory and the potential field due to the positive ions is assumed to be completely uniform. Thus the electrons can move from place to place in the crystal without any change in their energy, collide occasionally with the atoms, and have velocities determined at a constant temperature according to the Maxwell-Boltzmann distribution laws.

This model of a metal is eminently successful in explaining many properties of metals. For example, if an external electric field is applied to a metal, the negatively charged electrons are accelerated toward the positive pole of the field. The resulting current is limited by electron-atom collisions and is proportional to the applied voltage gradient according to Ohm's law. The opaqueness of metals for all wavelengths of light is explained by the ability of a *free* electron to oscillate in the electromagnetic field of an incident light beam regardless of its frequency.

Similarly, a free electron, once raised to a higher energy by the absorption of light, can return to its former energy by reemitting light of the same frequency in all directions. Because only the light rays directed toward the surface can get out of the crystal, this interaction appears as a reflection of the incident light and accounts for the so-called metallic luster. On the other hand, there are certain properties that the Drude-Lorentz theory cannot explain. The two most notable failures occur in the discrepancy between the observed and predicted specific heats of metals, discussed later in this chapter, and in the inability of this theory to explain why some substances are conductors of electricity and others are not.

Quantum theory. Before proceeding with a discussion of the free-electron theory and how it was changed to conform with the quantum-mechanical model of the electron, it is necessary to determine what restrictions are imposed by the laws of quantum mechanics on the energies that an electron can have inside a crystal. It has been shown in the previous chapter that the allowed-energy levels of an electron bound to a single atom are quantized. In this section, the permissible energy levels are determined for a free electron restricted to remain within the crystal but free to move within its confines. The exact solution of this problem is not attempted here; however, it is possible to obtain an approximate solution by considering an analogous although somewhat crude model.

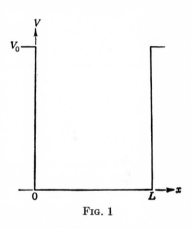

Fig. 1

For the sake of mathematical simplicity, consider first an electron limited to remain within a one-dimensional "crystal" of length L. Next, assume that the potential energy everywhere within this crystal is constant and equal to zero. At the two ends of the crystal the electron is prevented from leaving the crystal by a very high potential energy barrier represented by V_0 in Fig. 1. Inside the crystal the potential energy is zero, and the Schrödinger equation has the form

$$\frac{d^2\psi}{dx^2} + \frac{8\pi^2 mE}{h^2}\psi = 0. \tag{1}$$

The general solution of this equation by analogy to Chapter 9 is

$$\psi = C_1 \sin 2\pi \frac{\sqrt{2mE}}{h}x + C_2 \cos 2\pi \frac{\sqrt{2mE}}{h}x. \tag{2}$$

The values of the two coefficients can be determined according to the boundary conditions existing at $x = 0$ and $x = L$.

Before investigating the boundary conditions, consider the form of Schrödinger's equation on either side of the crystal, that is, in the regions where the potential energy is very large. Including the potential-energy term V_0, the Schrödinger equation can be written

$$\frac{d^2\psi}{dx^2} - \frac{8\pi^2 m(V_0 - E)}{h^2}\psi = 0. \tag{3}$$

The general solution of this equation for $V_0 > E$ is

$$\psi = C_3 e^{2\pi\frac{\sqrt{2m(V_0 - E)}}{h}x} + C_4 e^{-2\pi\frac{\sqrt{2m(V_0 - E)}}{h}x}. \tag{4}$$

An examination of the solution in (4) shows that, as x increases in either a positive or negative sense, the value of the wave function also increases. This obviously cannot be since this would mean that the probability of finding the electron outside the crystal would increase with increasing distance from the crystal, becoming infinite in the limit as $\pm x$ approached infinity. Consequently, $C_3 = 0$ when $x > L$ and $C_4 = 0$ when $x < 0$. This gives two different solutions, one for each side of the crystal.

When $x \geq L$,
$$\psi = C_4 e^{-2\pi\frac{\sqrt{2m(V_0 - E)}}{h}x} \tag{5}$$

and when $x \leq 0$,
$$\psi = C_3 e^{2\pi\frac{\sqrt{2m(V_0 - E)}}{h}x}. \tag{6}$$

It is now possible to consider the boundary conditions that solutions (2), (5), and (6) must satisfy. Since there is a finite probability of finding the electron anywhere in space, the wave function must be continuous everywhere. Similarly, it can be shown that $d\psi/dx$ must be continuous. Consider first the requirement that the slope be continuous at $x = L$. Differentiating equations (2) and (5),

$$\left(\frac{d\psi}{dx}\right)_{x=L} = 2\pi\frac{\sqrt{2mE}}{h}C_1 \cos 2\pi\frac{\sqrt{2mE}}{h}L$$
$$- 2\pi\frac{\sqrt{2mE}}{h}C_2 \sin 2\pi\frac{\sqrt{2mE}}{h}L \tag{7}$$

and

$$\left(\frac{d\psi}{dx}\right)_{x=L} = -2\pi\frac{\sqrt{2m(V_0 - E)}}{h}C_4 e^{-2\pi\frac{\sqrt{2m(V_0 - E)}}{h}L}$$
$$= -2\pi\frac{\sqrt{2m(V_0 - E)}}{h}\psi_{x=L}. \tag{8}$$

As the potential energy at the crystal surface increases, that is, as $V_0 \to \infty$, equation (8) becomes infinite unless simultaneously $\psi_{x=L} \to 0$. In the limiting case $V_0 = \infty$ and $\psi_{x=L} = 0$. A similar argument can be used to show that for an infinitely high potential barrier at $x = 0$ the wave function must be zero at that boundary also. Although infinitely high barriers are not encountered in crystals, the evaluation of the coefficients is greatly simplified by making this assumption. Considering the solution in (2) at $x = 0$,

$$\psi = 0 = C_1 \sin (0) + C_2 \cos (0)$$
$$= C_2. \tag{9}$$

At the other boundary, therefore,

$$\psi = 0 = C_1 \sin 2\pi \frac{\sqrt{2mE}}{h} L. \tag{10}$$

Excluding the trivial solution that C_1 also is zero, the only way (10) can be satisfied is for the sine to be zero. This occurs whenever

$$2\pi \frac{\sqrt{2mE}}{h} L = n\pi \qquad \text{where } n = 1, 2, 3, \ldots \tag{11}$$

From this it follows that the energy can have only the discrete values given by

$$E_n = \frac{h^2}{8mL^2} n^2. \tag{12}$$

Note that, if L is large, the energy levels are spaced very closely together. For example, if $L = 1$ cm,

$$E_n - E_{n\pm1} \sim 3.5 \times 10^{-19} \text{ eV.}$$

The potential barriers confining an electron to the interior of an actual crystal are not infinitely high and are determined in a complex way by the surface energies of the crystal. If this potential barrier at the surface of a crystal is high but not infinite, the wave function has the form shown in Fig. 2 for the case $n = 2$. (Compare this with Fig.

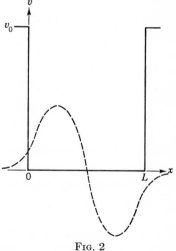

FIG. 2

1 in Chapter 9.) Note that the wave function is sinusoidal in the region $0 \le x \le L$ and exponential outside this region, in accordance with solutions (2), (5), and (6). Although the exact evaluation of the coefficients in these equations is not attempted here, it seems reasonable to

expect that the extension of the wave function beyond the potential barrier is inversely proportional to the height of the barrier. Furthermore, if the barrier is very narrow, it is possible that the wave function can extend beyond it. In this case there is a small but finite probability $(\sim|\psi|^2)$ of finding the electron on the other side of the barrier. This ability of the electron to penetrate a potential barrier is called the *tunnel effect* and is a direct consequence of the application of quantum mechanics to this problem.

In three dimensions, the crystal can be approximated by a cube of edge L inside which the potential energy is zero. It can be shown that the wave function inside such a cube is given by

$$\psi = C \sin \frac{n_x \pi}{L} x \sin \frac{n_y \pi}{L} y \sin \frac{n_z \pi}{L} z \tag{13}$$

where L is the length of a cube edge and n_x, n_y, n_z are any three integers greater than zero. The corresponding form of the energy is

$$E_{n_x n_y n_z} = \frac{h^2}{8mL^2} (n_x^2 + n_y^2 + n_z^2). \tag{14}$$

Remembering that the kinetic energy of an electron is related to its momentum p by

$$E = \frac{1}{2} mv^2 = \frac{p^2}{2m} \tag{15}$$

equation (14) can be written

$$E = \frac{p^2}{2m} = \frac{h^2}{8mL^2} (n_x^2 + n_y^2 + n_z^2). \tag{16}$$

Rearranging the terms in (16),

$$\left(\frac{2L}{h}\right)^2 p^2 = (n_x^2 + n_y^2 + n_z^2) \tag{17}$$

from which it follows that the momentum of an electron can be expressed directly in terms of its three quantum numbers.

This immediately suggests that a lattice can be constructed using unit vectors along the x, y, and z directions to connect lattice points corresponding to the integer values of the three quantum numbers. It is possible to define a vector $\mathbf{R}$ extending from the origin of this so-called *momentum lattice* to any of its lattice points. The length of this vector is given by

$$\mathbf{R}^2 = \mathbf{n}_x^2 + \mathbf{n}_y^2 + \mathbf{n}_z^2. \tag{18}$$

It follows from (17) and (18) that as $\mathbf{R}$ increases so does the momentum and hence the energy of the state represented by the lattice point. In the free-electron model of a metal containing some 10^{23} electrons, the lattice points are so closely spaced that it is not possible to show them in a drawing. The corresponding energy levels determined by (14) are so closely spaced that they form an almost continuous range of energies not unlike that predicted by classical mechanics. This quasi-continuous range of energies, nevertheless, does consist of discrete energy levels in complete agreement with the Pauli exclusion principle.

Fermi–Dirac statistics. The free-electron theory of metals has persisted to the present time primarily because it is a fairly close approximation to the actual state of metals, particularly for the lighter mono-valent elements. After the development of quantum mechanics, Sommerfeld modified the free-electron theory by replacing the classical statistics of Boltzmann by the quantum statistics of Fermi and Dirac. As a consequence, most of the failings of the earlier theory were removed. According to classical mechanics, all the electrons in a metal can have the same energy so that, at the absolute zero of temperature, they all occupy the lowest available energy levels. Quantum mechanics similarly requires that the valence or free electrons be indistinguishable; however, the state of each electron is determined by three quantum numbers n_x, n_y, n_z and by the spin quantum number which can have the two values $\pm\frac{1}{2}$. Moreover, the Pauli exclusion principle does not allow more than one electron to have the same four quantum numbers. This means that, in a metal crystal containing some 10^{23} free electrons, many of the occupied states must have fairly large quantum numbers. Enrico Fermi has shown that the probability that a particular quantum state is occupied is given by the so-called *Fermi factor*

$$f(E) = \frac{1}{e^{(E-E_0)/kT} + 1}. \tag{19}$$

Here E is the energy of an allowed state as determined by (14), and E_0 is the so-called *Fermi energy*. The meaning of (19) is best seen by plotting the Fermi factor as a function of the energy E. For energies less than the Fermi energy, the exponential term in (19) is negative. As the temperature approaches zero, this term approaches zero because $e^{-\infty} = 0$ and $f(E) = 1$. When $E > E_0$, then the exponential term becomes infinite as the temperature approaches zero and $f(E) = 0$. These values of the Fermi factor are plotted in Fig. 3*A* for the case $T = 0°\text{K}$. The meaning of $f(E) = 1$ in this figure, for all energy values less than E_0, is that all these quantum states are occupied at absolute zero while all the quantum states having energies greater than the Fermi energy value are unoccupied. As the temperature increases from absolute zero, electrons occupying states lying near E_0 can gain sufficient thermal energy to move into the higher unoccupied states. The actual change in energy is very small since an electron can gain only a few kT of energy (at room temperature $1kT \sim 0.03$ eV). The resulting change in the shape of the curve of the Fermi factor is shown in Fig. 3B in a highly exaggerated manner. Note that $f(E) = \frac{1}{2}$ when $E = E_0$.

It follows from the above that the highest occupied energy level in a metal at absolute zero has an energy equal to E_0. The actual value of this energy can be determined directly by making use of the lattice in *momentum space* discussed in the previous section. At absolute zero, according to this concept, the lattice points representing the allowed states are occupied out to some maximum value of R. Since each state can be occupied by two electrons having opposite spins, there are a total of $N/2$ occupied states in a crystal containing N free electrons. The

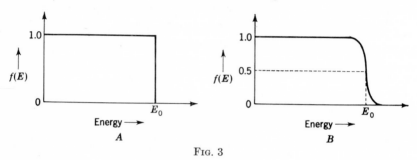

Fig. 3

lattice points representing these states lie in the positive octant of the lattice (because n_x, n_y, and n_z can have positive values only) and are enclosed by a sphere whose radius $R_{\max}$ is given by (16) and (17):

$$R_{\max} = \left(\frac{8mL^2E_0}{h^2}\right)^{\frac{1}{2}}. \tag{20}$$

The volume of the octant, $\frac{1}{6}\pi R_{\max}^3$, contains the $N/2$ occupied states, or $N/2$ lattice points. Because each unit cell in this lattice containing one lattice point has a volume equal to unity, the volume of this octant is

$$\frac{N}{2} = \frac{1}{6}\pi\left(\frac{8mL^2E_0}{h^2}\right)^{\frac{3}{2}}.$$

and

$$E_0 = \frac{h^2}{8m}\left(\frac{3N}{\pi L^3}\right)^{\frac{2}{3}}. \tag{21}$$

Note that E_0 is a function only of N/L^3, that is, the number of free electrons per unit volume, since all the other factors on the right side of (21) are constants. Consequently, the Fermi energy does not change when two identical metals are joined together; that is, the value of the Fermi energy is independent of the size of the metal.

The actual distribution of electrons among the available sites at any temperature is given by the so-called *Fermi-Dirac distribution*

$$N(E)\, dE = f(E)S(E)\, dE$$

$$= \frac{S(E)\, dE}{e^{(E-E_0)/kT} + 1}. \tag{22}$$

Here $N(E)$ is the number of electrons per unit volume having energies between E and $E + dE$, and $S(E)$ is the number of available quantum states in this energy range. Note that this distribution function obeys the Pauli exclusion principle. Since the denominator of (22) can never be less than unity, the number of electrons $N(E)$ having a particular energy E can never exceed the number of available states $S(E)$ having the same energy.

Zone theory

Quantum-mechanical approach. The solutions of the Schrödinger equation

$$\frac{d^2\psi}{dx^2} + \frac{8\pi^2 m}{h^2}(E - V)\psi = 0 \tag{23}$$

can be written

$$\psi = Ce^{\pm 2\pi i \frac{\sqrt{2m(E-V)}}{h} x} \tag{24}$$

remembering that $e^{ix} = \cos x + i \sin x$. The plus or minus sign preceding the exponent in (24) denotes two possible solutions, one for an electron moving in the plus x direction, the other for an electron moving in the minus x direction.

The kinetic energy of a free electron is

$$E - V = \tfrac{1}{2}mv^2$$

$$= \frac{p^2}{2m} \tag{25}$$

where p is the momentum of the free electron and is related to the De Broglie wavelength by

$$p = \frac{h}{\lambda}. \tag{26}$$

It is convenient to define a *wave number* k so that it corresponds to the number of wavelengths contained in one full period, that is,

$$k = \frac{2\pi}{\lambda}. \tag{27}$$

For a free electron, therefore,

$$k = \frac{2\pi}{h} p \tag{28}$$

from which it follows that k is proportional to the momentum. This interpretation of k, however, is correct only for a free electron. In the presence of a periodically varying potential field this is no longer true, since, as is shown later, k can have nonzero values even though $v = 0$.

The kinetic energy of a free electron now can be written

$$E - V = \frac{h^2 k^2}{8\pi^2 m} \tag{29}$$

which follows directly from (26) by substituting relation (28) for p. Finally, (29) can be substituted in (24) so that the general solution of Schrödinger's equation for an electron moving in a constant potential field can be written

$$\psi = C e^{\pm ikx}. \tag{30}$$

The above solution of the Schrödinger equation, for the case of a constant potential, leads to a somewhat paradoxical result. The wave function is sinusoidal. On the other hand, the potential field was assumed to be constant everywhere inside the crystal. The way out of this apparent inconsistency is to recognize the fact that the potential field in a real crystal is not constant. As might be expected, it varies in a periodic manner according to the periodicity of the crystal. To see what effect this model has on the solutions, consider the Schrödinger equation for a one-dimensional periodic potential field denoted $V(x)$:

$$\frac{d^2\psi}{dx^2} + \frac{8\pi^2 m}{h^2} [E - V(x)]\psi = 0. \tag{31}$$

The solutions of this equation were shown by Bloch to have the form

$$\psi(x) = u_k(x) e^{\pm ikx} \tag{32}$$

where $u_k(x)$ is periodic with the periodicity of the lattice, that is,

$$u_k(x + a) = u_k(x). \tag{33}$$

It follows from this that the so-called *Bloch function* (32) is modulated by the periodicity of the lattice, since

$$\begin{aligned} \psi(x + a) &= u_k(x + a) e^{\pm ik(x+a)} \\ &= \psi(x) e^{\pm ika}. \end{aligned} \tag{34}$$

The form of $u_k(x)$ is not unlike (10) and depends on the exact nature of the potential field. A simple model of a one-dimensional periodic potential field is shown in Fig. 4 where it is assumed that the potential energy is zero near the nucleus and equals V_0 halfway between adjacent nuclei which are separated by a. This model was first postulated by Kronig and Penney who used it to obtain solutions of the Schrödinger equation in the form of (32). Similarly to the case of the free-electron solutions, it is necessary that both ψ and $d\psi/dx$ be continuous throughout the crystal. Also, in order to simplify the attendant computations, an assumption is made regarding the potential barrier in Fig. 4, namely, that as V_0 increases, the width of the barrier w decreases, so that the product $V_0 w$ remains constant. Even so, the mathematics is still too

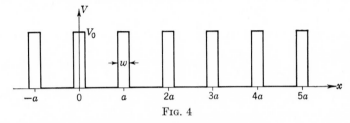

Fig. 4

complex to be discussed here, and only the results are presented. It turns out that solutions are possible only for energies given by the relation

$$\cos ka = P \frac{\sin \alpha a}{\alpha a} + \cos \alpha a \tag{35}$$

where

$$P = \frac{4\pi^2 ma}{h^2} V_0 w \tag{36}$$

and

$$\alpha = \frac{2\pi}{h} \sqrt{2mE}. \tag{37}$$

The meaning of this relation is best understood by considering the plot of the right side of (35) shown in Fig. 5. The left side of this equation imposes a limitation on the values that this function can have, namely, a maximum value of $+1$ and a minimum value of -1. These limits are indicated by horizontal dashed lines in Fig. 5. This limitation has the very important consequence that certain values of E are not allowed. Thus, the energy spectrum of an electron moving in the presence of a periodic potential field is divided into so-called *allowed* zones and *forbidden* zones. Note also that, as the potential barrier $V_0 w$ increases, P increases and the allowed zones become narrower.

Allowed-energy zones. It is equally fruitful to consider the meaning of (35) by considering the left side of this relation. It is immediately evident that $\cos ka$ can have only one value for a specific value of the energy E. Moreover, since $\cos ka$ is an even periodic function, it will have the same value whether ka is positive or negative or whether it is increased by integer multiples of 2π. Accordingly, the total energy E of the electron is an even periodic function of k with a period $2\pi/a$. Figure 6A shows a plot of the energy as a function of k. The parabolic energy dependence of a free electron given by (29) is also shown in this figure for comparison purposes. The energy gaps appear as regions for which

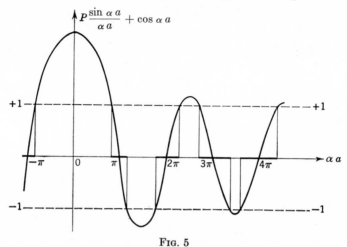

Fig. 5

there are no real values of k. [Actually, imaginary values of k are possible in (35); however, they represent solutions which lie in the forbidden region.] These energy gaps and the allowed zones are shown schematically in Fig. 6B in a representation of energy zones that is used in other parts of this book.

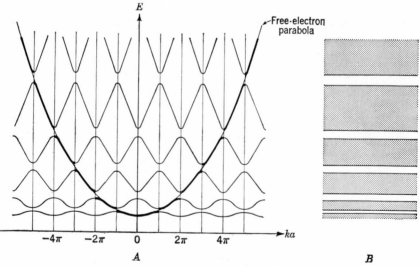

Fig. 6

When a parabola representing the energy of a free electron is compared with the energy curves for an electron in a periodic field, it becomes obvious that the discontinuities in the parabola occur at values of k given by

$$k = n\pi/a \qquad \text{where } n = \pm 1, \pm 2, \pm 3, \cdots . \tag{38}$$

Substituting (27) for k in (38),

$$2\pi/\lambda = n\pi/a$$

or $$n\lambda = 2a. \tag{39}$$

This equation can be compared with the Bragg law in Chapter 3 for the case of x-ray or electron diffraction at a Bragg angle of 90°. Accordingly, if a is the interplanar spacing between planes that are normal to the propagation direction of the electron, then (39) is the form of Bragg's law representing total reflection backwards. Use is made of this equivalence in the next section.

Brillouin zones. The parallelism between equation (39) and the Bragg law is a direct consequence of the wave nature of electrons. In order to understand this relationship more clearly, rewrite (38) for the case $n = 1$, using crystallographic notation. The direction of movement of the electrons is then denoted by the subscript $[uvw]$ so that

$$k_{[uvw]} = \frac{\pi}{d_{(hkl)}} \tag{40}$$

where $d_{(hkl)}$ is the interplanar spacing of the planes which are normal to $[uvw]$. (See Chapter 2 for a discussion of these relationships.) In two dimensions, directions are denoted $[uv]$ and the "planes" become (hk).

Consider the two-dimensional "crystal" having a square lattice, shown in Fig. 7. Next, consider electrons moving in the direction $[21]$ which is normal to the dotted lines (21). According to relation (40), total reflection of the electrons occurs when the wave number satisfies the condition

$$k_{[21]} = \frac{\pi}{d_{(21)}}. \tag{41}$$

Alternatively, consider the solid lines (01) forming the angle θ with $[21]$. An enlarged view of the triangle relating a_2, the interlinear spacing of (01), to $d_{(21)}$, which is measured in a direction parallel to $[21]$, is shown in Fig. 8. It is clear from this that $d_{(21)} = a \sin \theta$. Substituting this value for $d_{(21)}$ in equation (41),

$$k_{[21]} = \frac{2\pi}{\lambda} = \frac{\pi}{a \sin \theta}$$

which is Bragg's law for reflection by lines having an interlinear spacing a. It is clear from the above that condition (40), which determines the discontinuities in the allowed-energy ranges of the electrons in a crystal, can be interpreted to mean either total reflection of the electrons by planes that are normal to their direction of propagation or as Bragg reflection by other crystallographic planes. Obviously, the planes that

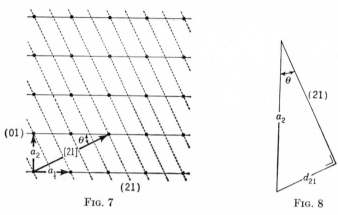

FIG. 7   FIG. 8

are chosen for the latter interpretation are the planes that most strongly reflect the electrons. For a crystal structure consisting of one atom placed at the lattice points of a primitive cubic lattice, these planes are the cube faces belonging to the form ((100)). In a simple face-centered cubic crystal the planes are ((111)) and ((200)) and in a simple body-centered cubic crystal ((110)). The polyhedra formed by these planes

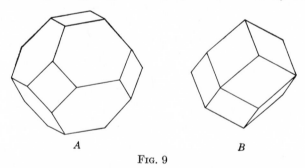

FIG. 9

are called the first *Brillouin zones* of these crystals. Figure 9*A* and *B*, respectively, shows the first Brillouin zones of a face-centered cubic crystal and a body-centered cubic crystal.

It should be realized that other planes in the crystal can reflect electrons also. In fact, for larger energies and, consequently, larger wave numbers, it is clearly seen in (40) that smaller d values are required to maintain the equality. Thus another set of planes (more closely spaced) is necessary to reflect the electrons having energies lying in the second allowed zone, and so on. The polyhedra formed by these planes are called the second, third, etc., Brillouin zones of the crystal. Use is made of these polyhedra in discussing the energies of electrons in crystals.

k **space.** In discussing the Brillouin zones of cubic crystals, it is conventional to select three axes, X, Y, Z, parallel to the three equivalent crystallographic axes a, and to denote directions parallel to these axes

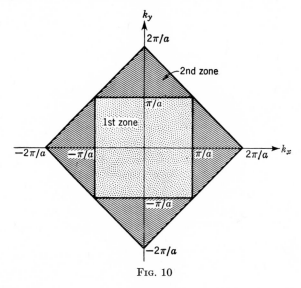

FIG. 10

by the subscripts x, y, z. Accordingly, condition (38) for these three directions can be written

$$k_x = \pm \frac{\pi}{a}$$

$$k_y = \pm \frac{\pi}{a} \tag{42}$$

$$k_z = \pm \frac{\pi}{a}$$

where the plus or minus sign corresponds to positive or negative values of x, y, and z. It is convenient to use the wave numbers k_x, k_y, k_z as coordinate axes for the construction of the Brillouin zones. The space defined by these axes is usually called *k space*, and since the distances in this space are reciprocal to distances in the crystal, according to (40), it is also called *reciprocal space*. (Note that for a free electron this is proportional to the momentum space discussed earlier in this chapter.)

The two-dimensional k space defined by k_x and k_y is shown in Fig. 10.

The first Brillouin zone for a simple cubic crystal is a cube and is shown in cross section in this figure.   The second Brillouin zone for a simple cubic crystal is a dodecahedron bounded by ((110)).   Its cross section in the XY plane is also indicated in Fig. 10.   Note that the second zone lies outside the first zone in k space because it is bounded by ((110)) planes which have a smaller interplanar spacing than the ((100)) planes.   This, of course, is because of the reciprocal relationships between distances in the crystal and distances in k space.

Fermi surfaces.   A very useful property of k space is that it can be used to show the distribution of the energy values of the valence electrons. If a plot of E as a function of k, like Fig. 6, is prepared for various directions in the crystal, it is possible to note the energy values of the various

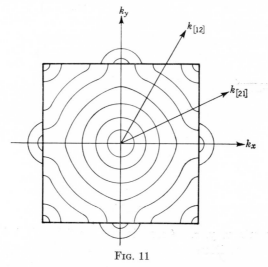

FIG. 11

points in k space.   By joining together points having the same energy values, a set of *energy contours* is obtained.   A typical set of such contours for the nearly free electrons of a simple cubic crystal is shown in Fig. 11. The inner contours are circles (spheres in three dimensions) because the electrons having these energies have wave numbers that are far removed from the critical values of (42); hence, the directions of motion of these electrons are not restricted in any way.   When the energy contours approach the zone boundaries, however, this is no longer true.   As the wave numbers approach the critical values of (42), the corresponding energy values increase very slowly (Fig. 6) and the contours in Fig. 11 begin to bulge toward the zone boundary.   Finally, the energy contours in the corners of the zone terminate on the zone boundaries because they correspond to k values that are larger than the wave numbers elsewhere in the zone.

Figure 11 also shows the first two energy contours of the second Brillouin zone. These contours do not join with any of the contours in the first zone because of the energy discontinuity that takes place at a zone boundary. The first contour of the second zone may correspond to an energy that is either greater or less than the outermost contour of the first zone. To see how this can happen, consider the energy curves for the first and second zones plotted in Fig. 12 as a function of k for two crystallographic directions. Figure 12A shows the energy curve for movement along the a_1 axis. As expected, this curve has a discontinuity at $k_x = \pi/a$, indicated by the top energy value for the first zone E_1 and the bottom energy of the second zone E_2. Figure 12B shows a similar plot for electron movement along [120]. It is clear from Fig. 11 that the top energy for the first zone is greater in this direction than in the [100]

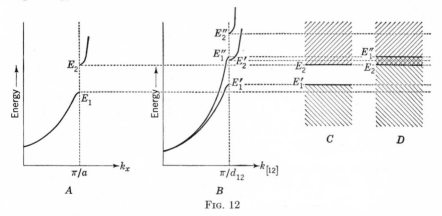

Fig. 12

direction; consequently, Fig. 12B shows two possible cases designated by E_1' and E_1''. The bottom energies of the corresponding zones are also higher for this direction, as indicated by E_2' and E_2''.

Essentially two possibilities exist regarding the relative magnitudes of the highest energy level of the first zone and the lowest energy level of the second zone, namely, either the first is greater or the reverse is true. Both possibilities are illustrated in Fig. 12. Consider the discontinuity in Fig. 12B represented by E_1' and E_2'. Figure 12C shows schematically the case when the first zone, terminated at the top by E_1', is separated from the bottom of the second-zone region. The width of this gap is determined by the lowest energy in that zone, E_2. Figure 12D shows the other case, where the top of the first energy zone, as determined by E_1'', lies above the bottom of the second zone, that is, $E_1'' > E_2$ and the zones overlap. The significance of *overlapping zones* becomes apparent when the occupation of the available energy levels by electrons is considered.

According to the usual boundary conditions restricting an electron to the interior of a crystal, the wavelengths that a free electron can have are limited to integral submultiples of the length of the crystal in the direction of propagation. Thus $k_x = 2\pi/\lambda = 2\pi n_1/L_1$; similarly, $k_y = 2\pi n_2/L_2$ and $k_z = 2\pi n_3/L_3$, and the volume corresponding to a single quantum state in k space is $(2\pi)^3/L_1 L_2 L_3 = 8\pi^3/V$, where V is the volume of a rectangular crystal whose sides are L_1, L_2, L_3. The volume of the first Brillouin zone for a simple cubic structure is that of a cube of edge $2\pi/a$. Hence, the total number of quantum states in this zone is $(8\pi^3/a^3)(V/8\pi^3) = V/a^3$, exactly equal to the number of atoms in the crystal. Since each quantum state can be occupied by two electrons of opposite spin, up to two valence electrons per atom can be accommodated

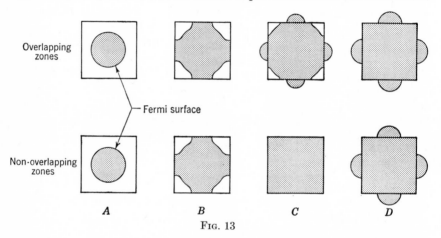

FIG. 13

in the first zone. For elements having more than two outer electrons, the quantum states in the second zone must be occupied. The sequence in which the electrons can occupy the available states depends on whether the zones overlap or not. These two cases are shown diagrammatically in Fig. 13. The first two diagrams (Fig. 13A and B) show the first zone partially occupied by electrons. The energy contour enclosing the occupied states is called the *Fermi surface* since it denotes the maximum energy that the electrons can have, that is, the Fermi energy. Figure 13C shows what happens when the number of electrons equals exactly twice the number of available energy levels, that is, when it just equals the total number of available quantum states because each energy level contains two quantum states having opposite spin numbers. Since each energy level can accommodate two electrons, the first zone is completely filled if the zones do not overlap. If the zones do overlap, then the quantum states at the bottom of the second zones have energies that are lower than the energies of the states in the corners of the first zone, and these states are occupied first as shown in the upper drawing in Fig. 13C. The consequence of overlapping zones, therefore, is that it is impossible to complete the filling of one zone without beginning to fill another zone. From this it follows that the outer zones of such crystals are only partially full.

Herein lies the explanation of the fact that certain substances are conductors and others are not. When zones overlap, the electrons having energies near the Fermi energy can move from one quantum state to another when an external source of energy is provided, say in the presence of an external electric field. Obviously, this is possible regardless of whether the first or the second zone is incompletely filled, as can be seen in Fig. 12D. On the other hand, if the zones do not overlap and the first zone is completely filled (Fig. 13C), then the electrons at the top of this zone cannot move into adjacent quantum states because these states are forbidden. Hence, the latter case represents an insulator. This is a direct consequence of the inclusion of the periodic nature of the structure of crystals in the calculations and is further discussed in later sections.

Density of states. In order to occupy the available quantum states according to a scheme like the one outlined in Fig. 13, it is necessary to determine the number of quantum states per unit energy range in each zone. This can be done quite easily by starting with the free-electron model. The energy of a free electron as a function of k is given by equation (29), and the Fermi surfaces for a free electron are spheres of radius $k = (k_x^2 + k_y^2 + k_z^2)^{\frac{1}{2}}$. The total number of quantum states up to some energy E, therefore, is determined by dividing the volume of a sphere of radius k by the volume of a single state, which was determined in the previous section to be $8\pi^3/V$. Remembering that each quantum state can contain two electrons having opposite spins, the total number of electrons that can be accommodated is given by

$$N = 2 \times \frac{4}{3}\pi k^3 \times \frac{V}{8\pi^3}$$

$$= \frac{8\pi}{3}\frac{(2mE)^{\frac{3}{2}}}{h^3} V \qquad (43)$$

where E is the kinetic energy of the electrons as determined by (29). The number of available states having energy levels lying between E and $E + dE$ is given by

$$\frac{dN}{dE} = 8\pi m\frac{(2mE)^{\frac{1}{2}}}{h^3} V. \qquad (44)$$

The quantity dN/dE is called the *density of states*† and can be given a simple meaning. First, notice that it increases with increasing crystal

† The density of states is frequently designated $N(E)$ without distinguishing between states that are actually occupied and those that are available but are not occupied. In this book, the terminology $S(E)$ is used for available states and the term $N(E)$ is reserved for those states that are actually occupied, in full accord with the Fermi distribution given in equation (22).

volume in order to accommodate the total number of electrons present, which also increases with the size of the crystal. Next, notice that it is a parabolic function of the energy, as shown in Fig. 14A for the case of free electrons. In actual crystals, this curve is modified by the Brillouin zones, as shown in Fig. 14B. For low energies the curve follows the free-electron parabola; however, as the energy of the nearest zone boundary (Fig. 12A) is approached, the energies level off and more states have nearly the same energy value at the boundary. Following this, the

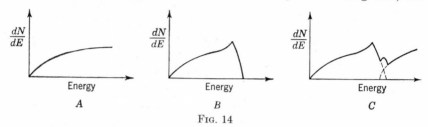

FIG. 14

corners of the zone are filled, causing the curve to fall as the number of available states decreases, until the curve falls to zero when the zone is completely filled. If two zones overlap, then these curves overlap and the resultant curve is obtained by a superposition of individual curves, as shown in Fig. 14C.

With this interpretation, the quantity dN/dE has the same meaning given to the quantity $S(E)$ in the Fermi distribution function (22). Accordingly, it is possible to determine how the available states given by

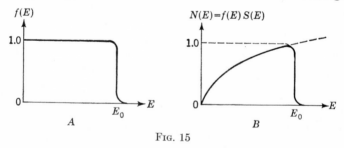

FIG. 15

(44) are occupied by electrons in a crystal at a particular temperature. Figure 15A shows a plot of the Fermi factor, and Fig. 15B shows a plot of the product $f(E)S(E) = N(E)$, in agreement with (22), for this temperature.

Electrical properties

Conductors and nonconductors. As already indicated, one of the successes of the zone theory is its ability to distinguish conductors of electricity from nonconductors. Consider a Brillouin zone that is only partly filled, as shown in Fig. 16. In the absence of an external electric field, each electron moves with a velocity determined by its energy; however, no net movement occurs, since for each electron with an energy determined by k there is a symmetrically located electron at $-k$ moving in the opposite direction. When an external field is applied, the distribution can be displaced in the direction of the electric field by moving the electrons into adjacent quantum states in the same zone, as indicated in Fig. 16 by the dashed circle. Obviously, only the electrons occupying energy levels lying near the Fermi surface can move into the higher energy states. Nevertheless, a net displacement of the electrons produces a net current, and a crystal with a partially filled zone is a conductor. As this process continues, it is possible that an electron ultimately

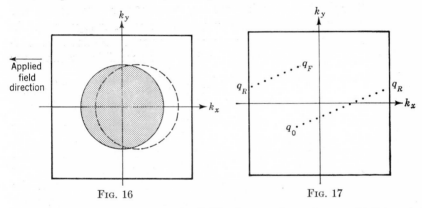

FIG. 16   FIG. 17

occupies a quantum state on the Brillouin-zone boundary. At this point, it cannot move farther in the same direction without crossing the boundary, that is, without a transition to a quantum state lying in the next zone. Such a transition is highly improbable so that the electron's velocity normal to the zone boundary is zero in this state. Physically, the electron can be pictured as being totally reflected by the crystallographic planes parallel to the zone boundary at this point. In terms of the zone model shown in Fig. 11, the reflected electron "reappears" in the zone at a translation-equivalent point on the opposite zone boundary. Such a successive occupation of available quantum states in the Brillouin zone is shown schematically in Fig. 17, where q_0 shows the initial quantum state of the electron, when an external field is applied; q_R is the quantum state of the electron when reflection occurs; and q_F is the final state when the external field is removed.

When the zone structure of a crystal is such that the energy values in two adjacent zones overlap (Fig. 14*C*), it is not possible to complete the filling of one zone without also occupying the lower-energy quantum states in the next zone. This means, of course, that such a crystal must have at least one partially filled zone and that it is a conductor of electricity. An interesting situation arises when one of the zones is very nearly filled while the next zone is only partly occupied. It was shown in the previous chapter that the relative energy of the 4s states is slightly lower than that of the 3d states for the first transition series in the periodic table of elements. The partial occupation of these states by the outer electrons of transition metals means that the corresponding Brillouin zones are also partly filled. For example, it can be shown that the 3d zone of nickel is 94 per cent filled, whereas the 4s zone is 70 per cent empty. Furthermore, it is believed that conductivity in these metals takes place by transitions in the 4s zone. Now, when a 4s electron undergoes a transition from a quantum state on the zone boundary to an empty state, it can be either "reflected back" into the same zone or "scattered" into the 3d zone because there are quantum states of equal energy present in both zones. Such scattering decreases the number of electrons contributing to the current and is believed to be responsible for the lower conductivity observed in the transition metals.

In case the Brillouin zones in a crystal are completely filled or completely empty and separated by a forbidden-energy region, the electrons cannot undergo transitions to adjacent quantum states and the crystal is an insulator. There are special cases of insulators in which one zone is very nearly filled and the next zone almost but not quite empty. This situation occurs in semiconductors and also leads to conductivity, as discussed in Chapter 12. By comparison with metals, however, the currents in semiconductors are many orders of magnitude smaller.

Conductivity in pure metals. The conductivity of most metals can be explained without recourse to the zone theory. According to the free-electron theory, electrons can undergo transitions from one quantum state near the Fermi surface to another adjacent and unoccupied state under the influence of an external field. If this process were allowed to continue without end, the electrons would continue to occupy ever-increasing energy states, a situation that is contrary to the observed steady-state current which is proportional to the applied field. The fact that the electrons cannot continuously increase their energy is explained by their collisions with the metal ions which occupy most of the space in a metal. These collisions are elastic so that the electrons transfer both energy and momentum in the process. Because of the much larger mass of the ions, an electron loses most of its newly gained energy and momentum so that its velocity, averaged over a period of time, is altered only slightly. There is, nevertheless, a small but finite increase in the velocity component parallel to the applied field. Thus, even though the electron follows an erratic path, bouncing from atom to atom in all directions, it does undergo a net displacement in a direction determined by the applied field.   The increase in its velocity component parallel to the applied field direction is called its *drift velocity*.

The average distance that an electron travels between collisions is called the *mean free path l*.   The electron's acceleration due to the field is proportional to its charge e and inversely proportional to its mass m. The conductivity σ or its reciprocal, the resistivity ρ, is thus given by

$$\rho = \frac{1}{\sigma} = \frac{mv}{n_c e^2 l} \tag{45}$$

where n_c is the number of *conduction electrons* and v is the average velocity as determined by their average kinetic energy E_0.

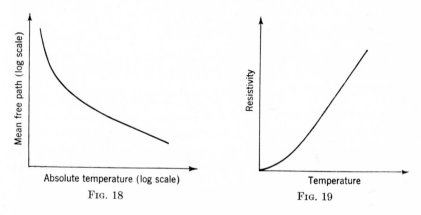

FIG. 18

FIG. 19

The vibration of the ions in a crystal increases with increasing temperature.   This has the effect of increasing the probability of an electron-ion collision or of decreasing the mean free path.   Conversely, as the temperature decreases, the mean free path should increase.   This is actually the case, as is shown in Fig. 18.   Note that the mean free path tends to infinity as the temperature approaches zero.   According to (45), this implies that the resistivity of a metal should tend toward zero as the temperature approaches zero.†   This conclusion is borne out by experiment, as shown by the curve of resistivity plotted as a function of temperature in Fig. 19.   Note that for all temperatures above a certain low temperature the resistivity is directly proportional to the temperature.

† This statement should not be interpreted to mean that *superconductivity* sets in at these temperatures.   It happens that many elements that are poor conductors at room temperature exhibit an anomalously high conductivity below a critical temperature, near 3 to 4°K.   A fairly satisfactory explanation based on somewhat subtle electron-phonon interactions has been recently proposed for this phenomenon. Because complete elucidation of this process is still in a state of flux, it is not discussed further here.

Quantitative calculations of the mean free path have been made for certain metals, using quantum mechanics. These calculations have led to results that are in good agreement with experimental values, particularly for the simpler metals such as the alkalis. The conductivities (expressed in millions of mhos per meter) of several metals at 20°C are compared with calculated values below.

	Fe	Na	Al	Cu	
Observed σ	10	22	35	59	$\times 10^6$ mhos/m
Calculated σ	..	22	..	161	$\times 10^6$ mhos/m

As discussed in Chapter 6, the electrical conductivity at each point in a crystal can be expressed by a first-order conductivity tensor. In crystals belonging to the cubic system, the conductivity is independent of direction. The conductivity (or its reciprocal, the resistivity) does depend on direction in crystals of lower symmetry. In the case of crystals possessing one unique axis, that is, in the hexagonal and tetragonal systems, the resistivity is different for current flow parallel to the unique axis and normal to it. Denoting the resistivity parallel to the c axis $\rho_\parallel$ and normal to it $\rho_\perp$, the resistivity along any direction in the crystal is given by

$$\rho = \rho_\perp + (\rho_\parallel - \rho_\perp) \cos^2 \phi \qquad (46)$$

where ϕ is the angle between the direction considered and the c axis. Note that, because $a_1 = a_2$ in these crystals, the resistivity has rotational symmetry about the c axis. Measured values of these two resistivities are given below (in 10^{-6} ohm-cm) for three metals having hexagonal closest-packed structures.

	$\rho_\parallel$	$\rho_\perp$	
Cadmium	8.36	6.87	$\times 10^{-6}$ ohm-cm
Magnesium	3.85	4.55	$\times 10^{-6}$ ohm-cm
Zinc	6.06	5.83	$\times 10^{-6}$ ohm-cm

Conductivity in alloys. The mean free path of an electron decreases in an alloy for two reasons. The first is an increase in the number of scattering centers caused by local inhomogeneities in the crystal structure produced by the difference in the sizes of the different atoms. This effect is particularly noticeable in the case of solid-solution alloys. Figure 20 shows the resistivity of the copper-gold alloys as a function of composition. In the unannealed or random solid solution, the resistivity reaches a maximum at the 50-50 composition, since this corresponds to the maximum possible distortion of the structure, and drops rapidly at both ends as the pure metals are approached. The increase in the resistivity is due to a discontinuity in the periodic potential encountered by the electrons in the vicinity of the solute atoms. The second curve in Fig. 20 shows the effect of annealing the alloy. At the compositions of the ordered alloys Cu_3Au and $CuAu$, the curve exhibits definite minima, corresponding to the increased mean free path of the electrons due to ordering, which restores a periodicity to the alloy. In practice, it turns out that annealing serves to decrease the resistivity also because it removes other imperfections present which may also act as scattering centers for electrons.

In a solid solution, the increased resistivity, due to the introduction of solute atoms, does not disappear at the absolute zero. The resistance that remains is usually called the *residual resistance*. The residual

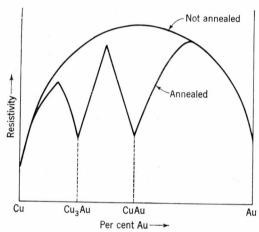

FIG. 20. Resistivity of annealed and unannealed copper-gold alloys. (After Seitz.)

resistance is independent of temperature in dilute alloys but varies with changes in the composition of an alloy. According to *Matthiessen's rule*, the resistivity of an ideal alloy can be expressed as the sum of the residual resistance and a resistivity term which varies with temperature in the same linear manner as the resistivity of a pure metal. Note that this term is not a linear function of temperature for very low temperatures, as can be seen in Fig. 19.

The second effect is due to the fact that the electron-to-atom ratio may be different in an alloy. If the Fermi surface for the electrons in an alloy lies near the Brillouin-zone boundaries, then Bragg reflection of the electrons becomes a contributing factor to the scattering of the electrons. When the zones overlap, it is further possible that an electron-ion collision results in a transfer of the electron from one zone to the other, for example, in the case of transition metals. The probability of such a transfer is proportional to the density of states in the neighborhood of the final state. As a consequence, if the final state lies on a high portion of the dN/dE curve in Fig. 14C, the probability of scattering is increased and an unusually high resistance results. It turns out that, in transition metals, the probability for transitions from s to d states is very high.

Hall effect. The conductivity σ can be defined in terms of the number of conduction electrons n_c by

$$\sigma = n_c e \mu \tag{47}$$

where μ is the *mobility* and is equal to the drift velocity per unit field. It has been shown by Hall that both the mobility and the mean free path of an electron can be determined experimentally. The so-called *Hall effect* is observed when a magnetic field is applied at right angles to a conductor carrying a current. This produces a potential difference across the conductor, in a direction that is mutually orthogonal to the direction of the current and that of the magnetic field. The reason for this effect becomes apparent from the following reasoning. An electron in an electric field $\mathcal{E}$ is acted on by a force that acts in the direction of the field and is proportional to the field strength and the charge of the electron, that is, $\mathbf{F} = e\mathcal{E}$. If a transverse magnetic field is then applied, the electron is also acted on by a magnetic force which is proportional to the electron's charge and velocity and to the applied magnetic field. The direction of this force is given by the vector relation $\mathbf{v} \times \mathbf{B}$, so that the total force on the electron is

$$\mathbf{F} = e\mathcal{E} + e(\mathbf{v} \times \mathbf{B}). \tag{48}$$

Note that if $\mathbf{v}$ is in the direction of the conductor (parallel to $\mathcal{E}$) and $\mathbf{B}$ is applied at right angles to this direction, then the vector $\mathbf{v} \times \mathbf{B}$ is at right angles to the direction of both the electric and magnetic fields.

The force in (48), therefore, causes the electrons moving down the wire to be deflected in a direction that is transverse to both fields. When such electrons reach the surface of the conductor, they build up a charge at the surface, which in turn produces an additional electric field inside the conductor. After a while, an equilibrium condition is attained between the force due to this field and the force in (48) and electrons can again move freely along the conductor. When this is the case, the magnitudes of the new transverse field $\mathcal{E}$ must be just equal to the magnitude vB, that is,

$$\mathcal{E} = vB. \tag{49}$$

The velocity can be expressed in terms of the current density J and the number of conduction electrons per unit volume, n_c, by

$$v = \frac{J}{n_c e}. \tag{50}$$

Substituting (50) for v in (49)

$$\mathcal{E} = \frac{J}{n_c e} B. \tag{51}$$

Finally, defining the *Hall constant R* by

$$R = \frac{1}{n_c e} \tag{52}$$

equation (51) can be written

$$\mathcal{E} = RJB. \tag{53}$$

Note that the Hall constant R has the same sign as the charge of the electron; that is, if the current is carried by electrons, or negative-charge carriers, as it is in most metals, then, by convention, R is negative. It turns out that the Hall constant is positive in certain metals, for example, in iron. The nature of such apparently positive-charge carriers is discussed in detail in Chapter 12.

Magnetic properties

Diamagnetism. When a substance is placed in an inhomogeneous magnetic field, it is either attracted toward the strong part of the field or repelled toward the weaker part. If it is attracted by the field, it is said to be *paramagnetic;* if repelled, it is said to be *diamagnetic.* The force F with which a diamagnetic substance is repelled when placed in a field of strength H and gradient dH/dx is determined by

$$F = \chi V H \frac{dH}{dx} \tag{54}$$

where χ is called the *magnetic susceptibility* and V is the volume of the substance. The magnetic susceptibility is a measure of the change in the magnetic moment of the atoms caused by an applied field. It is usual to speak of the *atomic susceptibility* χ_A which is determined according to Langevin's equation

$$\chi_A = \frac{N_0 e^2}{6mc^2} \sum \bar{r}^2$$

$$= -2.83 \times 10^{10} \sum \bar{r}^2 \tag{55}$$

where N_0 is Avogadro's number; e, m, c have their usual meaning for an electron; and $\bar{r}$ is the average radius of the orbits of the electrons. Note that the right side of (55) is negative, which indicates that the force in (54) is negative. This is in agreement with Lenz's law that *the magnetic flux produced by an induced current opposes the change in the magnetic field which produces it.*

In quantum mechanics, the Langevin equation is valid provided that the electron distribution is spherically symmetrical. Thus it is quite useful when dealing with inert gases, ions, and neutral atoms. The value of $\bar{r}$ is determined by the wave function, and since the susceptibility is proportional to $\bar{r}^2$, it follows that the outer electrons make the largest contribution. The value of χ_A, calculated using quantum mechanics, is in good agreement with the values found experimentally. For most elements, including Cu, Zn, Ga, Ge, As, Se, Br, Ag, Cd, Te, and the inert gases, the magnitude of the atomic susceptibility lies in the range 10^{-6} to 10^{-5}, whereas for Sb, Au, Hg, Tl, Pb, and Bi it is greater than 10^{-5}. Bismuth is exceptional in this regard; $\chi_A = -1.35 \times 10^{-4}$ in MKS units.

Paramagnetism. It is possible for an atom to have a net magnetic moment resulting from a particular combination of the orbital magnetic moments and the spin magnetic moments of its electrons. The unit for measuring the spin magnetic moment of an electron is the *Bohr magneton*

$$\beta = \frac{eh}{4\pi mc} = 9.27 \times 10^{-21} \text{ erg/gauss.} \tag{56}$$

If an external magnetic field is applied, the spin moments can line up either parallel to the field or antiparallel to the field.

The magnetic properties of many materials were first studied systematically by P. Curie before the end of the nineteenth century. He found that the *paramagnetic susceptibility* χ_P was inversely proportional to the absolute temperature.

$$\chi_P = \frac{C}{T} \tag{57}$$

where C is the Curie constant and is characteristic of the material. Langevin later applied classical mechanics to paramagnetism in gases and found that the Curie constant could be expressed theoretically

$$C = \frac{N_0 \bar{\mu}^2}{3k} \tag{58}$$

where N_0 is Avogadro's number

    k is Boltzmann's constant

    $\bar{\mu}$ is average magnetic moment per molecule.

It also follows from classical mechanics that, for free electrons in a metal, the Curie constant can be written

$$C = \frac{n\beta^2}{k} \tag{59}$$

where n is the number of free electrons per unit volume. By substituting (59) in (57) it is possible to calculate the paramagnetic susceptibility of any metal. The value obtained in this way is approximately 100 times larger than the values obtained experimentally. This is one of the properties of metals, therefore, that the classical free-electron theory cannot explain correctly.

The total magnetization M is defined as the magnetic moment per unit volume and is given by

$$M = \chi_P H$$
$$= \frac{n\beta^2}{kT} H. \tag{60}$$

Now, according to the Curie law (57), the susceptibility and, hence, the magnetization should vary with the temperature. Again, this is not the

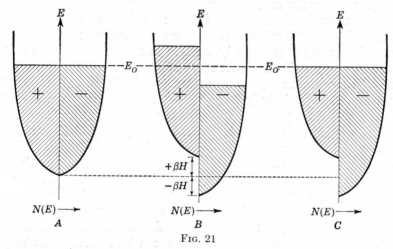

Fig. 21

case for many metals. The observed weak and temperature-independent paramagnetism can be explained by applying Fermi-Dirac statistics to this problem.

The distribution of electrons in a metal at the absolute zero of temperature is shown in Fig. 21 by plotting the parabola-shaped function representing the density of states as a function of energy. In the absence of an external magnetic field, the electrons occupy all the available states having energies less than the Fermi energy E_0. They are shown divided into two groups, in Fig. 21A, accordingly as their spins are plus or minus. When an external field is applied, the magnetic moments due to the spins line up either parallel or antiparallel to the field. Assuming that a plus denotes electrons which have antiparallel moments, these electrons undergo a shift in energy $+\beta H$, as shown in

Fig. 21*B*. This situation is not stable and, at equilibrium, some of the electrons in the antiparallel states undergo transitions to the lower-energy parallel states. This leads to the situation shown in Fig. 21*C*. The magnitude of the energy shift, even due to a fairly strong field, $H = 10^5$ gauss, is very small, $\beta H \sim 10^{-3}$ eV, so that, at room temperature, the thermal energy, $kT \sim 0.03$ eV, is sufficiently greater to keep the number of electrons having parallel and antiparallel moments very nearly equal. Not only does this explain the very small value of the observed susceptibility but also why the susceptibility is virtually independent of reasonable changes in temperature.

Ferromagnetism. It has been assumed, in the above discussion, that the magnetic moment of the atoms was due entirely to the electron spin. This is a fairly accurate picture for such metals as Li, Na, Mg, Al, and K. In these metals, the valence electrons are quite free to migrate through the crystals so that they contribute primarily spin moments, whereas the inner shells are filled and contribute only weak diamagnetism. On the other hand, if an atom has incomplete inner shells, then it is possible that not only the spin moments but also the orbital moments can contribute to the magnetic moment of the atom. This normally leads to large paramagnetic susceptibility in accord with the Curie law. Such relatively large susceptibilities are found among the rare earths and the platinum and palladium-group metals. An anomalous behavior is encountered in the case of Fe, Co, and Ni, which are paramagnetic at elevated temperatures but become *ferromagnetic* below a transition temperature called the *Curie* point. A ferromagnetic solid is one that can have a permanent magnetization after the external magnetic field is removed. This permanent magnetization was first explained by P. J. Weiss in 1907 as being due to a parallel orientation of the permanent magnetic moments of the constituent atoms. The paramagnetic → ferromagnetic transition can be likened, therefore, to the disorder → order transition discussed in Chapter 8. Above the Curie temperature, thermal agitation is responsible for keeping the magnetic moments randomly oriented, whereas below the Curie point the energy favors an ordered arrangement in which more magnetic moments are aligned in one direction than in another. In order to explain why an excess of magnetic moments along one direction is more stable than a uniform distribution, Weiss proposed that a *molecular field* exists in the crystal and favors such an alignment.

Heisenberg was the first to propose an explanation of this molecular field based on the principles of quantum mechanics. He treated the problem similarly to the Heitler-London treatment of the hydrogen molecule. In this treatment, an *exchange interaction* between electrons in different quantum states is shown to lead to a lower energy for a molecule than that obtained by a mere superposition of the wave functions of each atom. Experiments have proven that the magnetic moment, due to the electron spins rather than the orbital moments, contributes to the permanent magnetic moment of the iron-group atoms. The exchange forces, therefore, are necessary in order to explain why, in certain metals, the atoms have electrons with parallel magnetic moments. It is reasonable to expect that such exchange forces are negligible unless the atoms are brought closely together. It can be shown that, as two atoms approach each other, the electron spins of unpaired electrons in each atom assume parallel orientations. As they are brought closer together, the spin moments are maintained parallel by increasing forces. As the interatomic distance is decreased still further, however, these exchange forces decrease until finally they pass through zero and an antiparallel spin orientation is favored. It has been shown by Bethe that, for the iron group, the conditions favoring parallel orientations occur when the ratio between one-half the interatomic distance in a crystal and the average radius of the $3d$ shell is greater than 1.5. Some typical values of this ratio for these metals are

	Mn	Fe	Co	Ni
Ratio	1.47	1.63	1.82	1.98

As can be seen, the ratio for manganese is slightly less than 1.5, which explains why manganese crystals are not ferromagnetic whereas compounds containing manganese atoms spaced farther apart are. Notable examples are the Heusler alloys Cu_2MnSn and Cu_2MnAl. (Note that these ferromagnetic alloys contain neither Fe, Co, or Ni.)

According to the zone theory, two factors determine the energy of a crystal. The first is the Fermi energy, which makes a positive contribution to the total energy, and the second comes from the exchange integral and makes a negative contribution. A crystal then is ferromagnetic when the negative energy due to the exchange integral is greater than the positive-energy term due to the kinetic (Fermi) energy of the electrons, which tends to randomize the spin directions. The exchange integral used in this calculation is somewhat different from the one proposed by Heisenberg in that it is based on the electrostatic interaction between one electron and the electrons in an identical fictitious crystal having a hole in place of this electron. It turns out that this exchange integral is independent of interatomic distance and does not vary too much from atom to atom in the metal. In order to explain ferromagnetism, therefore, it is necessary to compare the Fermi energies of different metals. Although only nickel has been examined in detail, the results can be extended to show that the Fermi energy is smaller than the exchange energy in Fe, Co, and Ni.   As expected, it is somewhat greater in the case of Mn.   It should be noted that a small Fermi energy denotes a narrow energy zone, that is, a larger number of electrons having very closely spaced energies.   Thus this calculation supports the earlier conclusions that narrow, partially filled d zones, which do not overlap in neighboring atoms to any appreciable extent, are necessary and sufficient for ferromagnetism to occur.

More recently, Zener has proposed a different explanation for the occurrence of ferromagnetism.   The exchange integral, as calculated in the Heitler-London model for the bonding of two atoms, is negative. Heisenberg, therefore, was forced to postulate that the exchange integral was negative only when the atoms were brought very closely together and became positive when the unfilled d shells did not overlap appreciably.   It has never been proven, however, that such a reversal in the sign of the exchange integral actually occurs.   Zener has suggested that the exchange integral always remains negative and that ferromagnetism is due to an interaction between electrons occupying quantum states in the partially filled d and s zones.   The proposed interaction, which accounts for the excess of parallel spin moments of one kind, is similar to the interaction (Hund's rule) that causes unpaired electrons in different orbitals to have parallel spins.   According to this model, an over-all decrease in the energy is obtained when the electrons occupying states in the d zone have parallel spin moments and the s-zone electrons contribute a small moment in the same direction.   Because of the approximate nature of the calculations used to support the above stated competing theories, it is not possible to decide, at present, which one describes most correctly the interactions responsible for ferromagnetism.

On an atomic scale, the reason for the permanent magnetic moment of Fe, Co, and Ni atoms is best understood by considering their electronic structures.   Each atom has two $4s$ electrons and an incomplete $3d$ shell. If interactions favoring parallel spins are assumed, the electrons are distributed among the available states as follows:

$$
\begin{array}{lll}
\text{Fe } 3d^6 & \boxed{\uparrow\downarrow\,|\uparrow\,|\uparrow\,|\uparrow\,} & 4s^2\ \boxed{\uparrow\downarrow} \\
\text{Co } 3d^7 & \boxed{\uparrow\downarrow\uparrow\downarrow\uparrow\,|\uparrow\,|\uparrow\,} & 4s^2\ \boxed{\uparrow\downarrow} \\
\text{Ni } 3d^8 & \boxed{\uparrow\downarrow\uparrow\downarrow\uparrow\downarrow\uparrow\,|\uparrow\,} & 4s^2\ \boxed{\uparrow\downarrow}
\end{array}
\tag{61}
$$

According to this scheme, the atomic moments of these metals should be, respectively, four, three, and two Bohr magnetons.   The actual values turn out to be

	Fe	Co	Ni	
Atomic moment	2.22	1.70	0.61	Bohr magnetons

The nonintegral number of electron spins per atom determined from saturization magnetization measurements given above is explained by making use of the zone theory as follows: The 3d and 4s zones of these metals overlap, as shown for the case of nickel in Fig. 22. Since the relative occupation of these two zones is determined by the Fermi energy E_0, it is assumed that 0.6 electron occupies states in the 4s zone and 9.4 electrons in the 3d zone. Of these, five must have one kind of spin and 4.4 the other, leaving 0.6 spin of the same kind per atom. The accuracy of this model can be readily checked by alloying nickel with copper or zinc. The substitution of a copper atom for a nickel atom introduces one additional electron in the crystal, whereas zinc introduces

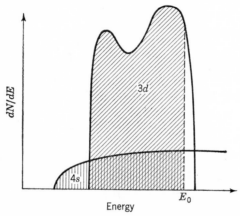

Fig. 22. Schematic representation of overlapping 3d and 4s states of nickel. On an average, 9.4 of the 10 available 3d states and 0.6 of the 2 available 4s states are occupied. (After Slater.)

two additional electrons. It is reasonable to expect that these electrons will prefer the lower-lying 3d states of nickel and, therefore, as more copper (or zinc) is added, the magnetic susceptibility should decrease. It has been shown from saturization magnetization measurements that this is indeed the case; the magnetization becomes virtually zero when 60 per cent Cu or 30 per cent Zn is added, that is, when enough electrons are added to fill completely the 3d zone of nickel.

Domain structure. The above discussion has explained why iron, cobalt, and nickel are ferromagnetic, but it has not accounted for such physical properties of magnets as, for example, the well-known hysteresis loop, relating the amount of magnetization to the strength of the applied field. Even before the atomic mechanism of ferromagnetism was clearly understood, Weiss assumed that a single crystal of iron consists of small regions or *domains*, within each of which the electrons have all their spins parallel, but that the spins of neighboring domains are not parallel.

When an external field is applied, the domains that have net moments parallel to the direction of the field have their energy reduced, whereas those domains that do not have their energy increased. The crystal's energy, obviously, can be lowered if all the domains align themselves parallel to the field. This can be accomplished in either of two ways. Either the direction of magnetization of an entire domain changes at once, or a domain that is favorably oriented grows in size at the expense of a less favorably oriented domain. When the external field is reversed in direction, all the domains must be reoriented, and, owing to several causes discussed below, this requires an additional field to overcome the factors opposing such reorientation so that a hysteresis loop results.

It turns out that magnetization is an anisotropic property in crystals. For example, it is easier to magnetize iron (body-centered cubic) along [[100]] than along any other directions, and most difficult along [[111]]. It is common practice to refer to these as *easy* and *hard directions* of magnetization, respectively. To show that this is a structure-sensitive property, the easy directions in nickel are [[111]] (normal to the closest-packed layers) and the hard directions are [[100]]. Similarly, the easy direction in the hexagonal closest packing of cobalt is [0001], normal to the hexagonal closest-packed layers. The magnetization of single crystals along certain directions is invariably accompanied by changes in their physical dimensions. For example, iron crystals expand along the direction of magnetization and contract at right angles to it so that the total volume tends to remain the same. In a nickel crystal, the dimensional changes are reversed; it contracts along the magnetization direction and expands in directions normal to it. Thus the magnetization of ferromagnetic crystals depends on the way that the structure is strained, a phenomenon called *magnetostriction*. As might be expected, magnetostriction is related to the elastic properties of the crystal and can be used to explain the formation of magnetic domains in crystals. With six [[100]] directions equally easy, it is natural that a single crystal of iron has domains containing magnetic moments aligned parallel to each of these six directions. Obviously, the domains must be separated by boundaries in which the magnetic moments undergo a gradual transformation from one orientation to the other. The exchange energy favoring parallel alignment of all moments prefers thick boundaries. It is opposed by the magnetic anisotropy which favors a minimum deviation from the easy directions of magnetization. A compromise between these opposing forces is reached, and it turns out that the boundaries have thicknesses of the order of hundreds of atoms in actual crystals. The domains themselves can have various sizes, determined primarily by the free energy of the boundaries, whose contribution to the crystal's energy decreases with increasing domain size, since the ratio of boundary area to domain volume decreases. Lest it be deduced from this that a single crystal consisting of a single domain has the lowest possible energy, it should be realized that such a crystal is a permanent magnet whose magnetic field contains magnetic energy. Thus the domain structure proposed by Weiss serves to lower the over-all energy, thereby neutralizing the individual permanent magnets.

When a weak magnetic field is applied parallel to an easy direction of a crystal, the domains having lower energies, because of their more favorable orientation, grow in size owing to the reorientation of the

FIG. 23. Magnetic domains in a single crystal of iron. (Photographed by R. V. Coleman and G. G. Scott.)

moments in the boundaries. The resulting movement of boundaries can actually be observed by sprinkling a fine powder of Fe_2O_3 on a polished crystal surface. The powder particles align themselves along the domain boundaries and a so-called *Bitter pattern* is obtained. Several domains can be seen in the Bitter pattern of a single crystal of iron shown in Fig. 23. It has been observed that the movement of domain boundaries is impeded by imperfections and proceeds in jumps. These jumps can be made audible by surrounding the crystal with an induction coil connected to an amplifier. This so-called *Barkhausen effect* is even more noticeable if the domains change their magnetization directions by rotation. The latter effect becomes more prominent when the strength of the field is increased.

In a polycrystalline material, magnetization is impeded by the random orientation of the grains. Consequently, only some of the grains have their easy directions parallel to the direction of the applied field. Moreover, magnetostriction in these crystallites produces strains in their neighbors which, in turn, affect the ease of magnetization in a more complicated way. Thus, if a material that is easily magnetized is desired, say, for transformers, it is necessary to find one having little magnetic anisotropy or magnetostriction. Such a material does not necessarily have higher saturation magnetization; it simply reaches saturation more rapidly. On the other hand, if a permanent magnet is desired, then strong magnetostriction is an asset. This is so because, once such a material is magnetized along a given direction, it is more difficult to change its magnetization direction. The alignment of the domains can be abetted by placing the magnet in a strong magnetic field and then annealing it, thereby inducing grain growth along the easy direction parallel to the field.

Thermal properties

Specific-heat theories. It is convenient to correlate the thermal behavior of a substance to its ability to absorb heat. The energy absorbed by a unit mass, when its temperature is raised by one degree, is defined as the *specific heat* of that substance. In measuring this quantity, either the volume or the pressure must be kept constant. It is more convenient to speak of the specific heat at constant volume defined by

$$C_V = \left(\frac{\partial E}{\partial T}\right)_V \tag{62}$$

where partial differentials are used because the energy may be a function of other variables in addition to temperature and the subscript denotes that the volume is kept constant. For relatively free atoms, in a monatomic gas, each atom can have three degrees of translational freedom which leads to an average kinetic energy of $\frac{3}{2}kT$ per atom, or

$$N_0\tfrac{3}{2}kT = \tfrac{3}{2}RT$$

per kilogram atomic weight, where R is the so-called gas constant. The specific heat for such an ideal gas, therefore, is

$$C_V = \frac{3}{2}\frac{\partial(RT)}{\partial T}$$
$$= \tfrac{3}{2}R. \tag{63}$$

The electronic contribution to the specific heat of such a gas is very small because the electrons and the nucleus of a gas atom act as an integrated whole.

The specific heat of solids has been found empirically to obey the so-called *law of Dulong and Petit,*

$$C_V = 3R. \tag{64}$$

Assuming that each atom in the crystal can absorb heat in the form of vibrational energy, it has been shown that the vibrational energy of N atoms can be represented by the energy of a system of $3N$ harmonic oscillators. According to classical mechanics, each harmonic oscillator has a potential and kinetic energy of $\frac{1}{2}kT$, or a total energy of $1kT$. Thus, for each atom there is a contribution of $3kT$ to the crystal's energy, which leads to (64) for the specific heat of a solid. The fact that this derivation does not take into account the specific heat due to energy absorbed by the electrons is not particularly disturbing in the case of nonmetals, if it is assumed that the electrons are located on the atoms and act in unison with them. In metals, however, it was assumed by Drude that the electrons were free. Then, according to classical mechanics, the electrons all have a minimum energy at absolute zero and gain energy as the temperature is raised. However, it has just been shown above that the Dulong-Petit law can be explained without considering the electronic contributions of the specific heat. This paradox was not resolved until the application of Fermi-Dirac statistics showed that only the electrons having energies near the Fermi surface can absorb energy by moving into adjacent unoccupied states. The application of the zone theory similarly explains why the electrons in insulators cannot absorb thermal energies, since the amount of energy absorbed is not sufficient to bridge the forbidden-energy region.

It is possible to estimate the *electronic specific heat* in metals. If it is assumed that only the electrons whose energies differ from E_0 by kT can absorb heat and that there are $2kT/E_0$ such electrons, then the electronic specific heat is given according to (63):

$$C_V \text{ (for electrons)} = \frac{3}{2} R \frac{2kT}{E_0}$$
$$= \frac{3R}{E_0} kT. \tag{65}$$

Since the electronic specific heat in (65) is proportional to kT, which is much smaller than the Fermi energy, it can make a noticeable contribution only at very low temperatures, when the atomic specific heat is very small also.

Einstein was the first to apply the quantum theory to the explanation of specific heats. He assumed that each atom in a solid can vibrate independently of all the other atoms. This means that a solid containing N atoms can be represented by $3N$ harmonic oscillators all vibrating with the same frequency ν. In this model, the vibrational energy can be represented by

$$E = 3N_0 \frac{h\nu}{e^{h\nu/kT} - 1} \tag{66}$$

from which the specific heat at constant volume

$$C_V = \frac{\partial E}{\partial T} = 3R \left(\frac{h\nu}{kT}\right)^2 \frac{e^{h\nu/kT}}{(e^{h\nu/kT} - 1)^2}. \tag{67}$$

The relatively naive model of Einstein proved fairly successful in explaining the specific heats of most materials, except at very low temperatures. Subsequently, Debye used a more sophisticated model to represent a solid, in which he tried to relate specific heat to the elastic properties of a solid. Before proceeding, however, it should be pointed out that the possible energy levels of a harmonic oscillator, according to quantum mechanics, are given by

$$E_n = (n + \tfrac{1}{2})h\nu \qquad n = 0, 1, 2, 3, \ldots \tag{68}$$

instead of by $nh\nu$ as Einstein assumed. This does not affect (67) since the additional term disappears when the energy term is differentiated to obtain the specific heat. The significance of (68) is that it clearly shows that, even in the lowest energy state corresponding to $n = 0$, the oscillator still has an energy of $\tfrac{1}{2}h\nu$. This is the *zero-point energy*, so called because it is independent of temperature and persists down to absolute zero.

Debye assumed that the vibrations in a crystal can be handled by the theory of elasticity. Thus the atoms are not assumed to vibrate independently, and the problem resolves to one of determining the normal modes of vibration of a continuous solid made up of individual atoms. It can be shown that the frequencies of vibration in such a solid are quantized according to

$$\nu = \frac{v}{2} \sqrt{\left(\frac{n_x}{X}\right)^2 + \left(\frac{n_y}{Y}\right)^2 + \left(\frac{n_z}{Z}\right)^2} \tag{69}$$

where v is the velocity of propagation and n_x, n_y, n_z are integers in the direction of the three axes X,Y,Z. By analogy to (18), the quantity under the square-root sign can be equated to a radius vector R in reciprocal space, that is,

$$\nu = \frac{v}{2} R. \tag{70}$$

The lattice points in the reciprocal lattice are the allowed frequencies, and it is easily seen that the frequency increases as the radius vector increases. The number of allowed frequencies, dN, lying in a shell between R and $R + dR$ is $4\pi R^2\, dR$. Since only positive integers are required, the part of the shell lying in the positive octant contains $\frac{1}{2}\pi R^2\, dR$ or $4\pi\nu^2\, d\nu/v^3$ points, and since each lattice point in the reciprocal volume has a unit volume associated with it that contains V allowed frequencies, the total number of allowed frequencies in the range $d\nu$ is

$$dN = \frac{4\pi\nu^2\, d\nu}{v^3}\, V. \tag{71}$$

If three mutually orthogonal directions of vibration are considered, one longitudinal and two transverse, then, in general, the velocities will be different for these vibrations and (71) becomes

$$dN = 4\pi\nu^2\, d\nu\; V \left(\frac{1}{v_l^3} + \frac{2}{v_t^3} \right). \tag{72}$$

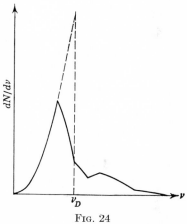

Fig. 24

Now, it turns out that the allowed frequencies are confined to Brillouin zones, similar to the case of allowed energies for electrons in solids. Figure 24 shows a plot of the number of vibrations per unit frequency range, in a simple cubic structure based on a primitive lattice. It is assumed in this plot that the velocity of the longitudinal wave is twice that of transverse wave. In order to simplify the calculations, Debye assumed that this frequency distribution can be approximated by the dotted curve in Fig. 24 which cuts off at a frequency called the *Debye characteristic frequency* ν_D. This leads to an expression for the specific heat of the form

$$C_V = 9Nk\, \frac{1}{x_0^3} \int_0^{x_0} \frac{x^4 e^x}{(e^x - 1)}\, dx \tag{73}$$

where $x = h\nu/kT$ and $x_0 = h\nu_D/kT$. Finally, defining the *Debye temperature*, $\Theta_D = x_0 T$, it can be seen that (73) gives the specific heat in terms of the ratio of the actual temperature to the Debye temperature. Since the maximum frequency is constant for a given material, so is the Debye temperature. Values of the Debye temperature for some elements are given below.

	C (diamond)	Na	Al	K	Cu	Sn	Pb
Θ_D	1840	159	398	99	315	160	88 °K

Equation (73) can be integrated numerically. When this is done, it turns out that the specific-heat curve is quite similar to that obtained by Einstein except at low temperatures. If $T \ll \Theta_D$, $x_0 \gg 1$, and the integration in (73) can be carried out from zero to infinity. Debye has shown that the integral is equal to $(\frac{4}{15})\pi^4$, so that, for low temperatures, (73) becomes

$$C_V = \frac{12}{5} \pi^4 Nk \frac{T^3}{\Theta_D^3}. \tag{74}$$

This is the famous *third power law* of Debye. The specific-heat curves due to Einstein and Debye are compared in Fig. 25.

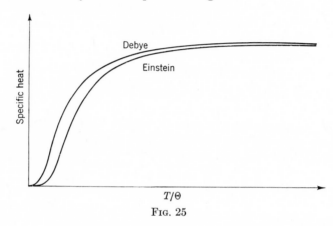

FIG. 25

Thermal conductivity and expansion. As shown in the discussion of specific-heat theory, the atoms in a solid vibrate about a mean position when the temperature is increased. The frequencies of vibration are limited in number and are independent of temperature above the characteristic temperature, so that, as the temperature increases, only the amplitude of vibration can increase. This increased amplitude of vibration has several interesting effects. It has already been shown, in the discussion of electrical conductivity in metals, that the atomic vibrations are responsible for the observed changes in the electrical resistance. It is possible to think of each mode of vibration as a type of imperfection in the true periodicity of the crystal, which can be represented by a *phonon* of energy $h\nu$ propagating through the crystal. An increase in the amplitude of vibration, therefore, means that more phonons having identical energies (frequencies) are added to the crystal. The mean free path of these phonons is only of the order of 10 to 100 Å, implying many collisions, and accounts for the poor heat conductivity of most materials. The exceptions, namely, the true metals, conduct heat by means of electrons in a manner entirely analogous to the conductivity of electricity already described. In fact, it has been shown that the ratio of the thermal to electrical conductivity is equal to a constant times the absolute temperature. Theoretically, this so-called *Wiedemann-Franz law* predicts that this constant equals 2.45×10^{-8} (volts/deg)^2 and is the same for all metals. Actually, small deviations from this value are observed in most metals, as shown below for several metals at 291°K.

	Fe	Cu	Zn	Ag	Pb
Wiedemann-Franz constant	2.88	2.28	2.31	2.36	2.45×10^{-8} (volt/deg)^2

The vibrating atoms also have the effect of changing the crystal shape and volume. The cohesion of crystals is discussed in Chapter 9, where it

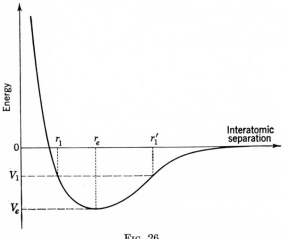

Fig. 26

is shown to be due to the attractive forces between the constituent atoms. To see how the thermal motion of the atoms changes the situation, consider the potential energy due to the interactions of two neighboring atoms. As shown in Chapter 9, the potential energy is given by a relation like

$$V = -\frac{\alpha}{r^n} + \frac{\beta}{r^m} \tag{75}$$

where α is the proportionality constant expressing energy of attraction
     β is the repulsive energy
     r is the interatomic separation.
Independently of the actual values of the exponents n and m, the potential-energy curve has the form shown in Fig. 26, when plotted against the interatomic separation. The equilibrium separation r_e and the potential

energy corresponding to this equilibrium separation, V_e, are also shown in Fig. 26. Now, suppose that the energy is increased to some higher value, V_1. The interatomic separation corresponding to this value can be either r_1 or r_1'. Physically this means that the atoms can alternate between these two positions. Because the potential-energy curve usually is not symmetric about r_e, the mean of these two positions corresponds to a larger average interatomic separation and results in a thermal expansion of the crystal.

Since the amount of thermal expansion that takes place depends on the interatomic forces, it is not surprising that it is dependent on the crystal structure. For example, because the bonding in covalent crystals such as diamond is very strong, the thermal expansion coefficient for diamond is correspondingly small. Similarly, in the case of ionic crystals, it usually depends on the valence of the ions; the larger their valence, the smaller the linear expansion coefficient. For comparison purposes, the linear expansion coefficients of a number of crystals are listed below.

	Diamond Na	Al	Cu	SiC	NaF	NaI
Linear expansion coefficient	1.1 62.2	25.0	16.8	6.6	39	$48 \times 10^{-6}/°C$

Note that the volume expansion coefficient is approximately equal to three times the linear coefficient (see Exercise 21).

It has been assumed in the above discussion that the crystal is thermally isotropic. Actually, most noncubic crystals exhibit pronounced anisotropies. As before, the specific values of the different expansion coefficients are related to the bonding and, hence, to the crystal structure. In fact, it has been observed, in certain crystals having complex crystal structures, that anisotropic thermal expansion can occur in two non-parallel directions, while the crystal actually contracts along a third direction.

Suggestions for supplementary reading

A. H. Cottrell, *Theoretical structural metallurgy*, 2d ed. (St. Martins Press, Inc., New York, 1957), especially pp. 44–93 and 108–115.

William Hume-Rothery, *Atomic theory for students of metallurgy* (Institute of Metals, London, 1946), especially pp. 151–211.

Frederick Seitz, *The physics of metals* (McGraw-Hill Book Company, Inc., New York, 1943), especially pp. 246–280 and 292–322.

Robert L. Sproull, *Modern physics* (John Wiley & Sons, Inc., New York, 1956), especially pp. 246–289.

C. Zener, Impact of magnetism on metallurgy, *Trans. AIME*, vol. 203 (1955), pp 619–630.

Suggestions for further reading

Adrianus J. Dekker, *Solid state physics* (Prentice-Hall, Inc., Englewood Cliffs, N.J., 1957).

Charles Kittel, *Introduction to solid state physics*, 2d ed. (John Wiley & Sons, Inc., New York, 1956).

Ursula M. Martius, Ferromagnetism, in *Progress in metal physics*, vol. 3 (Pergamon Press Ltd., London, 1952), pp. 140–175.

N. F. Mott and H. Jones, *The theory of the properties of metals and alloys* (Clarendon Press, Oxford, 1936; reprinted by Dover Publications, New York, 1958).

N. F. Mott, Recent advances in the electron theory of metals, in *Progress in metal physics*, vol. 3 (Pergamon Press Ltd., London, 1952), pp. 76–114.

John C. Slater, *Quantum theory of matter* (McGraw-Hill Book Company, Inc., New York, 1951).

Exercises

1. List at least six properties of metals familiar to you, for example, ductility, luster, etc. Explain these properties in terms of the Drude-Lorentz free-electron theory.

2. Redraw Fig. $3B$ plotting $f(E)$ as a function of $E - E_0$ in units of kT, at room temperature, in the range $-3kT \leq E - E_0 \leq 3kT$. This plot shows quite accurately the variation of the Fermi factor near the Fermi energy.

3. In order to see at what values of E the Fermi factor differs appreciably from unity, substitute $E_0 + \varepsilon$ for E in equation (19). Solve for ε when $f(E) = 0.2, 0.5, 0.8$.

4. Show that when $E - E_0 \geq 2kT$, $f(E) \sim e^{-(E-E_0)/kt}$. (Do this by actually calculating $f(E)$ for $E - E_0 = 2kT$, $3kT$, and $4kT$.)

5. The Fermi energy for Cs is 1.55 eV. By reversing the procedure used in deriving equation (21) in the text, determine the number of free electrons in 1 cm³ of cesium.

6. The linear coefficient of thermal expansion of silver is $17 \times 10^{-6}/°C$. Assuming that thermal expansion is the only reason why E_0 changes with temperature, what are the values of the Fermi energy at 100, 200, and 300°K. (There is one conduction electron per atom in silver.)

7. What is the value of E_0 for sodium at 100, 200, and 300°K? Make the same assumptions suggested in Exercise 6 and use $62.2 \times 10^{-6}/°C$ as the linear expansion coefficient.

8. Draw the first and second Brillouin zones, in cross section normal to the c axis, for a primitive hexagonal lattice. Assume that $((10\bar{1}0))$ planes terminate the first zone and $((11\bar{2}0))$ planes terminate the second zone. Are the Fermi surfaces likely to be more or less spherical when these zones are incompletely filled than in the case of the square zones shown in Fig. 10? Why?

9. Show the progressive occupation by electrons of the zones in Exercise 8 (see Fig. 13) for the case when the two zones overlap.

10. The Fermi energy for Cu is 7.1 eV. Assuming that this is the maximum kinetic energy of the electrons in copper, what is the number of electrons per cubic centimeter in copper as determined from equation (43)? How does this value compare with that determined directly from the density of copper (density = 8.92 g/cm³)?

11. The density of sodium at 20°C is 0.97 g/cm³. Assuming that each atom contributes one conduction electron, what is the mean free path l in sodium? ($E_0 = 3.2$ eV.)

12. The density of aluminum at 20°C is 2.70 g/cm³. Assuming that each atom contributes three conduction electrons, what is the mean free path l in aluminum? ($E_0 = 11.7$ eV.)

13. What is the relation between the mean free path l and the mobility μ of an electron?

14. Calculate the mobilities of sodium and aluminum from the conductivities listed in the text. How do you explain the difference in mobility in these metals?

15. Calculate the Hall constant R for sodium and aluminum.

16. What is the speed of a conduction electron in aluminum if the average kinetic energy is $E_0 = 11.7$ eV? How does this speed compare with the propagation speed of an electric pulse traveling through aluminum with the speed of light? How can the pulse of electricity travel faster than the electrons in aluminum?

17. Calculate the Curie constant for sodium. (To determine the number of conduction electrons, see Exercises 11 and 12.) Next, calculate the paramagnetic susceptibility for sodium metal and compare it with the value listed in a handbook.

18. Following the procedure in Exercise 17, calculate the paramagnetic susceptibility for aluminum and compare it with the listed value in a handbook.

19. Calculate the electronic specific heat for aluminum ($E_0 = 11.7$ eV) and for copper ($E_0 = 7.1$ eV) at 1, 300, and 1000°K.

20. Calculate the atomic specific heat of aluminum and copper at 1°K. How does it compare with the electronic specific heat determined in Exercise 19?

21. Prove that the volume coefficient for thermal expansion is equal to three times the linear expansion coefficient. Assume $l = l_0(1 + \alpha_l)$ and $v = v_0(1 + \alpha_v)$ and $v_0 = l_0^3$.

11

Structure of metals

There are different ways in which the ninety-odd elements in the periodic table can be classified. A classification frequently adopted is based on the way in which the elements combine to form solid compounds. Six elements, the so-called inert gases, have completely filled outer electron shells and normally do not participate in compound formation at all; therefore, they are not discussed further in this book. Approximately twelve to fifteen elements can be considered to be electronegative and to form predominantly ionic compounds in which they take the part of anions. The crystal structures of these elements are discussed in the last chapter of this book. The remaining seventy-odd elements are popularly called metals. They are electropositive and take the part of cations in ionic compounds. This classification is quite useful as a general scheme, but it does not take into account the mechanical or physical properties of the elements or of the compounds that they form. The above classification of metals, therefore, is most suitable to the purposes of a chemist who is primarily concerned with chemical properties. A metallurgist, on the other hand, must distinguish between true metals, which have the physical properties of high electrical and thermal conductivity, metallic luster, ductility, malleability, etc., and the metallike elements usually called *metalloids*. The latter may exhibit some of the physical properties of true metals to varying degrees; nevertheless, they can be distinguished from the true metals because the metalloids form predominantly covalent bonds as determined by the $8 - N$ rule. Also, all true metals have a negative coefficient of conductivity whereas most metalloids have a positive coefficient. For this reason, the metalloids are classified as semiconductors and are further discussed in Chapter 13.

The elements

Closest packings. It is not always easy to make the distinction between true metals and metalloids in practice. This is particularly true in the case of certain allotropic elements that can assume different crystal structures, which may or may not exhibit the physical properties of true metals. The allotropic modifications of such elements that exhibit metallic properties are discussed in this chapter; those that do not have metallic properties are discussed in Chapter 13. The origin of the metallic properties is, of course, the metallic bond. Accordingly, the elements discussed in this chapter form crystal structures in which the metallic bond is the principal bond between atoms.

It will be recalled from Chapter 9 that the metallic bond is an unsaturated covalent bond and that it is, therefore, an undirected bond. Consequently, the structures of most elemental metals are either the cubic or hexagonal closest packings shown on pages 60 and 61 or the body-centered cubic structure shown on page 69. The structures of most elemental metals are known and are listed in Table 1. Note that some of

Table 1
Crystal structures of metals

Li	Be										Zn	Ga	
BCC	HCP												
Na	Mg	Al											
BCC	HCP	FCC											
K	Ca	Sc	Ti	V	Cr	Mn	Fe	Co	Ni	Cu	Zn	Ga	
BCC	FCC	FCC	HCP	BCC	BCC	Cubic	BCC	HCP	FCC	FCC	HCP	Ortho.	
	BCC	HCP	BCC				FCC	FCC					
Rb	Sr	Y	Zr	Nb	Mo	Tc	Ru	Rh	Pd	Ag	Cd	In	Sn
BCC	FCC	HCP	HCP	BCC	BCC	HCP	HCP	FCC	FCC	FCC	HCP	Tetr.	Tetr.
	HCP		BCC										
	BCC												
Cs	Ba	La	Hf	Ta	W	Re	Os	Ir	Pt	Au	Hg	Tl	Pb
BCC	BCC	HCP	HCP	BCC	BCC	HCP	HCP	FCC	FCC	FCC	Hex.	HCP	FCC
		FCC	BCC									BCC	
Fr	Ra	Ac	Th	Pa	U	Np	Pu						
		FCC	FCC	Tetr.	Ortho.	Ortho.	Ortho.						
			BCC		Tetr.	Tetr.	FCC						
					BCC		Tetr.						

Rare-earth metals:

Ce	Pr	Nd	Pm	Sm	Eu	Gd	Tb	Dy	Ho	Er	Tm	Yb	Lu
HCP	HCP	Hex.		Hex.	BCC	HCP	HCP	HCP	HCP	HCP	HCP	FCC	HCP
FCC													

these structures, particularly those of metals lying to the right of the vertical line in Table 1, are more complex than the three simple types cited above. They are discussed further in a subsequent section. An examination of Table 1 also reveals that there are no simple rules determining the particular structure types assumed by the elements. Certain correlations can be made, of course. For example, the monovalent alkalis all have the body-centered cubic structure which is consistent with the fact that, having only one electron with which to form bonds, the average bond strength is increased by having each atom coordinated by eight other atoms rather than by twelve. On the other hand, such reasoning fails to explain why vanadium and chromium also have the body-centered cubic structure or why copper does not. Attempts to explain the particular structures adopted based on other qualitative considerations are equally fruitless. Consider the interatomic distances in some of the metals of the first long period given below.

V	Cr	Mn	Fe	Fe	Co	Co	Ni	Cu	
BCC	BCC	Cubic	FCC	BCC	HCP	FCC	FCC	FCC	
2.63	2.49	2.50	2.59	2.48	2.51	2.51	2.49	2.59	Å

Obviously the interatomic distances are not the criterion either, else why are the distances so different in face-centered cubic nickel and copper? Or why is chromium body-centered and nickel face-centered cubic when both have the same interatomic distances? This observation is particularly puzzling when it is realized that the interatomic distances determine the bonding energies and, hence, the cohesiveness of a particular crystal structure. Moreover, it should be noted that all the metals lying to the left of the vertical line in Table 1 (except manganese) have structures that are either closest packings or body-centered cubic. Except for cobalt, however, the c/a ratios of the hexagonal closest packings deviate from the ideal value of 1.633.

The only conclusion that can be drawn from the above is that the detailed electronic structures of the atoms must be the controlling factors in deciding which crystal structure is assumed. The proper approach, therefore, is to consider the role that the valence electrons have in the formation of the metallic bond. As shown in the discussion of cohesion in Chapter 9, there are essentially two ways of doing this. The one adopted by Pauling considers the electrons of each atom individually so that bonding is due to resonating electron-pair bonds. If such physical properties as ferromagnetism are also considered in determining the exact electron distributions, it then becomes necessary to postulate non-integral valencies for some of the atoms. Pauling's approach has been criticized for this reason as being physically untenable. The other approach, based on the model proposed by Wigner and Seitz, treats the valence electrons collectively and considers the interaction between the so-called free or conduction electrons and the positive ions constituting the metal. As shown below, this approach makes it possible to explain many crystal structures of metals in a way that is physically reasonable and consistent with their known physical properties.

Zone theory. It has been shown in the discussion of the zone theory, in the preceding chapter, that the assumption of a periodically varying potential energy distribution in a crystal leads to zones of allowed- and forbidden-energy values that electrons can have. Normally, the zones of allowed-energy values are separated from each other by forbidden-energy regions. It may happen, however, that along certain directions in a crystal the highest energy allowed in the first Brillouin zone is actually greater than the lowest energy value allowed in the second zone along another crystallographic direction. When this happens, the zones are said to overlap. The way that the allowed quantum states in each zone are occupied is determined by the number of electrons present and by the maximum energy that these electrons can have. It will be recalled that, at the absolute zero of temperature, the electrons fill the lowest energy states first and then proceed to fill higher energy states, up to the so-called Fermi energy. At temperatures other than zero, a small fraction of the total electrons present can exceed this value so that the Fermi energy becomes the average kinetic energy of those electrons that can transfer to unoccupied states, that is, the free electrons. It also has been shown that the number of states available in a zone is always an even number per primitive unit cell. (This is so because there are two quantum states for each allowed-energy value corresponding to the two possible values of the spin quantum number.) From this it follows that, when the number of valence electrons per atom is odd, the allowed-energy zone cannot be completely filled and the crystal must be a conductor. On the other hand, it does not follow that, when the average number of electrons per atom is even, the crystal must be an insulator. This is so because the two bands may overlap, making it impossible to fill one zone without also partially filling the next zone.

It is easy to understand from the above why all alkali metals having only one valence electron per atom are conductors. This does not exclude the possibility that the zones may also overlap in these metals, as shown for the case of sodium on page 233; it simply means that zone overlap is not necessary to explain conductivity in alkali metals. Going on to the next column of the periodic table, beryllium, magnesium, and the other alkali earths have an even number of electrons per cell. Nevertheless, these elements are electronic conductors of electricity, a fact which can be explained only if it is assumed that the zones overlap. Approximate calculations for beryllium and for calcium show that the zones do overlap for these metals. Next, it is interesting to note that, although boron has an odd number of electrons per atom, it appears that really pure boron is an insulator. (Strictly speaking, boron is a semiconductor because the forbidden-energy gap is quite narrow, $\sim$1.5 eV.) From the recently determined crystal structure of pure boron, it appears that boron contains an even number of atoms per primitive unit cell, so that the allowed zones can be assumed to be separated and completely filled (or completely empty). Conversely, the next element in the third column of the periodic table, aluminum, also has an odd number of electrons per atom but only one atom in the primitive cell of the face-centered cubic lattice, so that aluminum is a conductor. Carbon and silicon are not discussed in this section because, like boron, they do not form metallic bonds in the elemental crystals.

The transition elements are of special interest because they form metallic bonds regardless of the number of electrons per primitive unit cell. The conductivity in these metals can be explained by zone overlap, and the specific properties of transition metals can be shown to depend on the way that the overlapping zones are occupied. Consider the transition metals of the first long period, for which the overlapping zones of interest are the 3d and 4s zones. The way that the allowed states in these zones are occupied can be explained by considering the relative energies of the 3d and 4s electrons in the free atoms. In scandium, titanium, and vanadium, the 4s shell is completely filled while the 3d shell contains one, two, and three electrons, respectively. It can be shown that the exchange interaction between unpaired electrons (Hund's rule) favors the formation of completed *half-shells* containing electrons with parallel spins. Thus, when an additional electron in the next element, chromium, must be accommodated in the 3d shell, one of the 4s electrons is "demoted" to the 3d shell so that both shells are half filled. Now, a tendency to fill a half-shell implies a reluctance to start a new half-shell. Consequently, the next element, manganese, retains a half-filled d shell and accommodates the additional electron by completing the occupation of the 4s shell. Similarly, iron, cobalt, and nickel have two 4s electrons and six, seven, and eight 3d electrons, respectively. Finally, the 3d shell is completely filled in copper even though this requires that the 4s shell be half empty. (This suggests that the binding energy should be similar in chromium and copper, and this is indeed the case, as evidenced by the fact that the heats of sublimation for Cr and Cu are 80.0 and 80.3 kg-cal/mole, respectively.) Furthermore, it turns out that the energy required to demote a 4s electron decreases from 2.5 eV in calcium to 0.3 eV in vanadium and again from 2.1 eV in manganese to 0.02 eV in nickel. Now, in determining the occupation of allowed-energy zones in a crystal, additional interactions between atoms must be considered. It is not surprising, therefore, that the above distributions for isolated atoms are not obeyed exactly in crystals. For example, the very small energy required to demote a 4s electron in nickel helps explain why the 4s zone of Ni contains, on an average, only 0.6 electron per atom, while the $3d$ zone contains 9.4 electrons per atom.

It is now possible to attempt to account for the crystal structures adopted by some of the transition metals. Copper, silver, and gold have completely filled d shells, and nickel, palladium, and platinum have very nearly filled d shells. These filled shells produce a repulsion between adjacent atoms. Because the repulsive forces are nondirectional, this leads to the formation of a closest packing. This may also be the reason for the closest packings of cobalt, rhodium, and iridium. On the other hand, the lighter elements such as scandium, titanium, and vanadium have sparsely occupied d shells so that the d electrons can participate in bond formation. Pauling explains the decreasing interatomic separation from 3.21 Å in Sc to 2.63 in V by assuming that the increasing number of electrons present makes possible the formation of hybridized bonds. This also accounts for the stronger binding, say of titanium as compared with scandium. Pauling's model, however, does not fully explain the different crystal structures of these elements. Zener has suggested that magnetic interactions between the unpaired d electrons of adjacent atoms may explain some of the crystal structures assumed. Consider chromium, which has a completely filled $3d$ half-shell in which the electrons all have parallel spins according to Hund's rule. Because the $3d$ orbitals of adjacent chromium atoms overlap, it can be shown that the energy of the crystal is lowered if the spins of electrons in overlapping orbitals are oppositely directed. (This is analogous to the H_2 molecule formation discussed in Chapter 9.) This suggests that the most stable structure for Cr is one in which each atom is completely surrounded by atoms having oppositely directed spins. Now, such an arrangement is not possible in a closest packing, in which all atoms must be identical, but is possible in the body-centered cubic structure. Thus chromium has a body-centered cubic structure in which each Cr atom has eight nearest neighbors with opposite spins. By analogy to the exchange integral discussed in connection with ferromagnetism in the preceding chapter, it can be shown that an exchange integral favoring *antiparallel* spin orientations in overlapping $3d$ orbitals lowers the crystal's energy and increases its cohesion.

The above discussion has shown how the zone theory of solids can be used to explain why certain crystal structures are adopted by metals. It is also possible to explain the variations in the c/a ratio of metals in hexagonal closest packings with the aid of this theory. The first Brillouin zone for a primitive hexagonal lattice is a regular hexagonal prism; however, in the case of a hexagonal closest packing, it has the shape shown in Fig. 1. The reduced volume of this zone decreases the number of available states in the zone to slightly less than two per atom. Conse-

Table 2
Characteristics of hexagonal closest packings

Metal	Number of available states per atom	E_C/E_A	c/a
Be	1.731	1.196	1.585
Mg	1.743	1.137	1.625
Zn	1.799	0.863	1.861
Cd	1.805	0.859	1.890

quently, the valence electrons of divalent metals in hexagonal closest packings must occupy states in the next highest zone; that is, the zones overlap. Because the structure is anisotropic, however, the energy surfaces in the two zones can overlap normal to either the C face or the A face, depending on which face has the lower energy. Table 2 lists the number of available states per atom and the ratio of the energy value at C to that at A (in Fig. 1) for several metals having hexagonal closest-packed structures. The value of the c/a ratio for these metals is also listed in Table 2. It can be seen that when the ratio of the energy values at C and A is such that $E_C/E_A > 1.0$, then $c/a < 1.633$, the value of this ratio for a hexagonal closest packing of equal spheres. Conversely, when overlapping takes place normal to the C face, then $c/a > 1.633$. Note that the c/a ratio is much nearer to the ideal value in Be and Mg

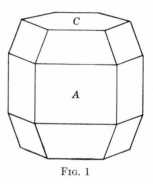

Fig. 1

than in Zn and Cd. This suggests that overlap parallel to the c axis distorts the hexagonal closest packing to a greater extent than does overlap along a. That this is indeed the case is brought out when the structures of zinc and cadmium are considered in detail below.

The way that zone overlap affects the size of atoms in crystals can also be seen in the case of aluminum. The interatomic distance between two Al atoms in the face-centered cubic structure (2.86 Å) is much larger than the diameter of a fully ionized Al^{+3} ion. This has been explained as being due to partial ionization of the aluminum atoms in elemental aluminum, a hypothesis that is consistent with its very low melting point (660°C) which is only 10° higher than that of divalent magnesium. More recently, Hume-Rothery and Raynor have suggested that the large interatomic distances can be explained more correctly by the zone theory. It turns out that the zones of aluminum overlap along the

[[100]] and [[110]] directions. Since the occupation of the zones is not completed until the second zone contains at least one electron per atom, this overlap implies that the outer electrons are not tightly bound, leading to a larger effective atomic size. This suggests that the effective size of aluminum atoms should be smaller in an alloy in which the zones do not overlap. The observed diameter of aluminum in copper and in silver alloys (face-centered cubic) is 2.71 Å, bearing out the above conclusion. Moreover, the effective size of Al is 2.83 Å in the direction of presumed zone overlap in a magnesium alloy (hexagonal closest packing) parallel to the c axis.

Complex structures. All the elements lying to the left of the vertical line in Table 1, except manganese, have one of the structures discussed

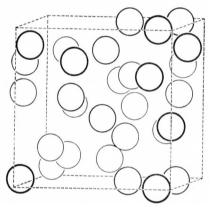

above. Manganese exists in four allotropic modifications whose stability is strongly temperature-dependent. The alpha modification is stable up to approximately 720°C and has a complex cubic structure containing fifty-eight atoms distributed among four sets of equipoints. The coordination numbers of the atoms range from 12 to 16, and the interatomic distances vary from 2.24 to 2.96 Å. The beta modification is stable up to about 1100°C and also has a complex cubic structure, shown in Fig. 2, which contains twenty

FIG. 2. β-Manganese structure. (The circles indicate the relative locations of the 20 atoms in the cubic cell.)

atoms distributed among two sets of equipoints. The coordination number for both kinds of atoms is 12; however, the interatomic distances vary from 2.36 to 2.67 Å. The density of available states in the Brillouin zone of β-Mn reaches a maximum at 1.41 electrons per atom and falls to zero at 1.62 electrons per atom. Certain alloys of monovalent metals, such as silver, with higher-valency elements also adopt this structure when the average number of valence electrons per atom is 1.5. This suggests that β-Mn may actually consist of very nearly equal amounts of monovalent and divalent manganese atoms. A divalent manganese atom has a completely filled $3d$ half-shell and an empty $4s$ shell, which has been shown to be a stable configuration. The existence of monovalent manganese atoms in ferromagnetic alloys indicates that this is also a possible electronic configuration for Mn in metals. The reasonableness of the above described proposal of mixed valencies is supported by the large number of different valencies that manganese exhibits in the different compounds that it forms. Nevertheless, the relative complexity of the α-Mn and β-Mn structures has prevented a quantitative elucidation of the reasons for their formation. Above 1100°C, the stable modification is called γ-Mn and is face-centered cubic although it becomes body-centered tetragonal if rapidly quenched. From 1137°C up to the melting point the stable modification is the body-centered cubic structure of delta manganese.

The elements lying to the right of the vertical line in Table 1 all have structures that are more complex than those encountered among the elements on the left side. Zinc and cadmium have structures which can be described as a distortion of the hexagonal closest packing in which $c/a \sim 1.9$ (Table 2). As a consequence, each atom has six nearest neighbors in a closest-packed layer, which are closer than the three nearest neighbors above and below, which are farther removed. The two kinds of interatomic distances are 2.66 and 2.91 Å in Zn and 2.97 and 3.29 Å in Cd. The resulting "layered" structure can be explained by assuming that the twelve electrons of one atom ($3d^{10}$ and $4s^2$) are not all paired so that they can form electron-pair bonds with six neighbors in accordance with the $8 - N$ rule. In the absence of a more quantitative theory, however, such speculations are not very meaningful. Interestingly enough, the next element in this column, mercury, also has a crystal structure in which each atom has six nearest neighbors that are close (3.00 Å) and six that are somewhat farther (3.46 Å). Unlike zinc and cadmium, the six closest neighbors in mercury lie in sets of three above and below each atom, while the farther nearest neighbors lie in the same plane. This arrangement is also a distortion of a closest packing obtained by compression along one of the 3-fold axes of a face-centered cube. The structure of mercury is anomalous in another way also in that mercury is a liquid down to -39°C.

Similarly, it is probable that some peculiarities in the electronic structures of Ga, In, and Tl account for their crystal structures. Gallium crystallizes in a very unusual structure in which each atom has one nearest neighbor at 2.44 Å and six others at 2.70 to 2.79 Å. The low melting point of gallium ($\sim$30°C) indicates that the bonds to these six neighbors are weak, whereas x-ray diffraction studies of liquid gallium indicate that the gallium atoms also tend to pair up in the liquid. Indium and thallium both have structures based on closest packings. Indium is actually body-centered tetragonal and has a structure obtained by elongation of a cubic closest packing along one of the 4-fold axes to give an axial ratio of 1.07. Thallium occurs in either the cubic closest packing or the hexagonal closest packing. Both structures are very nearly equally stable at room temperature, as evidenced by the similarities of the interatomic distances in both structures (3.45 and 3.43 Å). These interatomic distances are unusually high, however, and distinguish Tl, along with face-centered cubic lead (3.49 Å), from the other elements that have closest packings. (In this connection, note that the interatomic distances in the closest packings of so-called rare earths are also of the order of 3.5 Å.) It should be realized that these abnormally large atomic diameters need not persist in alloy structures in which the bonding may be different from that prevalent in the pure metals, similar to the case of aluminum discussed above.

FIG. 3. White-tin structure. (An exploded view of the coordination of an individual tin atom is shown in Fig. 4.)

A high-temperature form of thallium is body-centered cubic with an interatomic distance of 3.36 Å. Since the low-temperature form of thallium is a closest packing, the decrease in the interatomic distance in the high-temperature modification creates an interesting paradox. Both the less efficient packing and the increased thermal motion of the atoms suggest that the interatomic separations should increase. The actually observed decrease in the interatomic distances, therefore, must be explained on the basis of a change in the bond type. The metallic bond in closest packings is nondirectional whereas the bonding in the body-centered cubic modification apparently has a directional character similar to covalent or electron-pair bonding. This leads to a greater attraction and, hence, a decrease in the interatomic separation between adjacent atoms in the high-temperature form of thallium.

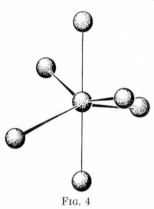

FIG. 4

Tin exists in two polymorphic modifications, the so-called gray tin below 18°C and white tin above this temperature. Gray tin has the so-called diamond structure shown on page 355 in which each atom is tetrahedrally coordinated by four other atoms. Because gray tin is a semiconductor, its structure is discussed further in Chapter 13. The stable modification at room temperature, white tin, has a more complex structure shown in Fig. 3. (This can be thought of as a distortion of the diamond structure.)   In the body-centered tetragonal structure, each tin atom has four nearest neighbors at 3.02 Å, disposed at the corners of a flattened tetrahedron, and two nearest neighbors above and below this tetrahedron, as shown in Fig. 4.   The slight zone overlap that must exist in the white-tin structure probably accounts for this atomic array, whereas the zone overlap disappears in the more symmetric gray-tin structure and the zones are separated by a very narrow energy gap.

Simple alloys

Substitutional solid solutions.   It has been shown in Chapter 4 that it is possible to replace atoms of one kind in a crystal by atoms of another kind, provided that the atoms are of similar size and valency. This results in a crystal structure called a solid solution or, more specifically, a *substitutional solid solution.*   A rapid survey of Table 1 shows that there are many pairs of metals which can form binary solid solutions with each other.   Very few metals, however, can form continuous solid solutions because most metals are only partially soluble in each other. The thermodynamic relations governing the formation of actual solid solutions have been discussed in Chapter 8.   The principal physical factors that determine the degree of solid solubility are discussed below. Although the empirical rules established by Hume-Rothery are derived from observations of a large number of alloys, certain exceptions are known to exist.   It turns out that two metals can form substitutional solid solutions for all composition ratios only when *all* the following conditions are fulfilled.

1. *Condition for atomic size.*   In order for extensive substitutional solid solution to occur, it is necessary that the atoms have atomic radii that differ by less than 15 per cent.   Generally, the more nearly alike they are, other things being equal, the greater the degree of solid solubility.   It is necessary to be careful in selecting the appropriate values to use for this comparison, however.   For example, it has already been shown that the effective radius of Al varies from 1.35 to 1.40 Å in solid solutions as compared with 1.43 Å in the pure metal.   Also, when using the values for metal radii given in Appendix 3, it is necessary to take into account any changes in the coordination number of the atoms in a solid solution.

2. *Condition for crystal structure.*   In order for continuous solid solubility to be possible, the two metals must have identical crystal structures, except for the dimensions of the unit cell which are governed by the atomic-size condition above.   Thus continuous solid solutions are possible between face-centered cubic Cu-Ni and Au-Ag, or body-centered

cubic Mo-W, but not between body-centered cubic molybdenum and face-centered cubic silver, even though their radii differ by less than 6 per cent.

3. *Condition for electronegativity.* If the two kinds of atoms in a solid solution are respectively electronegative and electropositive, then it is likely that they prefer to form stable structures rather than continuous solid solutions. Because these structures frequently have compositional variations over a certain range, it is proper to call such crystals *intermediate phases* rather than compounds, a word that implies strict stoichiometry. Some of the intermediate phases most commonly encountered are discussed further in a later section.

4. *Condition for relative valency.* Continuous solid solutions can occur only between atoms having the same valency in the alloy. It is generally true that elements of high valency dissolve to a larger extent in a lower-valency solvent than the reverse case. This is an example of the so-called *nonreciprocity* rule of solid solutions. A few examples are given below for alloys in which the conditions of size, structure, and electronegativity favor continuous solid solutions.

Solubility of	*Up to*
Cd in Ag	42.5% Cd
Ag in Cd	6.0% Ag
Zn in Cu	38.5% Zn
Cu in Zn	2.5% Cu
Si in Cu	11.5% Si
Cu in Si	2.0% Cu

Complete solid solubility is infrequent because all the above criteria must be obeyed quite closely. When they are obeyed, the substitutional solid solution is expected to follow *Vegard's law* which states that the change in unit cell dimensions should be linear with change in composition. (Because both metals have identical structures, the solid solution decreases the size of the larger metal's unit cell or increases that of the smaller metal.) It turns out that this law is obeyed fairly well by most isomorphous inorganic compounds; most metals, however, form notable exceptions. The observed deviations may be negative or positive, as shown in Fig. 5. It is generally found that Vegard's law is followed most closely in alloys in which intermediate phases do not occur, that is, in solid solutions of atoms most nearly alike in their chemical properties.

Order-disorder transformations. The above rules for solid solution need not be obeyed as closely at elevated temperatures. The increased thermal motion of the atoms tends to blur the differences between unlike atoms so that the solubility of larger atoms and of atoms having higher valencies increases with temperature. In fact, the stability of a structure having a particular composition is strongly dependent on temperature, as shown in Chapter 8. Now, except for some short-range order usually present, the atomic array in most solid solutions is completely random; that is, unlike atoms are distributed among the same equipoints of the structure. At certain temperatures, however, it is possible that the free energy of the solid solution is lower when the two kinds of atoms occupy different equipoints. As shown in Chapter 8, this transition from a random to an ordered array takes place at a characteristic temperature and, in practice, is usually helped along by annealing

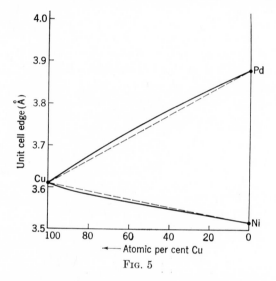

Fig. 5

the alloy. Some examples of the crystal structures of ordered and disordered solid solutions are considered below.

As an example of a substitutional solid solution that undergoes an order-disorder transformation, consider the copper-gold system. Because both copper and gold crystallize in the cubic closest packing, have radii that differ by less than 15 per cent, and lie in the same column of the periodic table, these two metals can form a continuous range of substitutional solid solutions, as shown by their equilibrium diagram in Fig. 6. The structure of this random solid solution can be represented by the face-centered cubic lattice array of "statistical" atoms shown in Fig. 7A. For example, at the 50-50 composition, CuAu, the statistical atoms are $\frac{1}{2}$Cu $-$ $\frac{1}{2}$Au, meaning that the probability of finding a copper atom at a particular site just equals that of finding a gold atom at the same site. At the 75-25 composition, Cu$_3$Au, the statistical atoms are $\frac{3}{4}$Cu $-$ $\frac{1}{4}$Au, and so forth. Below 500°C, the random solid solutions are no longer stable for all compositions. According to the equilibrium diagram in Fig. 6, the 50-50 alloy transforms to the ordered CuAu structure shown in Fig. 7B and the 75-25 alloy transforms to the ordered Cu₃Au structure shown in Fig. 7C. Both of these ordered structures are derivative structures having lower symmetry than their disordered counterparts. This is a direct consequence of ordering. The individual equipoints of the face-centered cubic lattice array in the disordered crystal are occupied statistically at random; hence, a small primitive rhombohedral cell can

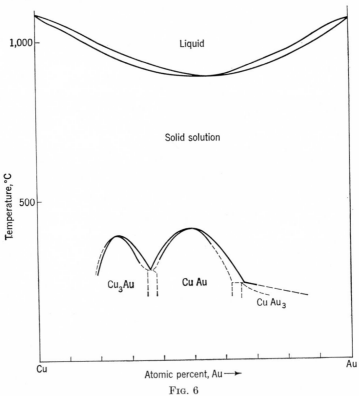

Fig. 6

be chosen to describe the lattice. When the atoms order, however, they occupy specific equipoints in a primitive, cubic unit cell, which is larger. This larger cell is said to describe a *superlattice* of the ordered crystal. Note that, in the case of CuAu, the 3-fold axes are suppressed by the ordering so that the space group goes from $Fm3m$, in the random solid solution, to $P\dfrac{4}{m}mm$, in the ordered tetragonal crystal. (In addition, certain translations of the face-centered cubic lattice are suppressed, and the ordering into successive Cu and Au layers causes a slight distortion along the 4-fold axis.) In the case of Cu_3Au, the space group of the ordered structure, $Pm3m$, is obtained by suppressing only the centering translations of the face-centered cubic lattice. Note that the above structural information was derived from x-ray diffraction investigations. It is possible to detect the order-disorder transition by other means also,

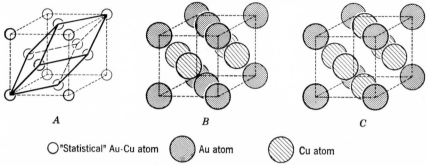

A   B   C

○ "Statistical" Au-Cu atom   ◉ Au atom   ◈ Cu atom

FIG. 7. Order-disorder in the copper-gold system.
A. Random solid solution.
B. Ordered CuAu structure.
C. Ordered Cu_3Au structure.

for example, by noting the changes in the electrical resistivity. In fact, the phase boundaries indicated by the broken lines in Fig. 6 are based on such less-direct observations.

Order-disorder transitions can take place in still another way also. When small amounts of copper are alloyed with the gamma phase of manganese, the resulting Mn-Cu alloy has the face-centered cubic structure of γ-Mn. The energy due to the exchange integral in these alloys favors an antiparallel spin orientation in nearest neighbors. As shown previously, it is not possible for each atom in a closest packing to surround itself entirely by unlike atoms. It is possible, however, to form an array in which each atom has more unlike than like atoms coordinating it. Such an arrangement is shown in Fig. 8 to consist of alternating (001) planes having opposite spin directions. Each atom in this array has four nearest neighbors in the same (001) plane with parallel spins and eight nearest neighbors, four in the plane above and four in the plane below, whose spins are antiparallel. (Because neutron beams interact with the magnetic moments of atoms, it has been possible

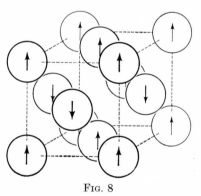

FIG. 8

to demonstrate, by means of neutron diffraction experiments, that the antiparallel spin array shown in Fig. 8 actually exists in a Mn-Cu alloy.) The symmetry of the spin arrangement in Fig. 8, of course, has tetragonal symmetry. If a face-centered tetragonal cell is chosen to describe this structure, it turns out that the c/a ratio is less than unity. This supports Zener's postulate that, because of the exchange integral favoring antiparallel spins, the energy of the crystal is lowered by this distortion of the cubic cell. This is so because the bonding forces normal to (001) planes are greater than those within (001) planes. In the high-temperature modification of this alloy (undoubtedly also in pure γ-Mn), the thermal energy (kinetic) is greater than that due to the magnetic interaction so that the spins of nearest neighbors are randomly oriented. Below approximately 250°C, the ordering effect of the exchange forces exceeds the randomizing effect of thermal motion so that the spins assume the ordered array in Fig. 8. Thus the cubic to tetragonal disorder → order transformation in this case does not involve atomic rearrangements (except for a small contraction parallel to c) but is occasioned by an ordered alignment of electron spins. This transformation is not unlike the paramagnetic-ferromagnetic transitions in Fe, Co, Ni, and their alloys. Further examples of similar transformations are also described in later chapters.

Intermediate phases

Electron compounds. As an example of a binary alloy system in which continuous solid solution is not possible because only two of the so-called Hume-Rothery rules are obeyed, consider the equilibrium diagram of the Cu-Zn system shown in Fig. 9. Copper crystallizes in a cubic closest packing, zinc in a slightly distorted hexagonal closest packing. Zinc is divalent and copper is monovalent so that more Zn can dissolve in Cu than the reverse case. Starting at the left, the α phase is a random solid solution rich in copper and has the face-centered cubic structure of copper. Skipping the mixed-phase region, the next pure phase is the so-called β brass phase having a composition of 45–50 atomic per cent zinc. Above about 470°C, the body-centered cubic structure is disordered (Fig. 10A), while below the transition temperature it orders into the cesium chloride arrangement shown in Fig. 10B. The specialized nature of this structure distinguishes it from the solid solution, and it is called an *intermediate phase*. At a composition of 61.5 atomic per cent zinc, a new intermediate phase, called the γ phase, appears. This phase has a complicated cubic structure with fifty-two atoms per unit cell and is stable over a rather limited compositional range. In fact, it more nearly approximates a stoichiometric compound than a

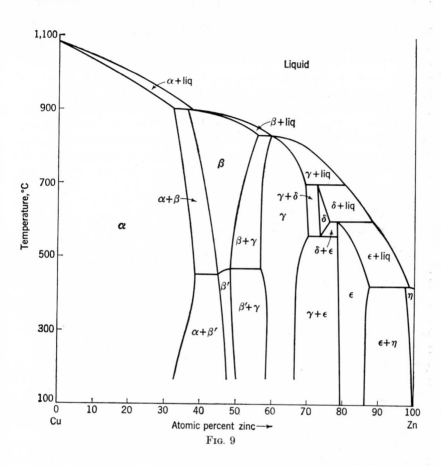

FIG. 9

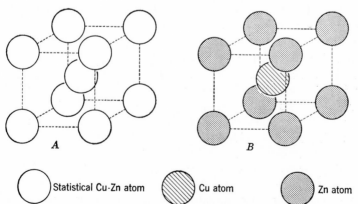

Statistical Cu-Zn atom   Cu atom   Zn atom

FIG. 10.   Intermediate phases in copper-zinc system.
A. Random solid solution.
B. Ordered CuZn structure.

295

typical intermediate phase.   On the other hand, the ϵ phase is again a typical intermediate phase having a compositional range of 82 to 88 atomic per cent zinc and a hexagonal structure based on a hexagonal closest packing.   Finally, the η phase is a zinc-rich solid solution accommodating up to 2.5 atomic per cent copper in the hexagonal closest packing of zinc.

If the normal valencies of $+2$, for zinc, $+1$, for copper, are assigned to the metals in this alloy, it turns out that the average ratios of electrons to atoms for the three intermediate phases in the Cu-Zn system are as follows:

In the β phase, CuZn,   the electron-to-atom ratio is $3:2$.
In the γ phase, Cu_5Zn_8, the electron-to-atom ratio is $21:13$.   (1)
In the ϵ phase, $CuZn_3$, the electron-to-atom ratio is $7:4$.

Similar phases are found to exist in other alloys also.   For example, in the Au-Zn and the Ag-Cd systems, three intermediate phases are found having identical structures and electron-to-atom ratios.   In fact, as was first pointed out by Hume-Rothery, when the electron-to-atom ratio is about $3:2$, the β structure appears in many systems, for example, AgMg, CuBe, Cu_3Al, and Cu_5Sn.   [In some alloys, when the electron:atom ratio is $3:2$, the intermediate phase has the β manganese structure (Fig. 2), for example, Ag_3Al and Cu_3Si.]   Further examples of these so-called *Hume-Rothery compounds* are Ag_5Hg_8, Cu_9Al_8, $Cu_{31}Si_8$, having electron:atom ratios of $21:13$ and structures very similar to the γ brass structure; and Ag_3Sn, Ag_5In, $CuCd_3$, Cu_3Ge, having electron:atom ratios of $7:4$ and structures that are based on hexagonal closest packings like that of ϵ brass.   It should be noted that alloys containing transition metals also form intermediate phases with similar structures.   These structures can be shown to occur at the same electron:atom ratios provided that the valency of the transition metals is assumed to be zero. Examples of such intermediate phases having the β-phase structure are CoAl, FeAl, and NiAl, while Co_5Zn_{21}, Ni_5Cd_{21}, and Rh_5Zn_{21} have the γ brass structures and $FeZn_7$ has the ϵ brass structure.

The importance of the electron:atom ratio to the stability of these structures becomes clearer when use is made of the zone theory of solids. Suppose that the allowed-energy zones of a particular structure are separated by large forbidden regions.   Then the structure can conveniently hold as many electrons as there are energy states available in a zone.   If higher-valency atoms are added to a structure in which such a zone is completely filled, the structure becomes unstable because it cannot accommodate the additional electrons without a relatively large increase in its energy.   When an alternate structure of lower potential energy exists, therefore, such a structure is preferred by the alloy.   Jones has calculated the electron:atom ratios at which the new phases should appear, and his values are compared with the empirical ratios of Hume-Rothery below.

Phase	β	γ	ϵ
Jones's ratio:	1.480	1.538	1.70
Hume-Rothery's ratio:	1.500	1.615	1.75

Although the calculations of Jones are based on certain simplifying assumptions, the agreement between the calculated values and the empirical values of Hume-Rothery is very good. In this connection, it should be realized that most of these intermediate phases can exist over fairly wide compositional ranges; hence, their electron:atom ratios can vary also. Owing to the importance of the electron:atom ratio in determining the stability of these intermediate phases, they are sometimes called *electron compounds*.

Ternary alloy phases. The equilibrium diagrams of some ternary alloys show that a considerable variation in the composition of certain intermediate phases is possible provided that the electron:atom ratio is not affected by the compositional change. Such intermediate phases are found particularly frequently in alloy systems of transition metals with aluminum and silicon. For example, in the system Fe-Ni-Al, an intermediate phase having the cesium chloride structure can accommodate a continuously variable amount of iron or nickel. It is reasonable, therefore, to classify such intermediate phases as electron compounds, similar to the Hume-Rothery compounds already discussed. Raynor has suggested that the transition metals act as acceptors of valence electrons, donated by the "electron-rich" aluminum or silicon atoms, in such phases as Co_2Al_9, $FeNiAl_9$, $FeAl_3$, $Ni_4Mn_{11}Al_{60}$, Mn_3SiAl_9, and others. He further predicted that, if Al and Si are assumed to contribute, respectively, three and four electrons per atom in these structures, then Cr, Mn, Fe, Co, Ni can accept, respectively, 4.66, 3.66, 2.66, 1.71, and 0.61 electrons per atom. Careful investigations of some of these phases indicate that the transition metals do, indeed, act as acceptors of electrons but not to the extent predicted by Raynor. Nor has the systematic variation in the number of electrons accepted been observed. Pauling has suggested a completely different explanation of the formation of these phases, based on the formation of more nearly covalent than metallic-type bonds between the transition-metal atoms and aluminum. There is little doubt that the exact nature of the bonding is certainly important in determining the stability of these structures; however, factors other than the electron:atom ratio may play a decisive role. Probably the most important one is the size factor. It should be realized, however, that the size of an atom is a function of its environment so

A

B

FIG. 11

that, like any single criterion that is selected as a parameter, it is not independent of other factors.

Laves phases. As a result of investigating a series of magnesium alloys, Laves and his co-workers found that intermediate phases having one of three structure types tend to recur for these and similar alloys. These so-called *Laves phases* are structurally quite similar and occur in alloy systems in which the radius ratio of the metals is in the range 1.08 to 1.32. (Ideally, $R_A/R_B = 1.260$.) The crystal structures of these phases are best understood by considering the two hexagonal closest-packed layers shown superimposed in Fig. 11*A*. As discussed in Chapter 3, closest-packed layers alternatively can be represented by layers of octahedra, like the one shown in Fig. 11*B*. Next, consider a group of four such octahedra shown in their arrangement about an occluded tetrahedron in Fig. 12*A*. These octahedra can be combined into a single polyhedron shown in Fig. 12*B*, and these so-called *Laves polyhedra*, arranged in a layer, are shown in Fig. 12*C*. (Compare with Fig. 11*B*.) Now, if the central sphere in each of the four hexagon-shaped faces of the Laves polyhedron is removed (this is equivalent

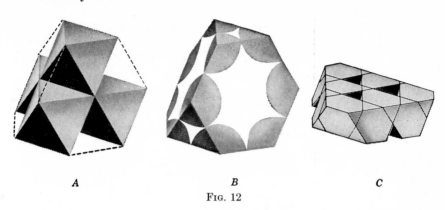

A   B   C
FIG. 12

to removing the four spheres at the corners of the occluded tetrahedron), a much larger sphere can be accommodated in the central tetrahedron. This is the reason, of course, why this modification of a closest packing is preferred by alloys having atoms whose radii differ by 20 to 30 per cent.

Since it is possible to take any two layers in a closest packing and transform them into double layers of Laves polyhedra by removing certain spheres, it is not surprising that the three Laves phases are simply three alternative ways of stacking such double layers. In fact, the $MgCu_2$-type structure also adopted by $AgBe_2$, $PbAu_2$, KBi_2, and others results from stacking these double layers in the sequence . . . ABC . . . ; similarly, the $MgZn_2$-type structure also adopted by $CaMg_2$, $TaMn_2$, KNa_2, and others has the simple hexagonal stacking sequence . . . AB . . . ; and the $MgNi_2$-type structure also adopted by $CrBe_2$, FeB_2, and others has the stacking sequence . . . $ABAC$ . . . . These structures can be thought of, therefore, in terms of the closest packings of Laves polyhedra in either the three-layer cubic closest packing (. . . ccc . . .), the two-layer hexagonal packing (. . . hh . . .), or the four-layer topaz packing (. . . $chch$ . . .). Although, undoubtedly, the electronic structure of the atoms is responsible for the stability of these structures, no simple relationships with their electron:atom ratios appear to exist, since the ratio varies from about 5:4 to 2:1 for the various phases. Other conditions which appear to favor the formation of Laves phases require that there be a small electronegativity difference between the constituent atoms and that their valencies be similar.

Sigma phases. An intermediate phase formed by alloys of the transition metals Mn, Fe, Co, and Ni with Cr, V, Mo, and W is of special interest to users of alloy steels because this so-called σ phase is hard, brittle, and nonmagnetic at ordinary temperatures. Consider the equilibrium diagram of the Cr-Fe system in Fig. 13, which shows the appearance of the σ phase at approximately the 50-50 composition.

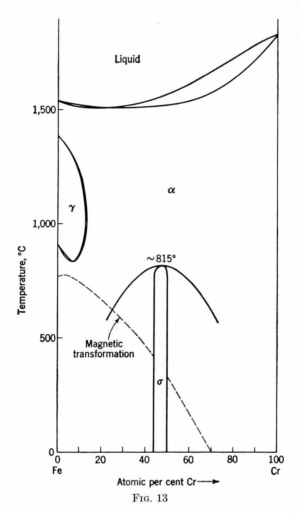

FIG. 13

Neither the composition range nor the stability range of this phase is the same in different alloys, however. This can be seen from the comparison of alloys of chromium with Mn, Fe, and Co below.

Alloy	*Composition range of* σ	*Stability range of* σ
Cr-Mn	17–28 at. % Cr	Stable up to melting point.
Cr-Fe	43–50 at. % Cr	Formed in solid state only.
Cr-Co	53–58 at. % Cr	Formed in solid state only.

The sigma phase also occurs in ternary alloy systems even when the three relevant binary systems do not contain it. This implies that the σ phase is stabilized by the addition of the third component, a conclusion that is borne out by the increased stability range of a σ phase formed in a binary system when small amounts of a third metal are added.

The crystal structure of the σ phase is known, but there is some uncertainty regarding the exact distribution of the different atoms among its equipoints. The large variation of its composition ratios in different alloys suggests that most of the equipoints are statistically occupied. The σ phase has a complex tetragonal structure with thirty atoms in each unit cell. (For Cr-Fe, $c = 4.559$ Å, $a = 8.7990$ Å.) The atoms are arranged in layers, and the interatomic distances between layers in the Fe-Cr system are 2.28 Å. This distance is much shorter than either the Fe-Fe distance in α-Fe (2.48 Å) or the Cr-Cr distance in chromium metal (2.49 Å) and suggests that the electronic structure of the constituent atoms must be different from what it is in the pure metals. The conditions governing the formation of this phase have not been clearly established. The proposed Brillouin zone can contain up to 6.97 electrons per atom, and calculations show that the mean electron:atom ratio for most binary σ phases is 6.93. This calculation has been questioned by D. P. Shoemaker, who derives a ratio of 5.76 electrons per atom based on the ionization states deduced from the known interatomic-bond distances. Thus it is not possible to reach specific conclusions until the valencies that transition metals can have in alloys are better established.

Size factors also appear to be important. For example, the stability of the σ phase decreases as the radius ratio increases. The largest ratio occurs in W-Fe and W-Co, where the radii differ by approximately 12 per cent and the phase is stable only at elevated temperatures. Recently, Frank and Kasper have proposed that the structures of the σ and related phases can be considered as sphere packings containing 12-, 14-, 15-, and 16-coordinated groups. Such polyhedra are accommodated by systematically omitting certain atoms in hexagonal closest-packed layers to form so-called *Kagomé nets*. The nets can be stacked in several ways to form large voids surrounded by either thirteen, fourteen, fifteen, or sixteen atoms. These structures can be analyzed, therefore, in terms of different ways of stacking such double layers, similar to the stacking of layers of Laves polyhedra, as discussed in the preceding section. In fact, it should be noted that the packing schemes of Frank and Kasper can be used not only to explain the structures of σ phases but also of Laves phases and a number of other intermediate phases that have been observed to form in transition-metal alloys. These phases are variously designated δ, μ, ξ, χ, P, and R phases, and all are structurally related to the σ phase.

Interstitial phases

Interstitial carbides and nitrides. In addition to substitutional solid solutions, alloys can be formed by *interstitial solid solutions*. It will be recalled from Chapter 3 that the octahedral voids in closest packings have $r/R = 0.414$ and the tetrahedral voids have $r/R = 0.225$. It is not surprising, therefore, that relatively small atoms like H, B, C, and N can enter into interstitial solid solution with larger metal atoms in closest packings. As might be expected, the smaller hydrogen and boron atoms tend to occupy tetrahedral voids in such packings while the larger carbon and nitrogen atoms prefer octahedral voids. From the physical properties of the solid solutions formed, it is deduced that the bonding between the solute and solvent atoms is metallic if the solvent atoms belong to the transition metals. It becomes more covalent in character for the more electropositive metals. Hägg has shown that stable solid-solution structures are formed if the radius ratio for octahedrally substituted atoms is less than 0.59 and that covalently bonded compounds form if the radius ratio exceeds this value. Many of the typical covalently bonded carbides, for example, SiC, adopt structures similar to the various polymorphs of ZnS, as described in Chapter 13.

Among the transition metals, Ti, V, Zr, Nb, Hf, and Ta form particularly stable carbides and nitrides. The transition metals are arranged in a cubic closest packing, and all the octahedral holes are occupied either by carbon or by nitrogen. The resulting sodium chloride–type structure is adopted by all these carbides and nitrides and is also found in the substitutional solid solutions formed by them. It is not surprising that the transition metal carbides or nitrides can form continuous substitutional solid solutions with each other, since they have the same structure and their atomic sizes are similar. The only exception is ZrC-VC. Because zirconium is 21 per cent larger than the smallest metal in this series, vanadium, only very limited solid solubility can exist. Other transition metals, for example, Cu, Ni, Co, and Fe, form metastable carbides at elevated temperatures which decompose at lower temperatures. The iron carbides are further discussed in a later section because of their importance in steels. Tungsten and molybdenum form nitrides in which the nitrogen atoms occupy only half of the octahedral voids, giving a composition Me_2N. Manganese and iron can also form nitrides in which only a quarter of the octahedral voids, namely, the voids at the body centers of face-centered cubes, are occupied, giving the composition Me_4N. Similar structures can be obtained by placing carbon or nitrogen in the octahedral voids of a hexagonal closest packing. In Fe_3N, one-third of the available voids between each layer are occupied in such a way that no two nitrogen atoms are nearest neighbors. If alternate layers have one-third and two-thirds of the available octahedral voids occupied by nitrogen, the structure of Fe_2N results. More complex iron nitrides are also possible, in which case the structures can be analyzed as combinations of these two simpler types. Similarly, in V_2C and Mo_2C the carbon atoms occupy half of the octahedral holes in a hexagonal

closest packing. In all these structures, the interstitial atoms tend to
be as far apart as possible.

It is interesting to note that,
although in carbides having the
sodium chloride structure the transition metals are arranged in a cubic
closest packing, these metals do not
adopt this arrangement in the pure
metal. Rundle suggested, therefore,
that the bonding in these carbides is
not purely metallic but has some
covalent character. This approach
is similar to the one used by Pauling
to explain the formation of intermediate phases in transition-metal–
aluminum alloys. It is assumed
that covalent-type bonds are formed
by the atoms through hybridized
orbitals. Since there are not enough
valency electrons available to form
six electron-pair bonds, the electrons
resonate between them and electrical
conductivity is possible. Hume-
Rothery also has shown that the carbide structures owe their stability to
hybrid bond formations, although
the hybrids he proposes differ markedly from those proposed by Rundle.
The very high melting points of these
so-called *refractory* carbides, 3000 to
4000°C, are cited as further proof
of the covalent nature of the bonds
formed.

**Interstitial hydrides and bo-
rides.** If all the tetrahedral voids in
a cubic closest packing are occupied,
the fluorite structure results, whereas
if only half of the tetrahedral voids
are occupied, the zinc blende structure is obtained. This is illustrated

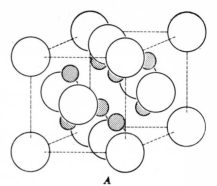

A

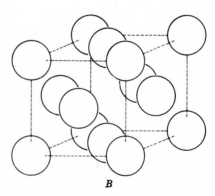

B

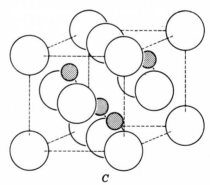

C

Fig. 14. Transition-metal hydride
structure types.

A. MeH$_2$ (fluorite type).
B. Cubic closest packing.
C. MeH (zinc-blende type).

in Fig. 14 which compares these two structures with the cubic closest
packing. Note that, since there are twice as many tetrahedral voids in a

closest packing than there are spheres, the fluorite structure has the formula MeX_2, such as TiH_2 or CrH_2, for example. Similarly, the zinc blende structure is adopted by compounds such as ZrH, CrH, and TiH. It is possible that even fewer tetrahedral voids are occupied. For example, one-quarter of the voids are occupied in Pd_2H and one-eighth in Zr_4H. The bonds formed by hydrogen in these structures are like the partially covalent bonds already discussed for the case of carbon.

The structures of borides are more complex. Although not enough of these structures have been determined to allow a complete evaluation of the rules that govern their formation, it is clear that bonding between adjacent boron atoms is an important factor. The diborides of Ti, V, Zr, Nb, and several other transition metals crystallize in a hexagonal crystal structure in which the metal atoms form hexagonal layers separated from each other by layers of boron atoms. Each boron atom is coordinated by three metal atoms above and below in the form of a trigonal prism. The abnormally high transition-metal–boron distances suggest that there is relatively strong bonding between adjacent boron atoms. Nevertheless, the bonds must be of the unsaturated covalent type in order to account for the fairly high conductivity. (The conductivity of several borides, for example, TiB_2 and ZrB_2, exceeds that of the parent metal.) The crystal structures of FeB and CoB also consist of boron polyhedra in the form of trigonal prisms. The Me-B distances are $\sim$2.15 Å whereas the B-B distances between prisms sharing a prism face are 1.77 Å, suggesting that the borons are linked in a type of continuous chain in these structures.

Steels. The interstitial solid solutions of carbon in iron are of special interest because they form the basis of what is probably the most widely used commercial alloy—steel. One can distinguish between *plain carbon* steels, which contain no intentionally added metals, *low-alloy* steels, to which up to 5 per cent of foreign metals are added, and *high-alloy* steels containing more than 5 per cent of alloyed metals. Normally, transition metals such as V, Cr, Mn, Ni, Mo, and W are alloyed with iron to produce high-alloy steels having unusual properties, for example, stainless steel, or the exceptionally hard tool steels. The role of carbon in such steels may be important in the formation of intermediate phases or it may be that of an unavoidable interstitial inclusion, in which case it is not specifically considered in discussing phase equilibria. (For example, see the σ phases previously discussed.) On the other hand, the distribution of carbides in the system Fe-C is of utmost importance in the manufacture of steels. For obvious reasons, a comprehensive discussion of steels is not possible here; nevertheless, some of the different phases found in the iron-carbon system are briefly described below.

As can be seen in the Fe-C equilibrium diagram (Fig. 15), iron can

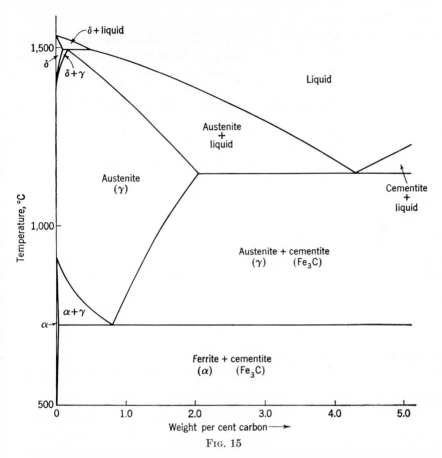

Fig. 15

exist in three allotropic modifications: body-centered cubic α-Fe below
910°C, face-centered cubic γ-Fe in the range 910 to 1400°C, and body-
centered cubic δ-Fe up to the melting point (1534°C). Alpha iron is
ferromagnetic up to 768°C and becomes paramagnetic, without change in
crystal structure, above the transition temperature. (Older texts call
this paramagnetic phase β-Fe but it is current practice to refer to it
simply as nonmagnetic α iron.) Because of the larger voids in the face-
centered cubic structure, γ-Fe is the only modification that dissolves
carbon interstitially to any large extent (up to 2.0 per cent by weight).
It has been shown that the carbon atoms occupy the octahedral voids
in a random fashion, and this interstitial solid solution is commonly
called *austenite*. Compared with this, the interstitial solid solution of
carbon in body-centered α-Fe, called *ferrite*, proceeds up to a maximum
concentration of 0.025 weight per cent carbon, at the eutectoid temperature. The intermediate phase in this diagram, called *cementite*, contains

6.67 weight per cent carbon so that its composition is Fe_3C. The structure of cementite is much more complex than that of the simple solid solutions and has an orthorhombic unit cell with $a = 4.524$ Å, $b = 6.743$ Å, and $c = 5.089$ Å. Each carbon atom is coordinated by six iron atoms at the corners of the distorted trigonal prism shown in Fig. 16, and the Fe-C distances vary from 1.85 to 2.68 Å. The iron atoms in this structure are divided among two equipoint sets so that they have either eleven or twelve nearest iron neighbors at distances ranging from 2.49 to 2.68 Å. This coordination number is sufficiently similar to that of a closest packing to indicate that the Fe-Fe bond is strongly metallic in character.

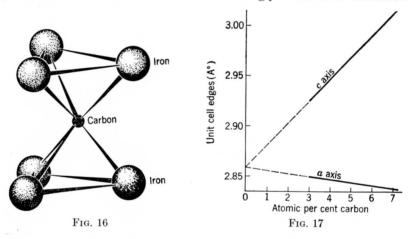

FIG. 16   FIG. 17

However, the peculiar coordination of carbon suggests that some covalent Fe-C bonds are also formed. The covalent character of some of the bonding is further attested to by the fact that, unlike most other intermediate phases, Fe_3C appears to be stable only when it has a very nearly stoichiometric composition. This does not exclude the possibility that other transition metals can substitute for Fe in cementite; in fact, Mn and Cr are frequently alloyed with cementite to make it more stable relative to the *graphite* modification of carbon.

When austenite is cooled very rapidly, it transforms to *martensite* by means of the so-called martensite transformation discussed in previous chapters. Martensite has a body-centered tetragonal structure which can be thought of as a slightly distorted NaCl structure. The length of the cell edges depends on the amount of carbon present, as shown in Fig. 17, in which the broken lines indicate the extrapolation to carbon-free α iron. The iron atoms actually vary slightly in their positions along the c axis, whereas the carbon atoms occupy their positions in a statistically random fashion. The variation in the c/a ratio, with increasing carbon content, is explained by the tetragonal distortion produced by

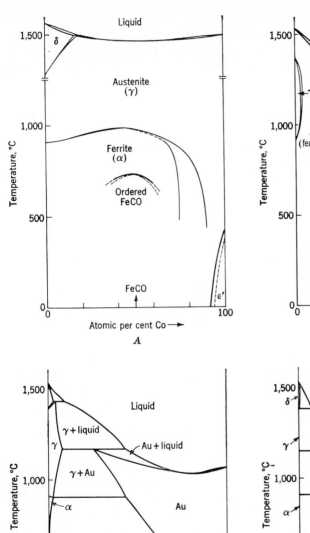

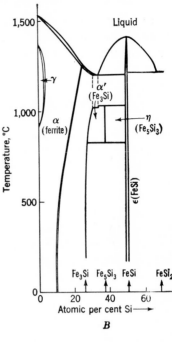

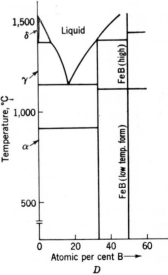

Fig. 18

307

the carbon atoms, which tend to push the iron atoms further apart, parallel to *c*. It appears that at least 2.5 atomic per cent of carbon must be present to produce the tetragonal distortion at room temperature. This is the reason why martensite containing less carbon has not been observed (Fig. 17). The austenite → martensite transformation proceeds quite rapidly but is never actually completed, so that some retained austenite is invariably present. On the other hand, if austenite is cooled more slowly, it transforms into a lamellar intergrowth of ferrite and cementite called *pearlite* (see p. 199).

An interesting feature of the equilibrium diagrams of iron alloys is the effect that different alloying metals have on the relative stabilities of the allotropic modifications of iron. Since the structures of α and δ iron are the same, a metal whose size and other properties favor solid solubility will alloy equally readily with both. Hence, the appearance of many equilibrium diagrams is like the Fe-Cr diagram shown in Fig. 13, in which the α and δ solid solutions cannot be distinguished. Note that the stability range of the γ modification in this diagram is enclosed in a sort of loop, commonly called a *closed γ field*. The extent of the γ field is determined by the type of metal entering into the solid solution. Four possibilities are usually distinguished: the *open γ* field (Fig. 18*A*), the *closed γ* field (Fig. 18*B*), the *expanded γ* field (Fig. 18*C*), and the *contracted γ* field (Fig. 18*D*). The way in which an alloyed metal affects the stability of the γ phase is determined by several factors. When the relative sizes of the metals are considered, it becomes apparent that the greater solubility of smaller atoms tends to increase the stability of the phase so that these can be said to open the γ field. Conversely, larger atoms tend to close the γ field. Other factors, however, must be considered also. For example, metals that crystallize in a cubic closest packing tend to stabilize the γ phase, whereas metals crystallizing with a body-centered cubic structure tend to stabilize the α phase, so that they decrease the extent of the γ field. The relative stabilities of these two phases also can be expressed thermodynamically by observing the change in the latent heat of transformation from the γ to the α structure. If the heat absorbed per unit concentration of solute in α is greater than that in γ, then the γ phase is favored, and vice versa. Recently, Zener has shown that some discrepancies which arise when this approach is adopted can be resolved by considering the effect of magnetic interactions on the free energies of the two modifications of iron.

Suggestions for supplementary reading

Charles S. Barrett, *Structures of metals*, 2d ed. (McGraw-Hill Book Company, Inc., New York, 1952), especially pp. 213–252 and 558–561.

F. C. Frank and J. S. Kasper, Complex alloy structures regarded as sphere packings, I. Definitions and basic principles, *Acta Cryst.*, vol. 11 (1958), pp. 184–190.

William Hume-Rothery and G. V. Raynor, *The structure of metals and alloys*, 3d ed. (Institute of Metals Monograph 1, London, 1956).

C. Zener, Impact of magnetism upon metallurgy, *Trans. AIME*, vol. 203 (1955), pp. 619–629.

Exercises

1. Why is cesium, with one valence electron per atom, a conductor, since a body-centered unit cell of cesium contains two atoms?

2. How do you explain that scandium, with three valence electrons per atom and a hexagonal closest packing, is a conductor?

3. Look up the structures of gray and white tin and compare the interatomic distances in both structures. Why are the distances in gray tin shorter?

4. The outer electronic configuration in Al is $3s^2\,3p^1$. Explain why these valence electrons must be distributed between two zones, since Al has a face-centered cubic structure with four atoms in the face-centered cell. Why must the two zones overlap? Relate the directions of overlap, [110] and [111], to the bonding in Al.

5. If copper in CuO is divalent, why do you think only 2.5 per cent of copper can dissolve in divalent zinc?

6. What is the structure of ordered and disordered $CuAu_3$? Deduce the answer from the discussion of the copper-gold system in this chapter.

7. Assume that ordered structures having the composition Cu_7Au and Cu_3Au_5 were possible. Suggest probable ordered structures for these two alloys consistent with retaining high symmetry. Specifically, propose structures that belong to the cubic, hexagonal, and tetragonal systems containing not more than two formula weights per cell.

8. Calculate the electron:atom ratios of the following intermediate phases: Cu_3Ga, $NiAl$, Cu_9In_4, $Cu_{31}Si_8$, $CuZn_3$. Classify these phases, assuming that they are Hume-Rothery phases.

9. Classify the following Hume-Rothery phases: $Na_{31}Pb_8$, $Cu_7Zr_4Al_2$, and Cu_3Ge.

10. Calculate the electron:atom ratios of various Laves phases listed in the text. What conclusions can you draw about the importance of this ratio in determining the stability of these phases?

11. The Laves phases are not known to exhibit polymorphism. Since their structures are based on closest packings, why do you suppose this is so?

12. Look up the paper by Frank and Kasper describing the 12-, 14-, 15-, and 16-coordinated atom groups in transition-metal alloys [*Acta Cryst.*, vol. 11 (1958), p. 184]. Why is the 12-coordinated icosahedron not possible in closest packings in which the CN is also 12? What are the simple geometrical relations between the other coordination polyhedra?

13. The nitrogen atoms in Mn_4N are in random interstitial solid solution. If the structure were to order, what would become of the symmetry of Mn_4N?

14. Relate the three structures of austenite, martensite, and ferrite according to the relative stabilities of the carbon atoms in the available interstitial sites.

12

Properties of semiconductors

The importance of semiconductors to modern technology is already well known to the reader. The utilization of semiconductors in radios, welders, solar batteries, and many, many more devices has stimulated intensive research efforts to understand their properties better. It is usually the case that the result of a particular measurement depends on several characteristics of the crystal being investigated. In order to determine an individual characteristic, therefore, it is often necessary to measure two or more properties that have this trait in common. For example, the density of charge carriers in a crystal is best determined by measuring the conductivity and the Hall effect of a semiconductor, because both depend on the carrier density and mobility. A number of interrelations between electrical and optical properties of semiconductors and their dependence on the individual characteristics of different crystals are considered in this chapter. These interrelations are of interest not only for understanding semiconductor properties but also because they are directly utilized in many semiconductor devices, some of which are also mentioned below.

It will become evident in the discussions of this and the next chapter that most semiconductor properties are structure-sensitive and highly dependent on the nature and amount of imperfections present in a crystal. In fact, impurities and other imperfections, even when present in trace amounts, can seriously complicate the interpretation of many measurements. Following the discovery of transistors in 1949, procedures for growing very pure crystals of silicon and germanium have been developed. Consequently, much of the understanding of semiconductor properties has come directly from the study of the properties of these two crystals. Such studies have shown how one can take advantage of the modifying effect of imperfections in a beneficial way. For example, an otherwise nonconducting crystal can be converted to a semiconductor by incorporating certain impurities in the crystal, a process popularly called *doping*. This role of impurities can be best understood by considering what their inclusion does to the allowed-energy values that electrons can have in a crystal. Before proceeding with this discussion, therefore, some of the energy relations are briefly considered below.

Band theory

Energy bands. According to the zone theory discussed in Chapter 10, the presence of a periodic potential field in a crystal leads to zones of allowed- and forbidden-energy values that electrons can have. The resulting energy distribution along some crystallographic direction through a row of atoms is shown in Fig. 1. The periodically varying potential energy of an electron is determined by the periodic field. Because it is inversely related to the binding energy, the potential energy exhibits minima at the atomic nuclei and maxima halfway between them. The total energy that the $1s$, $2s$, $2p$, etc., electrons can have is shown by the shaded regions in Fig. 1. (The relative values of these energies can be compared with those shown in Fig. 9 of Chapter 9 at the equilibrium interatomic separation.) An interesting feature of this diagram is that the inner electrons appear to have allowed energies that are localized

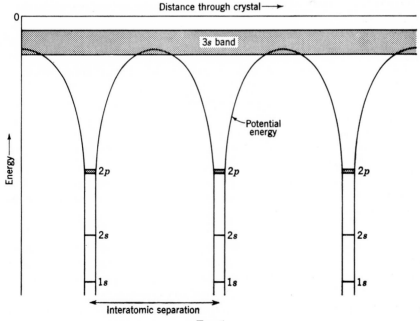

Fig. 1

in the vicinity of the nuclei. This is physically reasonable because the inner electrons are very tightly bound to the nuclei. According to quantum mechanics, their wave functions are concentrated near the nuclei so that the probability of finding an inner electron farther away decreases markedly outside the regions indicated. By comparison, the 3s electrons do not appear to be localized at any particular atom in Fig. 1. This is the case, for example, in sodium metal where the 3s wave functions of adjacent atoms overlap to such an extent that the allowed-energy values for these electrons are virtually independent of position in the crystal and constitute a continuous *band* extending through the entire crystal. It follows from the above that the energy-band model shown in Fig. 1 is particularly useful in discussing the energies that electrons can have in different parts of a crystal. Because the inner electrons do not play an important role in determining the properties of semiconductors, they are usually omitted in such models. In nonmetals, the broad bands that lie above the inner electron bands can be divided into two groups: the *valence bands*, whose available states are occupied by valence electrons, and the *conduction bands*, whose available states are occupied by electrons that can participate in electrical conductivity. As discussed in previous chapters, these bands are separated by *forbidden bands* of energy in all nonmetals. Moreover, at the absolute zero of temperature, the available states in the valence bands of a nonmetal are completely filled while those in the conduction bands are completely empty. At higher temperatures, transitions between states in the highest filled valence band and the lowest empty conduction band are possible. Hence these two bands and the forbidden band that separates them are of particular interest and are the only ones normally considered in using the band model.

The energy corresponding to the highest and lowest energy level available in a band depends on direction in a crystal, as shown in Chapter 10. It will be recalled from the discussion of Brillouin zones that the most convenient way of relating energy to direction is to express it as a function of the wave vector **k**. For example, the variation of the allowed energies at the top of the valence band and bottom of the conduction band along [100] in a silicon crystal is shown in Fig. 2A. Now, in order to show this variation along all possible directions, it is necessary to construct a three-dimensional model. Because such drawings are relatively difficult to construct and to interpret, it is more usual to consider the variations along a particular direction in the crystal. For most of the discussions in this book it is sufficient to consider the highest allowed energy in the uppermost valence band and the lowest allowed energy in the lowermost conduction band. Consequently, the energy-band models used in this chapter will not show the detailed variations in Fig. 2A. Assuming

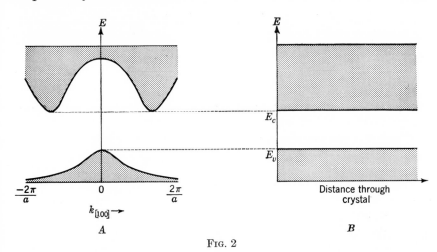

E_c

E_v

$-\dfrac{2\pi}{a}$ 0 $\dfrac{2\pi}{a}$

Distance through crystal

$k_{[100]} \longrightarrow$

A

B

Fig. 2

that the width of the forbidden band in silicon is correctly defined by the maxima and minima along [100] in Fig. 2*A*, then the model used from now on appears as shown in Fig. 2*B*.

Intrinsic semiconductors. The energy-band model of crystals lends itself particularly well to the discussion of their electrical properties. It has already been shown that a crystal composed of N primitive unit cells has $2N$ energy states available in each allowed band. If the primitive unit cell contains an odd number of electrons, it is not possible to fill at least one of the allowed bands and the crystal must be a conductor. On the other hand, when the primitive unit cell contains an even number of electrons, the crystal is a conductor only if the valence and conduction bands are not separated from each other by a forbidden-energy band. When the bands are separated by a forbidden-energy region, then the crystal is an insulator. It is possible, however, that, when the energy gap is sufficiently narrow, some of the electrons occupying states at the top of the valence band may gain sufficient thermal energy to transfer to empty states in the conduction band. Since such electrons can contribute to conductivity, the crystal then becomes a semiconductor. Because the temperature at which conductivity becomes appreciable depends on the width of the forbidden band which, in turn, depends on the crystal structure, such crystals are properly called *intrinsic* semiconductors. The difference between the electrical properties of a metal and a semiconductor is due to the difference in the density of conduction (free) electrons present in each. Moreover, the density of conduction electrons in a semiconductor increases with temperature so that its conductivity also increases. Conversely, the free-electron density in a metal changes little with increasing temperature while its conductivity decreases because of the increased thermal scattering.

The difference between an insulator and an intrinsic semiconductor can be described quantitatively with the aid of the Fermi distribution function

$$f(E) = \frac{1}{e^{(E-E_0)/kT} + 1} \tag{1}$$

which expresses the probability for the occupation of a quantum state whose energy is E. As discussed in Chapter 10, this function can be used to determine the occupation of quantum states having energy values that are larger or smaller than the Fermi energy E_0. At the absolute zero of temperature, $f(E) = 1$ for $E < E_0$ and $f(E) = 0$ for $E > E_0$. Since the number of available states in the valence band of an insulator just equals the number of valence electrons present, all these states are occupied at absolute zero so that E_0 must be greater than the energy of the uppermost state in the valence band, E_v. Similarly, because the conduction band is completely empty at absolute zero, the Fermi energy must be less than the lowest allowed energy in the conduction band, E_c. It follows from this discussion that the Fermi energy of an insulator has a value that lies somewhere in the forbidden-energy region. Its exact position in the forbidden band depends on temperature in a way that is considered next.

The probability that the quantum states at the bottom of the conduction band are occupied by an electron can be determined by substituting E_c for the energy in (1). Similarly, the probability that the quantum states at the top of the valence band are occupied can be determined by substituting E_v for the energy in (1). For simplicity of argument, assume that only electrons occupying quantum states at the top of the valence band can gain sufficient thermal energy to transfer to states at the bottom of the conduction band. If there are N such electrons per unit volume in the crystal at absolute zero, then the density of occupied states in the conduction band, N_c, at some other temperature is given by

$$N_c = N(E_c) = N f(E_c) = \frac{N}{e^{(E_c-E_0)/kT} + 1}. \tag{2}$$

The density of states of energy E_v that remain occupied in the valence band is given by

$$N(E_v) = N f(E_v) = \frac{N}{e^{(E_v-E_0)/kT} + 1}. \tag{3}$$

The density of unoccupied states of energy E_v in the valence band, N_v. can then be determined by subtracting (3) from N.

$$N_v = N - \frac{N}{e^{(E_v-E_0)/kT} + 1}. \tag{4}$$

But the number of empty states in the valence band must equal the number of occupied states in the conduction band, so that in an intrinsic semiconductor

$$N_c = N_v$$

$$\frac{N}{e^{(E_c - E_0)/kT} + 1} = N\left[1 - \frac{1}{e^{(E_v - E_0)/kT} + 1}\right]. \tag{5}$$

After dividing both sides of (5) by N and clearing fractions, it follows that

$$e^{(E_v - E_0)/kT} + 1 = [e^{(E_v - E_0)/kT} + 1 - 1][e^{(E_c - E_0)/kT} + 1]$$
$$= e^{(E_v + E_c - 2E_0)/kT} + e^{(E_v - E_0)/kT} \tag{6}$$

and after canceling like terms on both sides of the equal sign

$$1 = e^{(E_v + E_c - 2E_0)/kT}. \tag{7}$$

Taking natural logarithms of both sides in (7),

$$\ln 1 = 0 = \frac{E_v + E_c - 2E_0}{kT} \tag{8}$$

and

$$E_0 = \tfrac{1}{2}(E_v + E_c). \tag{9}$$

According to this analysis, the Fermi energy lies halfway between the top of the valence band and the bottom of the conduction band in an

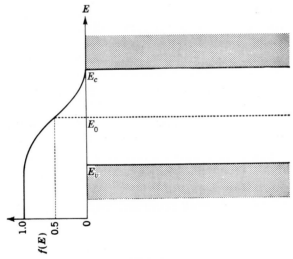

Fɪɢ. 3

intrinsic semiconductor, as shown in Fig. 3. It should be realized that the above analysis is not rigorous because it was assumed that the electrons undergo transitions only from the quantum states of energy E_v to those of energy E_c. In real crystals, of course, transitions are possible between other quantum states also. Although it is not shown here, it turns out that the result obtained in (9) is not appreciably altered if these other transitions are also taken into account. Note, however, that only electrons whose energies differ from E_0 by $\sim kT$ can undergo such transitions.

When all the quantum states in a band are taken into account, then (2) must be altered to include these other states. In such a case, it is convenient to define the number of conduction electrons per unit volume as the *effective* density of states in the conduction band, n, by

$$n = \int_{E_c}^{\infty} N(E) \, dE = \int_{E_c}^{\infty} S(E) \, f(E) \, dE. \tag{10}$$

Assuming that the conduction electrons are like the free electrons in a metal, it is possible to use relation (44) of Chapter 10 to determine the density of available states in the conduction band.

$$S(E) = \frac{8\pi m}{h^3} \sqrt{2m(E - E_c)} \tag{11}$$

where $E - E_c$ is the kinetic energy of a conduction electron. For $(E_c - E_0) \gtrsim 4kT$ the Fermi distribution function (1) can be approximated by

$$f(E) \sim e^{-(E-E_0)/kT} \tag{12}$$

so that, on substituting relations (11) and (12) for $S(E)$ and $f(E)$ in (10),

$$n = \frac{8\pi m}{h^3} \sqrt{2m} \, e^{E_0/kT} \int_{E_c}^{\infty} (E - E_c)^{\frac{1}{2}} e^{-E/kT} \, dE. \tag{13}$$

Multiplying the right side of (13) by $\sqrt{kT/kT} \; e^{-E_c/kT} e^{E_c/kT} = 1$,

$$n = \frac{8\pi m}{h^3} \sqrt{2mkT} \, e^{(E_0-E_c)/kT} \int_{E_c}^{\infty} \left(\frac{E - E_c}{kT} \right)^{\frac{1}{2}} e^{-(E-E_c)/kT} \, dE. \tag{14}$$

It is convenient to change the variables at this point in the calculation of the effective density of states in the conduction band. Let $z = (E - E_c)/kT$ and $dz = (1/kT) \, dE$. Making this substitution in (14), note that the lower limit of integration is now zero because $z = 0$ when $E = E_c$ and

$$
\begin{aligned}
n &= \frac{8\pi mkT}{h^3} \sqrt{2mkT} \, e^{(E_0-E_c)/kT} \int_0^{\infty} z^{\frac{1}{2}} e^{-z} \, dz \\
&= \frac{8\pi mkT}{h^3} \sqrt{2mkT} \, e^{(E_0-E_c)/kT} \left(\frac{\pi}{4} \right)^{\frac{1}{2}} \\
&= 2.52 \times 10^{19} \, e^{(E_0-E_c)/kT} \quad \text{(number of electrons/cm}^3\text{)} \tag{15}
\end{aligned}
$$

at room temperature ($\sim 300°$K).

The meaning of (15) is that the number of electrons occupying quantum states lying in the conduction band is equal to a constant times the probability that these states are occupied, since $f(E_c) \sim e^{-(E_c-E_0)/kT}$ according to (12). Note that the above calculations were carried out on the assumption that all the conduction electrons in a semiconductor were like the free electrons of a metal. Actually this is not the case, and a more complete analysis shows that an additional term must be included to allow for possible interactions between electrons and the periodic potential of the crystal structure. It is convenient to lump this additional term with the mass of the electron m to give a single new term m^*, called the *effective mass* of an electron. The effective mass is very nearly the same as the normal electron mass for a really free electron but becomes considerably larger when the electron occupies a quantum state lying near the edge of a band. In fact, it is possible for the effective mass to become negative. This is the case, for example, when Bragg reflection of a conduction electron occurs in the presence of an external field so that an increase in the electron's energy increases its velocity in a direction opposite to the applied field direction. Although not specifically employed in Chapter 10, the effective-mass concept is useful in explaining the conductivity in transition metals for this reason. Because most of the discussions in this chapter deal with quantum states lying near the band edges, the effective mass rather than the real electron mass is used in many equations. It turns out, moreover, that when the effective mass m^* is substituted for m in (14), it has the correct form. Note that this substitution, however, changes the value of the constant in (15) which is different, therefore, for different crystals.

Because the Fermi energy of an intrinsic semiconductor can be assumed to lie halfway in the forbidden-energy band, it is convenient to define the width of this band, or the so-called *energy gap*, by

$$E_g = 2(E_c - E_0) = 2(E_0 - E_v). \tag{16}$$

Strictly speaking, this relation is valid only when the effective masses of electrons in the conduction and valence bands are exactly the same. Nevertheless, this relation is quite useful in the determination of the energy-gap width in a semiconductor. Substituting (16) in the exponent of (15),

$$n = Ce^{-E_g/2kT} \tag{17}$$

and

$$\ln n = \ln C - \frac{E_g}{2kT}.$$

Figure 4 shows a plot of $\ln n$ as a function of reciprocal temperature. As can be seen in this plot, the width of the energy gap can be determined directly whenever the effective density of conduction electrons at several temperatures is known. Moreover, it is possible to determine the value of C by extrapolation to $1/T = 0$. This extrapolated value can then be used to calculate the average effective mass of the electrons.

Extrinsic semiconductors. In the previous section it has been tacitly assumed that only the electrons occupying quantum states in the valence band can transfer to states lying in the conduction band. Insofar as lower-lying energy bands are concerned, this assumption is valid because excessively large energies are required to free an electron lying in the inner shells of an atom. However, crystals are never perfect and usually contain some foreign atoms which may be present in substitutional or interstitial solid solution. These atoms have valence electrons

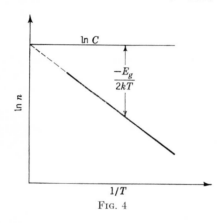

FIG. 4

which are bound to their nucleus by forces differing from those binding such electrons in the other atoms. In terms of the band model, this means that there are quantum states present in the crystal which differ in energy from those shown in Fig. 3. If the electrons occupying these quantum states can contribute to conductivity in a crystal, then such a crystal is called an *extrinsic semiconductor*. Technological developments in recent years have enabled the growth of rather pure crystals of germanium and silicon containing known amounts of impurity atoms of selected types. Since the impurity atoms enter these crystals in substitutional solid solution, their effect on the band model is easily understood.

Both germanium and silicon atoms have four valence electrons, and each forms four electron-pair bonds in the diamond structure described in the next chapter. If the substitutional impurity atoms have five or more valence electrons, they are said to "donate" excess electrons to the crystal because only four of their electrons are required in bond formation. The energy of these so-called *donor states* is usually somewhat less than the energy of the states at the bottom of the conduction band, as shown in Fig. 5A. Conversely, if the impurity atoms have three or less valence electrons, they can "accept" electrons. The energy of these so-called *acceptor states* is usually slightly greater than that of the quantum states at the top of the valence band, as shown in Fig. 5B. In this connection it should be noted that donor or acceptor atoms are spatially localized; that is, the atoms occupy certain atomic sites in the structure. Accordingly, their quantum states in the energy-band model are also spatially localized.   Usually the horizontal axis in energy-band model representations like those shown in Fig. 5 represents some direction in a crystal. It is conventional, therefore, to indicate these quantum states by short dashes in order to distinguish them from, say, the valence band which is continuous throughout the crystal.   It is for this reason also that donor and acceptor states are frequently called *localized states*.

The energy level of a donor state depends on the energy required to remove the excess electron from the impurity atom, similar to the

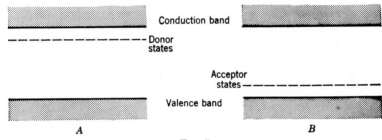

FIG. 5

ionization of an atom in a gas.   By analogy to equation (20) in Chapter 9, these energy levels are given by

$$E_n = \frac{2\pi^2 m e^4}{n^2 h^2 \kappa_e^2} \tag{18}$$

where κ_e is the dielectric constant in the crystal and is equivalent to $1/Z$ for the isolated atom.   ($\kappa_e = 15.8$ for Ge and 11.7 for Si.)   For $n = 1$ this equation gives a value of approximately 0.05 eV for the ionization energy of a donor atom in germanium.   When calculating ionization energies in a crystal, however, it is necessary to replace m in (18) by the effective mass of a conduction electron.   If the correct effective-mass value is substituted for m in (18), this value decreases by almost a factor of 5, so that the correct ionization energy is approximately 0.01 eV. Since this is the energy required to ionize an electron from the donor states to the conduction states, it means that the donor states lie approximately 0.01 eV below the bottom of the conduction band in Fig. 5A. Similar arguments lead to the result that the acceptor states lie approximately 0.01 eV above the top of the valence band.   Experimental values for donors in germanium give 0.0127, 0.0120, and 0.0097 eV for P^{+5}, As^{+5}, and Sb^{+5}, respectively.   Experimental values for acceptors in germanium give 0.0104, 0.0102, 0.0108, and 0.0112 eV for B^{+3}, Al^{+3}, Ga^{+3}, and In^{+3}, respectively.

As in the case of an intrinsic semiconductor, the relative occupation of the various quantum states at any temperature is predicted by the Fermi distribution function.   In the case of an extrinsic semiconductor containing donor atoms only, the Fermi energy must lie above the donor states and below the conduction states at absolute zero. At a slightly higher temperature, some of the electrons in the donor states may be ionized to the conduction band. The density of electrons occupying quantum states in the conduction band n is given by (14). This number must be exactly equal to the number of vacant or ionized donor states. Defining n_d as the number of donor states per unit volume, the number of vacant donor states is given by

$$
\begin{aligned}
n_d - n_d\, f(E_d) &= n_d \left[1 - \frac{1}{e^{(E_d-E_0)/kT} + 1} \right] \\
&= n_d \left[\frac{e^{(E_d-E_0)/kT} + 1 - 1}{e^{(E_d-E_0)/kT} + 1} \right] \\
&\simeq n_d e^{(E_d-E_0)/kT}
\end{aligned}
\tag{19}
$$

when $E_d - E_0 \lesssim -4kT$, that is, when E_0 lies more than a few kT above the donor states. Equating the number of occupied conduction states (14) to the number of empty donor states (19),

$$
2 \left(\frac{2\pi m^* kT}{h^2} \right)^{\frac{3}{2}} e^{(E_0-E_c)/kT} = n_d e^{(E_d-E_0)/kT}.
\tag{20}
$$

After rearranging the terms in (20) and taking natural logarithms of both sides,

$$
\frac{2E_0 - E_c - E_d}{kT} = \ln \frac{n_d}{2(2\pi m^* kT/h^2)^{\frac{3}{2}}}
$$

and

$$
E_0 = \tfrac{1}{2}(E_c + E_d) + \frac{kT}{2} \ln \frac{n_d}{2(2\pi m^* kT/h^2)^{\frac{3}{2}}}.
\tag{21}
$$

It can be seen in (21) that the Fermi energy lies halfway between the donor states and the bottom of the conduction band at absolute zero. Since the argument of the logarithm is a fraction, the second term in (21) is negative and the value of E_0 decreases as T increases. Note, however, that when E_0 drops to a value that does not lie more than a few kT above the donor states, then the approximation made in deriving (19) is no longer valid.

So far in this discussion, the electrons occupying quantum states in the valence band have been ignored. As the temperature increases, however, the number of valence electrons that can transfer to quantum states in the conduction band increases, as described in the preceding section. Since there is a finite number of donor electrons and a much larger number of valence electrons in a crystal, at some temperature the number of valence electrons occupying quantum states in the conduction band becomes predominant and the crystal becomes an intrinsic semiconductor. At this temperature, therefore, the Fermi energy lies approximately halfway between the top of the valence band and the bottom of the conduction band.

If a crystal contains predominantly acceptor impurity atoms (Fig. 5*B*), the electrons at the top of the valence band require relatively little energy to transfer to the unoccupied acceptor sites. Consequently, as the temperature increases from absolute zero, the Fermi energy moves from a position halfway between acceptor states and the top of the valence band to a position halfway in the energy gap, as the crystal enters the intrinsic temperature range. Most crystals, of course, contain both donors and acceptors. Suppose that a crystal is grown containing an excess of donor atoms; then the smaller number of acceptor states are first occupied by electrons from the donor atoms rather than by electrons transferring from states in the valence band. At absolute zero, all the states in the valence band are filled. Similarly, all the acceptor states are filled by donor electrons, as far as possible. At a higher temperature, the donors become ionized and the donor electrons transfer to empty quantum states in the conduction band. The number of effective electrons at this temperature, therefore, is determined by the number of donor atoms less the number of acceptor atoms present. When the temperature is sufficiently high to allow most of the electrons occupying acceptor states to transfer to states lying in the conduction band, then the semiconductor is very near to its intrinsic range. Nevertheless, such a crystal has a higher density of occupied states in the conduction band than of empty states in the valence band at all temperatures, except at or very close to absolute zero. This excess is equal to the difference in the densities of donor and acceptor atoms present. The reverse distribution obtains, of course, when a crystal contains more acceptor than donor atoms. The conductivity in both kinds of crystals is considered next.

Conductivity

It has been suggested in the previous section that semiconductors can be distinguished from insulators by measuring their conductivity. Conductivity has been defined in Chapter 10 by

$$\sigma = en_c\mu \tag{22}$$

where e is the electronic charge
n_c is the number of charge carriers contributing to conductivity
μ is their mobility.
For a typical germanium crystal at room temperature, n_c is of the order of 2×10^{15} electrons/cm^3, and $\mu = 3600$ cm^2/(volt-sec). Substituting these values in (22) gives a conductivity of approximately 1 mho/cm or a

resistivity of 1 ohm-cm. By comparison, the resistivity of an ideal
insulator, of course, is infinite, and for most actual insulator crystals it
is extremely large ($\sim10^{15}$ ohm-cm). On the other hand, the resistivity
of a typical metal such as aluminum is of the order of 10^{-6} ohm-cm.
This is because the number of free electrons contributing to conductivity
in a metal is of the same order as the number of atoms per cubic centimeter ($\sim10^{22}$) which is approximately 10^7 larger than the number of
conduction electrons in germanium.

Electrons and holes. Under an externally applied electric field, the
free electrons in a crystal gain sufficient additional energy to move into

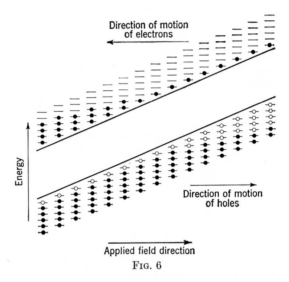

Fig. 6

higher unoccupied quantum states, provided that the Pauli exclusion
principle is not violated thereby. In an intrinsic semiconductor, this
means that the electrons occupying quantum states in the conduction
band move into adjacent unoccupied quantum states and the electrons
remaining in the valence band can move into the quantum states that
have been vacated by the thermal excitation of electrons to the conduction band. These vacated quantum states are usually called *holes*.
When an external electric field is applied, the electrons move in a direction opposite to the direction of the applied field so that it appears that
the holes are moving in the same direction as the applied field. A very
simple way to look at this process is to consider the quantum states near
the positive end of the applied field as having lower energies than those
near the negative end. This has the effect of skewing the band model,
as shown in Fig. 6. If the applied field is positive to the left of Fig. 6
and negative to the right, then the electrons (black dots) move "down-

hill" from right to left, whereas the holes in the valence band (open circles) move "uphill" from left to right.

The electric current produced by the applied field can be determined as follows: Each electron produces a current that is proportional to its charge $-e$ and its velocity v. For comparison purposes, it is convenient to speak of the current density J, or current per unit volume V, defined by

$$J = -\frac{ev}{V}. \tag{23}$$

If there are n electrons per unit volume, the total current density is $\sum_{i=1}^{n} (-e/V)v_i$. In the absence of an applied field, the motions of the electrons are random so that the sum is essentially equal to zero. (An equal number of electrons have positive and negative velocities.) Singling out one electron for consideration, the preceding statement can be written

$$\sum_{i=2}^{n} \frac{-e}{V} v_i + \frac{-e}{V} v_1 = 0$$

$$\sum_{i=2}^{n} \frac{-e}{V} v_i = \frac{e}{V} v_1. \tag{24}$$

The meaning of (24) is that a positively charged electron moving with a velocity v_1 (right side of this relation) produces exactly the same current density that is produced by all the electrons after one of them has been removed. Thus it is evident that a hole behaves like a positively charged electron. As will be seen later, it is frequently convenient to speak of conductivity by holes as distinct from conductivity by electrons. Since conductivity is actually due to the motion of electrons, what is meant by such statements is that electronic conductivity takes place by means of transitions in the conduction band, whereas hole conductivity takes place by transitions in the valence band.

Consider a germanium crystal ($E_g = 0.72$ eV) containing 1 ppm (one part per million) of arsenic atoms in substitutional solid solution. Since the crystal contains approximately 10^{22} Ge atoms/cm³, this means that the impurity density is 10^{16} As atoms/cm³. Arsenic is a donor, and its donor states lie 0.012 eV below the bottom of the conduction band. According to (21), therefore, the Fermi energy lies 0.16 eV below the bottom of the conduction band (see Exercise 2) or 0.148 eV below the donor states. For simplicity, let the energy at the top of the valence band equal zero so that the crystal has the band model shown in Fig. 7.

The density of donor electrons occupying quantum states in the conduction band at room temperature must equal the number of unoccupied donor sites.

$$n = n_d \left[1 - \frac{1}{e^{(E_d - E_0)/kT} + 1} \right]$$
$$= 10^{16} \left[1 - e^{-(E_d - E_0)/kT} \right]$$
$$= 10^{16} \left[1 - e^{-(0.708 - 0.560/0.025)} \right]$$
$$= 10^{16} (1 - 0.0027)$$
$$\simeq 10^{16} \quad \text{(electrons/cm}^3\text{)}. \tag{25}$$

The number of holes in the valence band, p, at room temperature is similarly calculated with the aid of a relation like (15) for holes (see Exercise 4).

$$p = 2.51 \times 10^{19} \, e^{(E_v - E_0)/kT}$$
$$= 2.51 \times 10^{19} \, e^{(0 - 0.56)/0.025}$$
$$\simeq 10^{10} \quad \text{(holes/cm}^3\text{)}. \tag{26}$$

It is clear from the above calculations that the bulk of the conductivity in a germanium crystal doped with 1 ppm of arsenic takes place by electron transitions in the conduction band. Accordingly, such a crystal is called an *n-type semiconductor*, and the electrons are called the *majority carriers* of current and the holes the *minority carriers*. If a crystal is doped with an excess of acceptor-type impurity atoms, so that the holes become the *majority carriers*, it is called a *p-type semiconductor*.

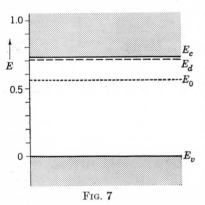

FIG. 7

It should be noted that the product np, that is, the number of effective electrons occupying quantum states in the conduction band times the number of effective holes left in the valence band, is constant at a specific temperature and does not depend on whether the semiconductor is in the intrinsic or extrinsic temperature range. This is so because the product np is independent of the exact position of the Fermi energy E_0. If n and p are determined by equations like (15),

$$np = (2.51 \times 10^{19})e^{(E_0 - E_c)/kT} \times (2.51 \times 10^{19})e^{-(E_0 - E_v)/kT}$$
$$= 6.3 \times 10^{38}e^{-(E_c - E_v)/kT}$$
$$= 6.3 \times 10^{38}e^{-E_g/0.025} \tag{27}$$

at room temperature ($\sim 300°$K).

The temperature dependence of conductivity. The conductivity of a semiconductor now can be expressed by

$$\sigma = en\mu_n + ep\mu_p \tag{28}$$

where n is the density and μ_n the mobility of electrons occupying states in the conduction band, and p is the density and μ_p the mobility of the holes. In an intrinsic semiconductor, the number of electrons occupying states in the conduction band just equals the number of holes or unoccupied states in the valence band so that (28) reduces to (22) with $n_c = 2n = 2p$ and $\mu = \frac{1}{2}(\mu_n + \mu_p)$. Some typical values of these quantities for silicon and germanium at 300°K are given below.

	μ_n	μ_p	$\sigma_{intrinsic}$
Si	15×10^2 cm²/volt-sec	4×10^2 cm²/volt-sec	4×10^{-5} mho/cm
Ge	36×10^2	17×10^2	2×10^{-2}

Accordingly, the conductivity in the intrinsic range can be written

$$\sigma = 2ne\,\tfrac{1}{2}(\mu_n + \mu_p)$$
$$= ne\,(\mu_n + \mu_p). \tag{29}$$

Substituting (15) for n,

$$\sigma = 2.51 \times 10^{19}\,e(\mu_n + \mu_p)e^{-E_g/2kT} \tag{30}$$

where $-E_g = 2(E_0 - E_c)$.

It is clear from this that the energy gap can be determined directly from conductivity measurements by plotting $\ln \sigma$ as a function of $1/T$ since μ varies very slowly with temperature. In practice, such a plot gives only an approximate value, however, because the constant coefficient in (30) actually depends on the effective masses of the two types of carriers. The correct form of (30) is

$$\sigma = 2e\left(\frac{2\pi kT}{h^2}\right)^{\frac{3}{2}} (m_n^* m_p^*)^{\frac{3}{4}}(\mu_n + \mu_p)e^{-E_g/2kT}. \tag{31}$$

The conductivity in the extrinsic range is determined by the density of donor or acceptor states in the crystal and the relative mobilities of the electrons and holes. As shown in the sample calculations in the previous section, the density of the minority carriers in this range is negligibly small. Accordingly, an expression like (31) can be used to determine the temperature dependence of conductivity in the extrinsic region. Figure 8 shows a schematic plot of $\ln \sigma$ as a function of $1/T$ for a typical impurity-containing semiconductor.

Mobility of charge carriers. One of the factors affecting the conductivity of a semiconductor is the mobility of the charge carriers,

Mobility was defined in Chapter 10 as the *average drift velocity per unit electric field* (cm/sec ÷ volts/cm). As might be expected, the average drift velocity is different for the two types of carriers in semiconductors because their mechanisms of motion are different. Figure 9 shows schematically the migration of a free electron and a hole under the influence of an applied field. The free electron moves in a random path between the atoms in a direction opposite to the applied field direction (Fig. 9A), whereas the hole moves in the direction of the applied field by means of discrete electron jumps, as indicated in Fig. 9B. As the electrons move through the crystal, they are scattered by inhomogeneities in the crystal. These inhomogeneities are caused by the following:

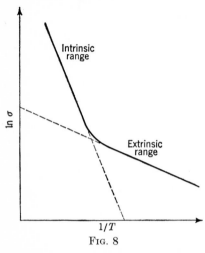

FIG. 8

1. Thermal vibrations of the atoms.
2. Impurity atoms in substitutional solid solution.
3. Interstitial atoms.
4. Other imperfections such as vacancies, dislocations, etc.

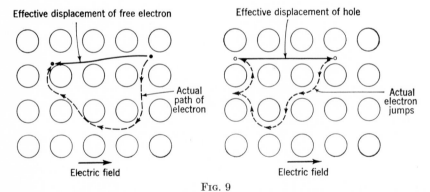

FIG. 9

The time that an electron spends between collisions is called the *mean free time* τ_r. It can be shown that the average drift velocity $\langle v \rangle$ in the direction of the field ε is given by

$$\langle v \rangle = -\frac{e\tau_r}{m}\varepsilon \tag{32}$$

where the minus sign indicates that the velocity vector has an opposite sense to the field vector. Defining the *drift* mobility by

$$\mu = \frac{\langle v \rangle}{-\mathcal{E}} = \frac{e\tau_r}{m} \tag{33}$$

the conductivity (22) can be determined by

$$\sigma = n_c e \mu$$
$$= \frac{n_c e^2 \tau_r}{m}. \tag{34}$$

In carrying out an actual computation, it is necessary to pay strict attention to the units used. Assuming a conductivity of 1 mho/cm, and 10^{16} donor-electrons/cm^3 for an n-type semiconductor,

$$\mu = \frac{\sigma}{n_c e}$$
$$= \frac{1 \ (\text{mho/cm})}{10^{16} \ (\text{cm}^{-3}) \times 1.6 \times 10^{-19} \ (\text{coulomb/sec})}$$
$$= 6.25 \times 10^2 \ (\text{cm}^2/\text{volt-sec}) \tag{35}$$

since 1 amp = 1 coulomb/sec and 1 volt = 1 amp × 1 ohm. Using the value in (35) for the mobility, the mean free time can be determined with the aid of (34).

$$\tau_r = \frac{\mu}{e/m}$$
$$= \frac{6.25 \times 10^2 \ (\text{cm}^2/\text{volt-sec}) \times 300 \ (\text{volts/esvolt})}{4.8 \times 10^{-10} \ (\text{esu})/9.1 \times 10^{-28}(g)}$$
$$= 3.5 \times 10^{-13} \ (\text{sec}). \tag{36}$$

It is also possible to determine the mobility with the aid of the Hall effect. For semiconductors, the Hall constant R is determined by the carrier density n_c (Chapter 10):

$$R = \frac{1}{n_c q} \tag{37}$$

where q is the charge of the carrier whose sign determines the sign of the Hall constant. The relations between the applied electric field $\mathcal{E}$ and magnetic field B are illustrated in Fig. 10. It will be recalled from Chapter 10, equation (53), that

$$\mathcal{E}_y = RJ_x B_z \tag{38}$$

where B_z is the magnetic field strength in the z direction and J_x is the current density along the x direction defined by

$$J_x = n_c q \langle v_x \rangle.$$ (39)

Combining (37), (38), and (39),

$$\mathcal{E}_y = \frac{1}{n_c q} n_c q \langle v_x \rangle B_z$$

$$= \frac{\langle v_x \rangle}{\mathcal{E}_x} \mathcal{E}_x B_z$$

$$= \mu \mathcal{E}_x B_z$$ (40)

so that the mobility can be determined by measuring $\mathcal{E}_y$ when a known $\mathcal{E}_x$ and B_z are applied to the crystal.   Note also in Fig. 10 that it is possible

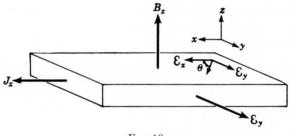

FIG. 10

to use these quantities to define a *Hall angle* θ such that

$$\tan \theta = \frac{\mathcal{E}_y}{\mathcal{E}_x} = \mu B_z.$$ (41)

Thus it is possible to measure the mobility of the charge carriers in a semiconductor by means of the Hall effect, that is, by measuring the so-called Hall angle defined in (41).

As already shown, it is possible to measure the mobility in another way also, namely, by measuring the conductivity.   In fact, the two kinds of measurements can be combined.   Since the Hall constant R is a measure of the carrier density, dividing both sides of (37) by μ gives

$$\frac{R}{u} = \frac{1}{n_c q \mu} = \frac{1}{\sigma}$$

so that $$\mu = R\sigma.$$ (42)

Whether relation (42) or (41) is used to determine the mobility, it should be borne in mind that these procedures determine the mobility of the majority carriers.   In order to determine the respective mobilities of holes and electrons, therefore, it is necessary to make separate measurements on p-type and n-type crystals. Such measurements should be conducted at temperatures corresponding to the extrinsic range of the semiconductors.

Lifetime of minority carriers. The discussion of conductivity so far has ignored the role of minority carriers in extrinsic semiconductors. A crystal containing an excess of, say, donor atoms also contains some acceptor atoms. Some of the n-type impurities *compensate* for the p-type impurities present while the rest contribute conduction electrons, making the crystal an n-type semiconductor. As long as the density of p-type impurities is small relative to the density of n-type impurities, their effect on conductivity can be ignored in many considerations. On the other hand, the role of minority carriers can become important in certain applications of semiconductors, particularly when the mobilities of the two kinds of carriers are quite different. Because of their relatively smaller density, for example, the role of minority carriers is more markedly affected by any imperfections already present in a crystal (or artificially produced). For example, as discussed in later sections, it is possible to inject into a crystal either electrons or holes from external sources. In order properly to understand the resulting phenomena, it becomes necessary to distinguish between the majority and minority carriers of current and the possible interactions between electrons and holes in a semiconductor.

In addition to donor or acceptor impurities, other kinds of imperfections in a crystal can also produce empty quantum states lying in the forbidden-energy band. Not too much is known about the relation between various imperfections, such as interstitial atoms, vacancies, dislocations, etc., and the energies of the quantum states that they introduce. It is possible, nevertheless, to discuss the role that these quantum states have in the conduction process. It is easy to show that these quantum states have definite energies and that they are localized in the crystal so that they contribute so-called *localized energy states*. In an n-type semiconductor, the localized states lying far above the top of the valence band are normally empty. There exists a certain probability, therefore, that a free electron may transfer from a state in the conduction band to such a lower-lying state. Because this state has a lower energy, the transition must be accompanied by the release of energy, usually in the form of a quantum of light or phonon (Fig. 11A). The crystal imperfection, therefore, appears to act as a trap for electrons, and it is common practice to refer to its localized energy state as an *electron trap*. Similarly, a p-type semiconductor can contain *hole traps*, as shown in Fig. 11B. When an imperfection first "captures" a hole and subsequently an electron, it is called a *recombination center* (Fig. 11C). In principle, all imperfections can act as recombination centers. The distinction is

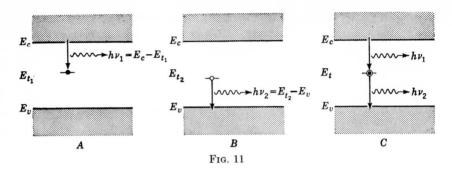

FIG. 11

usually made on the basis of the respective transition probabilities. It is called an electron trap if an imperfection has a larger probability of capturing electrons when empty than of capturing holes when full, and a hole trap when the probabilities are reversed. If the probabilities are nearly the same, it is called a recombination center.

The above transitions can be reversible. For example, an electron that is trapped in an electron trap may be later thermally excited to a quantum state in the conduction band. Similarly, an electron may be excited to a hole trap so that the hole in the valence band is restored. At a particular temperature, therefore, the crystal reaches an equilibrium between the number of filled and empty traps. By comparison, the probability of the recombination of a conduction electron with a hole in the valence band is very small. Now, when an excess of minority carriers is injected into a crystal, the equilibrium between the filled and empty traps is upset. (The way that excess carriers can be introduced in a crystal without disturbing its average charge neutrality is described in a later section.) Suppose that excess holes are injected into an n-type crystal. These holes must wander around the crystal until they can recombine with an electron trapped in an electron trap. The length of time that elapses subsequent to injection and prior to recombination is called the carrier *lifetime* τ. It is important not to confuse this quantity with the mean free time discussed in the previous section.

In a typical crystal, there are usually many more imperfections present at the surface of the crystal than there are in the interior. Consequently, the lifetime of minority carriers, as usually measured, consists of two components, a *bulk* lifetime τ_v and a *surface* lifetime τ_s, related by

$$\frac{1}{\tau} = \frac{1}{\tau_v} + \frac{1}{\tau_s}. \tag{43}$$

The bulk lifetime depends on the number of imperfections present in the crystal's interior and can be altered significantly by varying the purity of the crystal or by stressing the crystal thermally or mechanically. As might be expected, the surface lifetime is very sensitive to the way that the surface has been treated. It can be increased by carefully etching the surface or decreased by abrading it.

Optical properties

Absorption spectrum. Many semiconductors such as Si, Ge, InSb, and others exhibit typical metallic luster when viewed with ordinary

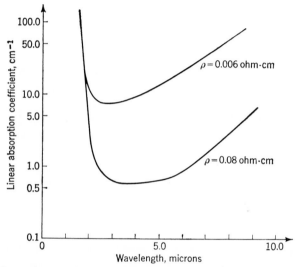

FIG. 12. Absorption coefficients of two n-type germanium crystals at room temperature.

light. When viewed with longer-wavelength infrared radiation, however, the crystals are rendered transparent. Figure 12 shows the variation of the linear absorption coefficient with changes in the wavelength of the incident light used for two germanium crystals. Starting with the longer wavelengths and moving toward the shorter wavelengths (move from right to left in Fig. 12), it is observed that the absorption coefficient decreases, indicating that the crystals become more transparent to shorter-wavelength radiation. This is consistent with the greater energy of the photons of shorter-wavelength radiation ($E = hc/\lambda$). At 2 μ (1 μ = 10^{-6} m), however, the absorption coefficient begins to rise until at approximately 1.7 μ it becomes extremely high. The reason for this abrupt increase in absorption becomes evident when the band model of germanium is considered. The energy of the radiation corresponding to a wavelength of 1.7 μ is 1.15 $\times$ 10^{-12} erg or 0.72 eV, which is the width of the energy gap in germanium. Thus a photon having this energy is capable of exciting an electron occupying a quantum state at the top of the valence band to a quantum state at the bottom of the conduction band. In the process, the energy of the photon is absorbed and the crystal appears to be opaque to radiation of this energy. Still shorter-wavelength radiation also can excite electrons from lower-energy quantum states to other states in the conduction band. The increased number of free electrons thus produced accounts for the metallic luster of germanium, since these electrons can absorb energy by transition to higher-energy quantum states in the conduction band and reradiate it by

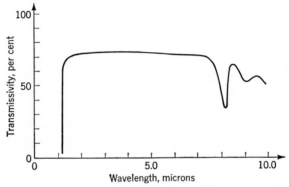

FIG. 13. Transmissivity of polycrystalline *p*-type silicon at room temperature.

transition to unoccupied lower-energy states. (Actually, these transitions take place through electron-phonon interactions because direct transitions are not allowed.) Note that a lower-resistivity germanium crystal has greater absorption at all wavelengths for this reason, as is shown by the two curves in Fig. 12. Lower resistivity, of course, means that there are more conduction electrons present.

The transmission spectrum of a silicon crystal is shown in Fig. 13. Since the energy gap in silicon is 1.09 eV, the transmission drops to zero at about 1.1 μ. Note that there are sharp dips in the transmission values at longer wavelengths. In terms of the energy-band model, this means that electronic transitions take place between quantum states lying in the forbidden-energy region and the conduction band or between states in the valence band and the localized states. The energy values of the localized states can be determined from the values of the wavelengths at which the absorption maxima occur. It can be seen from this discussion that absorption measurements can be used to determine the nature of the band model of semiconductors. Although it is possible to determine the energies of donor or acceptor states by this means, it is necessary to perform the experiments at very low temperatures in order to minimize thermal excitation of the electrons.

Photoconductivity. The increase in the carrier density produced by the irradiation of a semiconductor contributes to the crystal's conductivity. When an electric field is applied to the crystal and radiation of an appropriate wavelength is allowed to fall on it, an increase in its conductivity is observed. This property of *photoconductivity* is utilized in a large number of device applications, the most obvious being simply to use the crystal as a detector of radiation. Since pronounced photoconductivity occurs whenever the crystal is irradiated with radiation having an energy greater than the gap width, various kinds of radiation such as visible light, x-rays, electrons, or nuclear radiation can be detected in this way. Although the general nature of the photoconductive process has been studied extensively, an exact theory of this process has not been developed as yet. Some of the difficulties arise in describing the process whereby an electron excited to a quantum state in the conduction band by the absorption of a photon can recombine with the hole produced in the valence band. As previously stated, the electron and hole do not recombine directly. This is so because the probability for such a transition, measured by the so-called *capture cross section*, is very small ($\sim 10^{-21}$ cm²) as compared with the capture cross section of an imperfection ($\sim 10^{-15}$ cm²). Direct recombination becomes a significant factor, therefore, only when the concentration of free electrons is very high ($\sim 10^{19}/$cm³). Consequently, recombinations usually take place through recombination centers with a rate that depends on the nature of the imperfection, that is, its relative electron and hole affinity. The difference in the mobilities of electrons and holes also affects the recombination process. The description of photoconductivity given below is derived from empirical observations rather than from fundamental principles. Such theories are usually called *phenomenological* theories for this reason.

If the absorption of photons produces f electron-hole pairs per unit time, the increase in the density of electrons and holes is given by

$$\Delta n = f\tau_n \qquad \text{and} \qquad \Delta p = f\tau_p \tag{44}$$

respectively. Here τ is the *effective lifetime* and the subscripts denote the type of carrier. The resulting change in conductivity can be determined with the aid of (28).

$$\begin{aligned} \Delta\sigma &= e\Delta n\mu_n + e\Delta p\mu_p \\ &= ef(\tau_n\mu_n + \tau_p\mu_p). \end{aligned} \tag{45}$$

Some aspects of (45) are worth noting. The relative contribution to the observed conductivity may be different for holes than for electrons. This can be caused by differences in either their relative lifetimes or their mobilities or both. Also it is apparent that, in order to measure an increase in conductivity, $\Delta\sigma$ must be of the same order as the conductivity in the absence of radiation. This means that crystals having small values of *dark conductivity*, for example, certain insulators, generally are better photoconductors.

If F is the total density of free carriers per unit time produced in the crystal, then the photocurrent I_L is given by

$$I_L = eF \frac{\tau}{T_r} \quad \text{(amp)} \tag{46}$$

where T_r is the time spent by an electron in transit between the two electrodes. This is called *transit time*, and it is determined by the interelectrode separation L and the average drift velocity of the carriers according to

$$T_r = \frac{L}{\langle v \rangle} = \frac{L}{\mu \mathcal{E}} \tag{47}$$

where μ is the mobility and $\mathcal{E}$ the applied field. Noting that the applied field (volts/cm) is equal to the applied voltage V divided by the interelectrode separation, it is often more convenient to express (47) as

$$T_r = \frac{L^2}{\mu V}. \tag{48}$$

Note in (46) that the larger the effective lifetime of the carriers relative to the transit time, the larger the photocurrent becomes. Physically, the following events take place. Suppose that the lifetime of the electrons is greater than the lifetime of holes. This means that a hole is quickly trapped while the free electron is swept out of the crystal by the applied field. In order to preserve charge neutrality, another electron is emitted by the negative electrode, the process continuing until the free electron recombines with the hole. Thus, for each photon absorbed, there appears to be more than one free electron contributing to conductivity. This apparent gain can be expressed directly by a *gain factor*

$$G = \frac{\tau}{T_r}. \tag{49}$$

It follows from the definition of the gain factor G in (49) that it can be used as an indication of the efficiency of a photoconductor. According to (47), one way to change the gain is to change the interelectrode separation. Another way to change the gain factor is to change the composition and perfection of the crystal. This is so because the effective lifetime of the charge carriers is inversely proportional to their average velocity $\langle v \rangle$, the number of trapping centers N, and their capture cross section S, according to

$$\tau = \frac{1}{\langle v \rangle SN}. \tag{50}$$

It is possible to combine photoconductivity with the Hall effect to obtain an interesting new effect. The conduction electrons and holes produced on the surface of a suitably irradiated semiconductor tend to diffuse into the bulk of the specimen. When such a crystal is then placed in a transverse magnetic field B, the electrons and holes are deflected through the Hall angle to opposite sides of the crystal. This produces a current which can be measured, and the phenomenon is called the *photoelectromagnetic effect*, frequently abbreviated to PEM effect. If the PEM current I_L is measured simultaneously with the photocurrent I_M, it is possible to obtain a relation for the effective carrier lifetime in terms of both effects.

$$\tau = D \left(\frac{I_M}{\mathcal{E}}\right)^2 \left(\frac{B}{I_L}\right)^2 \tag{51}$$

where D is the diffusion constant for the crystal and $\mathcal{E}$ is the applied field.

This is one example of the way in which different semiconductor properties can be combined to produce new effects. Such combinations are equally useful in the study of a particular property and in the design of a new device. The number of combinations possible is quite large and limited only by man's ingenuity. Some of the more important effects utilized to date are described in the rest of this chapter.

Photovoltaic effect. It is possible to grow a single crystal containing both p-type and n-type regions. The boundary between two such regions is called a *p-n junction* and has some very interesting properties which are described in a later section in this chapter. Consider a crystal composed of two such different regions and a transition zone between them, as shown in Fig. 14. When light is incident on this crystal, electron-hole pairs are produced in the crystal and the electrons diffuse into the n region while the holes diffuse to the p region. In the absence of an externally applied field, the light-induced current develops a *photovoltage* across the crystal, and the phenomenon is called the *photovoltaic effect*. Such a crystal obviously can be used as a battery whose energy is derived from, say, visible light. In order to see how this so-called *photovoltaic cell* functions, some of its important properties are described below.

Suppose that an external voltage V is applied to the crystal in such a way that the p region is biased positive with respect to the n region; then, in the absence of light, the current is given by

$$I = I_0 - I_0 e^{eV/kT} \tag{52}$$

where I_0 is the so-called dark current and the second term represents a current in the reverse direction whose origin is discussed in a later section. If light is now allowed to fall on the crystal, an additional

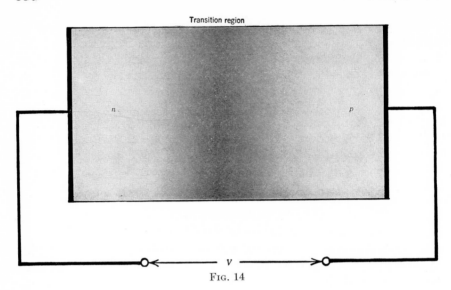

Transition region

Fig. 14

photocurrent I_L is produced, and the total current becomes

$$I = I_L + I_0 - I_0 e^{eV/kT}. \tag{53}$$

When no external voltage is applied to such a crystal, $I = 0$ and the crystal becomes a photovoltaic cell. The voltage developed across the two ends of the crystal then can be determined directly from (53). Denoting this *photovoltage* V

$$I = 0 = I_L + I_0 - I_0 e^{eV/kT}. \tag{54}$$

Rearranging the terms in (54),

$$e^{eV/kT} = \frac{I_0 + I_L}{I_0} \tag{55}$$

and taking natural logarithms of both sides in (55)

$$\frac{eV}{kT} = \ln\left(1 + \frac{I_L}{I_0}\right).$$

This relation can be solved for the photovoltage

$$V = \frac{kT}{e} \ln\left(\frac{I_L}{I_0} + 1\right). \tag{56}$$

For very large light intensities, $I_L/I_0 \gg 1$ so that according to (56) the voltage varies logarithmically with the photocurrent. This is the reason why photovoltaic cells are so useful in ordinary light meters.

Luminescence. An electron that has been excited to the conduction band can return to a lower-lying allowed state provided that such a transition is accompanied by the emission of an appropriate quantum of energy. The number of different transitions possible is determined by the number and kinds of allowed states lying in the forbidden-energy band. Consequently, these phenomena can be rather complicated so that they are not discussed at length in this chapter; however, some of the more important ones are listed below. The term *luminescence* is used to describe the phenomenon whereby a crystal absorbs energy, usually in the form of radiation, and reemits it in the form of visible light. If the crystal emits light simultaneously with its excitation, the process is called *fluorescence;* if it takes 10^{-7} sec or longer to emit its light, then the process is called *phosphorescence* and the crystal is called a *phosphor.* Furthermore, there are two distinct processes for luminescence, both of which require that impurity atoms called *activators* be present in the crystal. In the first process, the incident quantum of energy is absorbed by an activator atom by a transition of one of its electrons from one quantum state to another. When the excited atom returns to its ground state, it loses energy by emitting a photon of energy

$$h\nu = E_{\text{excited}} - E_{\text{ground}}. \tag{57}$$

Because the allowed transitions are characteristic of the energy levels of the activator atoms, this process is called *characteristic luminescence.*

The second process is more complicated. Consider a divalent metal sulfide in which a number of monovalent cations have been substituted for the metal normally present in the crystal. Other ions, called *coactivators*, must be added to the crystal in order to preserve charge neutrality. When an electron-hole pair is produced by an absorbed photon, the hole wanders through the crystal until it is trapped at the site of an activator ion. (The actual process can be pictured as a diffusion of the extra electron belonging to the activator ion until it combines with the newly created hole.) Thus the activator first acts as a hole trap. When the free electron later recombines with the trapped hole, a photon of light is emitted by the crystal. The color (frequency) of the emitted light depends on the nature of the trapping centers present which in turn depends on the type of imperfection introduced. For example, two processes have been suggested to explain why copper-activated ZnS emits blue and green light. (Actually, emission bands having other frequencies are also observed but they are relatively much weaker.) Based on the known ionization energies for copper, it has been shown that the blue light is emitted whenever Cu^{+1} substitutes for Zn^{+2}. On the other hand, in order to explain the strong emission of green light, it is necessary to assume that the substitutional copper is divalent and that the ionized electron combines with interstitial Cu^{+1} ions so that the interstitial copper atoms are neutral.

The above example has been cited merely to illustrate the involved nature of the luminescence process. Without going into further detail, some other ways to produce luminescence in crystals are listed below. When luminescence is produced by either visible light or ultraviolet, infrared, or x-radiation, it is called *photoluminescence*. When a phosphor is irradiated with high-energy electrons that lose their energy by electron-electron collisions in the crystal, the secondary electrons lose their extra energy by recombinations at trapping centers and the process is called *cathodoluminescence*. It is also possible to produce luminescence by exciting the electrons electrically. The phosphor is placed in an insulating medium having a very high dielectric constant and an alternating electric field is applied across the crystal. The very large electric field strength built up inside the phosphor is sufficient to "empty" an activator quantum state. When a free electron recombines with the hole thus produced, light is emitted. This process is called *electroluminescence*, and it has been observed that the emitted light is a function of the voltage and frequency of the applied field. Finally, suppose that a phosphor has been excited by any of the above means at very low temperatures. The decreased thermal energy (velocity) of the electrons retards the luminescence process until the temperature of the crystal is raised so that it appears that the luminescence is thermally produced. This is called *thermoluminescence* and is particularly useful in studying the energy levels of the impurity quantum states because the amount of thermal energy gained by the electrons upon heating the crystal can be measured quite accurately.

Junction properties

Some of the more common properties of individual single-crystal semiconductors have been described above. An additional group of properties become important when the contacts between semiconductor crystals and other crystals are considered. The photovoltaic effect already described is one example of the properties of a semiconductor-semiconductor junction. Another very important one is the transistor effect described at the end of this chapter. Similarly, the properties of metal-semiconductor junctions are very important because such contacts must be made in order to measure the current flowing in a semiconductor, and so forth. The simplest kind of contact to understand is the one formed between two metals. Consequently, metal-metal contacts are briefly considered first.

Metal-metal junctions. The energy-band models of two dissimilar metals at absolute zero are shown in Fig. 15*A*. The work that must be done to remove an electron which is inside the crystal to a distance far removed from the crystal is called the *work function* Φ of that crystal. At absolute zero, this can be represented in the band model by the energy required to raise an electron from the Fermi energy to the so-called *vacuum level*. When these two metals are brought in intimate contact with each other, some of the electrons in metal 1, shown to the left in Fig. 15*A*, occupy quantum states that have larger energies than those of unoccupied states in metal 2. The electrons near the Fermi level in metal 1, therefore, flow into metal 2 until *at equilibrium the Fermi energy in both metals is at the same energy level*. In the process, the surface of metal 2 becomes negatively charged while the surface of metal 1 becomes positively charged, as indicated in Fig. 15*B*. This produces a potential difference between the two metals called the *contact potential V* determined by

$$eV = \Phi_2 - \Phi_1. \tag{58}$$

Since a local electric field cannot exist inside a metal because of its high conductivity, the change in the free-electron distribution in the two metals that produced the potential in (58) takes place on the contact surface between them. Note also that it is possible to measure the difference in the work function of the two metals according to (58) by measuring the contact potential.

When a potential is applied across the metal-metal junction so that a current I flows through it, heat is generated (or absorbed) at the junction in addition to the so-called Joule heat (I^2R) normally produced. The generated heat is proportional to the current, and the phenomenon is called the *Peltier effect*. If current flow from metal 1 to metal 2 generates heat, the corresponding *Peltier coefficient* is said to be positive.

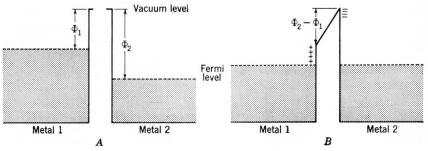

Fig. 15

When the current between these two metals is reversed, the Peltier coefficient changes its sign and the reverse current absorbs heat.

It is possible to take advantage of this effect in still another way. Suppose that the two sides of the junction are maintained at different temperatures. The electrons in the hot metal gain thermal energy so that they occupy higher quantum states. At equilibrium, the Fermi energy is at the same level in both metals so that some of the electrons must flow from the hot metal to the cold one. This produces a *thermoelectric emf* at the contact, and this phenomenon is called the *Seebeck*

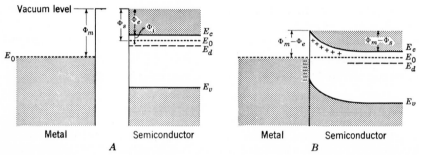

FIG. 16. Energy-level diagrams of metal–*n*-type semiconductor contact with $\Phi_m > \Phi_s$.

A. Before contact is made.
B. After contact is made.

effect. It follows from the above discussion that the thermoelectric emf produced at the metal-metal contact can be used to measure temperature; this is, of course, the explanation of how a thermocouple operates. Similarly, the Peltier effect can be used to heat or cool the metal-metal junction by passing an electric current through it. This is the principle on which the so-called electronic refrigerator is based.

Metal-semiconductor junctions. In the case of a semiconductor, the energy relations are slightly more complex because there are no occupied quantum states whose energy equals E_0. The energy-band model of an *n*-type semiconductor is shown on the right in Fig. 16*A*. The work function of the semiconductor can be construed to consist of two parts: the energy difference between the Fermi energy and the bottom of the conduction band, called the *internal* work function Φ_i, and the work required to remove a free (conduction) electron from the crystal, called the *external* work function Φ_e. Suppose that a metal having a work function Φ_m and an *n*-type semiconductor having a work function $\Phi_s = \Phi_e + \Phi_i$, such that $\Phi_m > \Phi_s$, are brought in intimate contact with each other. If it is assumed that the donor levels in the semiconductor are completely ionized at room temperature, the electrons occupying states in the conduction band of the semiconductor will flow into the metal until *at equilibrium the Fermi energy in both the metal and the semiconductor is at the same energy level.* In the process, the surface of the metal becomes negatively charged and the surface of the semiconductor, which is now depleted of electrons, becomes positively charged. Now, the electrons occupying quantum states in the conduction band came from donors near the surface of the semiconductor crystal, so that the effect of the electron transfer is that an insulating region is produced near the surface of the semiconductor. This layer is called a *barrier layer* for reasons that will become obvious shortly. Since the Fermi energy in both crystals has the same energy, the energy levels in the bulk of the semiconductor are lowered by an amount $\Phi_m - \Phi_s$, as shown in Fig. 16B. Thus the region that has been depleted of electrons represents a potential barrier to further flow of electrons from the semiconductor. This barrier can be expressed in terms of a *diffusion potential* V_D by

$$eV_D = \Phi_m - \Phi_s. \tag{59}$$

Note that the height of the barrier on the metal side is $\Phi_m - \Phi_e$. At room temperature, some of the electrons in the metal gain enough energy to surmount the barrier and enter the semiconductor. Similarly, some of the electrons in the semiconductor may cross over into the metal. At equilibrium, however, the two currents are equal and opposite so that they cancel each other and no net current flows.

Suppose that, after equilibrium has been established, a potential V is applied to the system. (Since the metal is assumed to be a perfect conductor, this has the effect of making the semiconductor more positive or more negative relative to the conductor.) If a positive potential $+V_0$ is applied to the semiconductor, the height of the potential barrier at the contact, for electrons flowing from the semiconductor to the metal, is increased from eV_D to $e(V_D + V_0)$, as shown in Fig. 17A. If a negative potential $-V_0$ is applied, then the height of the barrier decreases to $e(V_D - V_0)$, as shown in Fig. 17C. The height of the potential barrier for electrons flowing from the metal to the semiconductor is not affected by the applied potential and remains $\Phi_m - \Phi_e$, as can be seen in Fig. 17B for the equilibrium situation. This means that the current flowing from the metal to the semiconductor remains the same whereas the current flowing from the semiconductor to the metal depends on the polarity of the applied field. Suppose that the voltage applied to the semiconductor is positive; the current flow from semiconductor to metal is impeded, and it is said that the semiconductor is biased in the direction of *difficult current flow* or that a *reverse bias* has been applied. Conversely, if the applied voltage aids the current flow, then the semiconductor is biased in the direction of *easy current flow*, and it is said that a *forward*

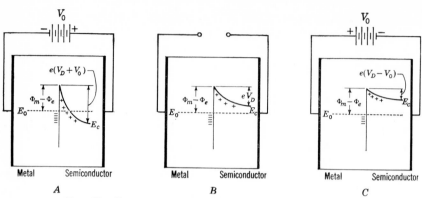

FIG. 17.   Rectifying, metal–*n*-type semiconductor contact.

A. Energy-level diagram for a reverse bias.
B. Energy-level diagram for equilibrium.
C. Energy-level diagram for a forward bias.

bias has been applied.   This metal-semiconductor contact, therefore, acts like a rectifier, and it is called a *rectifying contact*.

The contact behaves differently if the work function of the metal is less than that of the *n*-type semiconductor.   The energy-band models for the case $\Phi_m < \Phi_s$ are shown before contact is made in Fig. 18A and after contact in Fig. 18B.   Since, initially, the Fermi energy in the semiconductor is lower than the Fermi energy in the metal by an amount $\Phi_s - \Phi_m$, electrons flow from the metal into the semiconductor, leaving a positive charge on the metal surface.   These electrons collect on the surface of the semiconductor and form a negative surface charge.   After equilibrium has been established, the negative surface charge on the semiconductor has the effect of depressing the bottom of the conduction band at the contact, as shown in Fig. 18B.   When the potential is applied,

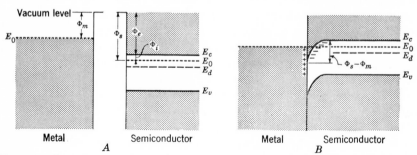

FIG. 18.   Energy-level diagrams of metal–*n*-type semiconductor contact with $\Phi_m < \Phi_s$.

A. Before contact is made.
B. After contact is made.

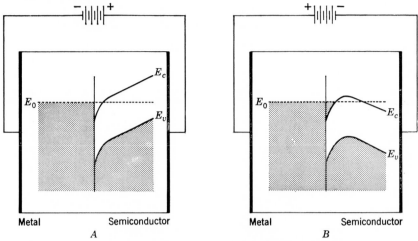

FIG. 19. Ohmic, metal–n-type semiconductor contact.
A. Energy-level diagram when metal is negatively biased.
B. Energy-level diagram when metal is positively biased.

therefore, the energy of the quantum states in the bulk of the semi-conductor is shifted, as shown in Fig. 19. Suppose that the semiconductor is made positive with respect to the metal; then the energy levels shift as shown in Fig. 19*A*, and the current carried by the electrons from the semiconductor to the metal flows "downhill" without encountering an appreciable barrier. When the semiconductor is made negative with respect to the metal (Fig. 19*B*), then the current carried by electrons flowing from the metal to the semiconductor similarly flows "downhill." The current flow in these cases is directly proportional to the applied voltage in accordance with Ohm's law, and the contact is said to be an *ohmic contact* not unlike a metal-metal contact. In making a metal-semiconductor contact, therefore, an ohmic contact can be made by choosing two materials such that $\Phi_m < \Phi_s$, or a rectifying contact can be made by choosing $\Phi_m > \Phi_s$. It should be noted that this condition applies only to n-type semiconductors.

The situation is exactly reversed when a p-type semiconductor forms a contact with a metal. The energy-band models of a metal and p-type semiconductor, having $\Phi_m > \Phi_s$, are shown before contact in Fig. 20*A* and after contact in Fig. 20*B*. As in all cases of two substances in contact, *at equilibrium the Fermi energy in both materials is at the same energy level*. This is the key to understanding all contact phenomena. Since before equilibrium is established the Fermi energy is higher in the semiconductor than in the metal, electrons flow out of the semiconductor into the metal. Because the semiconductor is p-type, the electrons that occupied acceptor states near the crystal's surface move to the metal and leave a positive surface charge on the semiconductor while creating a negative charge on the metal surface. Suppose that a potential is then applied in either direction. The holes in the semiconductor can flow "uphill" into the metal, or, if the field is reversed, the thermally created holes in the metal can flow "uphill" into the semiconductor, without any difficulty. The contact, therefore, is ohmic. On the other hand, if $\Phi_m < \Phi_s$, a barrier layer is formed and the contact acts as a rectifier. It is left to the reader to work out the energy-band model for this case. (See Exercise 19 at the end of this chapter.)

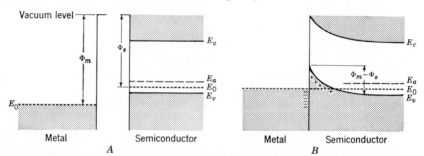

FIG. 20. Energy-level diagrams of metal–p-type semiconductor contact with $\Phi_m > \Phi_s$.

A. Before contact is made.

B. After contact is made.

p-n junctions. The junction between the n-type region and a p-type region in the same semiconductor crystal is called a *p-n junction*. Such a junction has already been encountered in the section describing the photovoltaic effect. There are several ways that such junctions can be prepared. If a crystal is grown from the melt by slowly withdrawing the solidified crystal, the change from p to n type is readily accomplished by suddenly adding an excess of donor impurities to the melt. Alternatively, an *alloy junction* can be formed by placing a suitable metal in contact with a semiconductor, say indium with n-type germanium, and heating them in a furnace until the metal melts. The molten indium dissolves the germanium in contact with it until the melting point of the solution equals the furnace temperature. Upon slow cooling, the molten region of the germanium crystal solidifies and retains the indium in solid solution. This region now is p-type whereas the host crystal was n-type. Alternatively, a semiconductor can be heated in the presence of a donor or acceptor gas so that these atoms can diffuse into part of the crystal to form a *diffusion junction*. Other procedures have also been developed and undoubtedly many more will follow.

Since the density of electrons is larger in the n-type region than in the p-type region, electrons on the n side of the contact diffuse into the p-type region where they recombine with free holes. As this process continues, the p side of the junction becomes negatively charged and the n side becomes positively charged until, at equilibrium, a potential barrier eV_D deters further diffusion. The region on both sides of the contact is said to contain a *space charge* and is usually called the space-charge region or the *transition* region. At equilibrium, the Fermi energy

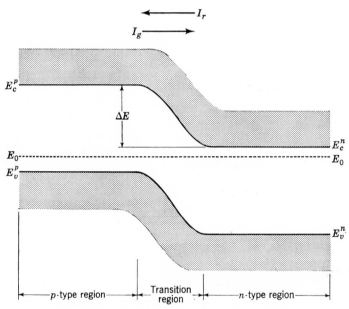

Fig. 21. Energy-level diagram for a p-n junction. (See also Fig. 14.)

has the same value throughout the entire crystal so that the energy-band model looks like Fig. 21. It is clear from this picture that the small number of thermally excited electrons occupying quantum states in the conduction band of the p-type region can flow "downhill" into the n-type region. This produces a thermally generated current I_g which is directly proportional to the number of thermally excited electrons in the p-type region

$$n_p = e^{-(E_c^P - E_0)/kT} \tag{60}$$

where the superscript p denotes the energy values in the p-type region. At the same time, the number of electrons occupying quantum states in the conduction band of the n-type region is $n_n = e^{-(E_c^n - E_0)/kT}$. These electrons can cross over into the p-type region and recombine with free holes there. To do this, however, they must be able to overcome the potential barrier $\Delta E = E_c^p - E_c^n$. This produces a current I_r, shown

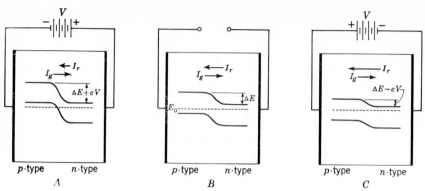

FIG. 22.   *p-n* junction.

A. Energy-level diagram for a reverse bias.
B. Energy-level diagram for equilibrium.
C. Energy-level diagram for a forward bias.

flowing to the left in Fig. 21.   This current is proportional to the number
of electrons that can surmount the energy barrier; that is, it is proportional to

$$e^{-[\Delta E+(E_c^n-E_0)]/kT} \;=\; e^{-(E_c^p-E_0)/kT}. \tag{61}$$

But the right side of (61) is the same as that of (60).   Consequently, at
equilibrium, the current flowing to the right, given by (60), must equal
the current flowing to the left, given by (61).   The equilibrium situation
is indicated by the two arrows drawn at the top of Fig. 21.

Suppose that an external voltage is applied to the junction so that the
p-type region is made even more negative with respect to the *n*-type
region.   The effect on the band model of applying this so-called reverse
bias is shown in Fig. 22A.   If the applied voltage is V, the energy barrier
is increased from ΔE to $\Delta E + eV$† and virtually no electrons can cross
over from the *n*-type region to the *p*-type region and the *recombination*
current I_r is very small.   The so-called *generation* current I_g is not
particularly affected by the reverse bias, because the number of thermally
excited electrons in the *p*-type region is not changed.   The same energy
relations apply to the currents produced by holes.   The potential barrier
due to a reverse bias limits the flow of holes from the *p*-type to the *n*-type
region.   (Remember that holes prefer to go "uphill.")   Thus I_r for
holes is reduced and I_g remains unaffected, since the applied voltage does
not alter the number of thermally generated holes appreciably.

For comparison, the effect on the band model of applying a forward

---

† By convention, $V < 0$ when the *p* side is negative and $V > 0$ when the *p* side is
positive.   Hence, when a reverse bias is applied, the potential barrier is $\Delta E - (-|V|)$
$= \Delta E + V$.

bias is shown in Fig. 22C. The thermal current I_g again is not affected. Because the energy barrier is decreased by the applied voltage, I_r increases according to the Boltzmann distribution law by a factor $e^{eV/kT}$. Since, at equilibrium, I_r equaled I_g, and since the value of I_g is not changed, the increased current can be expressed by

$$I_r = I_g e^{eV/kT}. \tag{62}$$

This relation applies to both the electron and hole currents and is represented by a longer arrow in the direction of I_r in Fig. 22C.

The net current I is equal to the difference between the two currents, $I_r - I_g$, which, according to (62), can be written

$$\begin{aligned} I_r - I_g &= I_g e^{eV/kT} - I_g \\ &= I_g(e^{eV/kT} - 1). \end{aligned} \tag{63}$$

If the combined current due to holes and electrons is represented by the so-called *dark current* I_0, then (63) can be written in its more familiar form†

$$I = I_0(e^{eV/kT} - 1). \tag{64}$$

It should be noted that (64) applies equally well to the case of a reverse bias. In such a case, the magnitude of eV is much larger, but since V is negative, $e^{eV/kT} \ll 1$ when $eV \gtrsim 4kT$. This means that, when a reverse bias is applied, an increase in the applied voltage produces a saturation effect, at which point the current has the constant value $-I_0$.

Transistors. Although a discussion of the device applications of semiconductors has been intentionally avoided in this chapter, the discovery of the transistor has had such a profound influence on semiconductor physics as to place it in a category by itself. For this reason, a brief phenomenological description of the properties of transistors is given below.

Historically, the first transistor was discovered by Bardeen and Brattain in 1949. It was called a *type A* transistor and later became known as a *point-contact* transistor because it consisted of a germanium crystal to which two metal points were connected, as shown in Fig. 23. Suppose that the device shown in Fig. 23 consists of an *n*-type germanium crystal and is to be used as an amplifier. One of the metal points, called the *emitter*, is made positive with respect to the *n*-type crystal (forward bias) and the other point, called the *collector*, is made respectively negative (reverse bias). The emitter injects holes into the crystal (note that these are minority carriers in an *n*-type crystal), and these holes are attracted

---

† Relation (64) is the same as (52) encountered in the discussion of the photovoltaic effect. A minus sign was used in (52) to indicate that the applied voltage caused the current to flow in the opposite direction from the photo-induced current.

to the collector because of its large negative bias. The consequence of injecting a relatively small number of minority carriers is that there is a considerable increase in the current of the collector circuit and a corresponding voltage increase takes place. (Another way to see this is to note that the injection of holes creates a positive field in the space-charge region.) Thus this device acts as a power amplifier with a gain that can range up to a maximum value of about 100.

Shortly after the discovery of the point-contact transistor, Shockley suggested that *p-n* junctions rather than metal-semiconductor junctions could be used in transistors. The resulting *junction transistor* has the

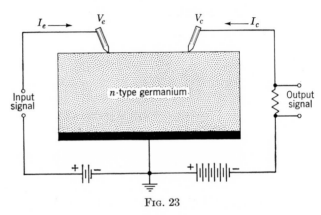

Fig. 23

advantage of greater mechanical rigidity and is capable of attaining greater gains. Consequently, commercial transistors are normally made by arranging two junctions in the sequence *p-n-p* or *n-p-n*. The principles of operation are the same for junction transistors as for point-contact transistors. Consider the *n-p-n* transistor pictured in Fig. 24 with the electrical connections arranged so as to form an amplifier. The *n*-type region on the left is called the *emitter* and contains many more donors than there are acceptors in the *p*-type region, which is called the *base*. Consequently, a much larger current of electrons flows into the base than the number of holes flowing in the reverse direction. The base is usually very narrow so that the electrons can easily diffuse across it into the *n*-type region, to the right, which is called the *collector*. In fact, in a properly made transistor, the collector current very nearly equals the emitter current.

The energy-band model for a junction transistor can be readily constructed by combining properly the energy-band models for two *p-n* junctions (Fig. 22). The resulting band model for an *n-p-n* arrangement is shown in Fig. 25A, when no external fields are applied, and in Fig. 25B, when the left junction (*n-p*) is biased in a forward direction and the *p-n* junction is biased in a reverse direction. Consider first what happens at the emitter-base junction. A relatively small applied voltage ($V > 4kT/e \sim 0.1$ volt) produces a large recombination current, according to (62). The increased number of electrons flowing into the base region reach the second junction without any appreciable loss in number due to recombinations in the p region. In fact, the small voltage applied to the first junction is usually sufficient completely to saturate the base

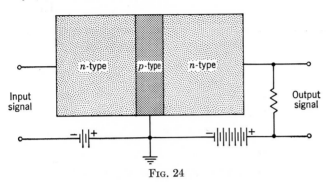

Fig. 24

region, so that no electrons have to be injected by the electrode attached to the base. Since the second junction has a reverse bias, the electrons entering the collector (n-type region in Fig. 25B) are rapidly accelerated to the positive electrode. This results in a considerable voltage and power gain in the collector circuit. Because the forward impedance in the n-p junction is very small, while the reverse impedance in the p-n junction is quite large, the current flow across the first junction controls the amount of current flowing across the second junction. (In the absence of current flow across the n-p junction, a smaller current flows in the collector circuit because of electrons injected into the p-type region from the base electrode.) The increase in the collector current produced by the electron flow across the emitter-base junction, therefore, is the

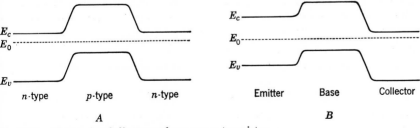

Fig. 25. Energy-level diagrams for a n-p-n transistor.

A. Before external voltages are applied.
B. After a forward bias has been applied to left junction and a reverse bias has been applied to right junction. (See also Fig. 24.)

basis of the amplifier action of this device. The fact that very small voltages and currents are required for their operation is one of the reasons why transistors are preferred over vacuum tubes in many applications. Other reasons are their much smaller size and virtually indefinite useful life. The chief limitation of transistors is their poor performance at elevated temperatures.

Suggestions for supplementary reading

William Shockley, *Electrons and holes in semiconductors* (D. Van Nostrand Company Inc., Princeton, N.J., 1950).

Solid-state electronics issue, *Proc. IRE*, vol. 43 (1955), pp. 1701–1940.

Robert L. Sproull, *Modern physics* (John Wiley & Sons, Inc., New York, 1955), pp 300–315 and 325–379.

Transistor issue, *Proc. IRE*, vol. 45 (1958), pp. 949–1098.

Aldert van der Ziel, *Solid state physical electronics* (Prentice-Hall, Inc., Englewood Cliffs, N.J., 1957).

Suggestions for further reading

Adrianus Dekker, *Solid state physics* (Prentice-Hall, Inc., Englewood Cliffs, N.J., 1957), pp. 305–365.

Charles Kittel, *Introduction to solid state physics*, 2d ed. (John Wiley & Sons, Inc., New York, 1957), pp. 347–401.

Eberhard Spenke, *Elektronische Halbleiter* (Springer-Verlag, Berlin, 1956).

Exercises

1. Assume that the conduction band and the valence band in an insulator both contain 10^{22} quantum states/cm³ and that all states in a band have the same energy. Show that in the intrinsic range $n \simeq 10^{22}\, e^{-E_g/kT}$.

2. Assume that a germanium crystal contains 10^{16} donor atoms/cm³ ($E_d = 0.010$ eV). If the number of conduction electrons is given by equation (15) and the number of vacant donor sites by $10^{16}\,[1 - f(E_c - 0.01)]$, what is the value of $E_c - E_0$?

3. Derive the expression for E_0, for holes, by analogy to the derivation of relation (21).

4. Derive the expression for p by analogy to the derivation of n in equation (15).

5. Calculate E_0 for a germanium crystal containing 10^{16} phosphorus atoms/cm³ at 300°K. (Ionization energy for P is 0.0127 eV.)

6. Calculate E_0 for germanium containing 5×10^{15} gallium atoms/cm³ at 300°K. (Ionization energy for Ga is 0.0108 eV.)

7. In germanium, the intrinsic electron density at 300°K is 2.5×10^{13} cm⁻³. Assume that $\rho = 50$ ohm-cm and that the lowest impurity concentration that can be attained is 10^{12} impurities/cm³. Can Ge be considered to be intrinsic at room temperature? ($E_g = 0.72$ eV.)

8. In silicon, the conduction electron density at 300°K is 1.4×10^{10} cm⁻³. Assume a value for intrinsic conductivity in silicon of 10^{-5} mho/cm and an impurity density of 10^{12} cm⁻³. By analogy to Exercise 7, is this silicon crystal intrinsic at room temperature? ($E_g = 1.09$ eV.)

9. Assuming that intrinsic electron density in Ge at 300°K is 2.5×10^{13} cm^{-3}, what is the value of σ in the intrinsic range? Use the values of mobility given just before equation (29).

10. Using the values given just before equation (29) in the text, what is the intrinsic density of holes in silicon at room temperature?

11. Suppose that a single crystal of germanium weighing 100 g contains 2×10^{-6} g of antimony in a random solid solution. What is the density of Sb atoms in this crystal? (The density of Ge is 5.46 g/cm^3.) Next, suppose that all these atoms are ionized. If the mobility of the electrons at room temperature is 3600 cm^2/volt-sec, what is the conductivity of this crystal? What is the resistance of a prism $2 \times 2 \times 20$ mm cut from this crystal?

12. Using the values given just before equation (29), what is the mean free time of an electron and a hole in germanium at room temperature? In silicon at room temperature?

13. A dip in the transmission curve of silicon doped with boron is observed at liquid helium temperatures. If the dip occurs at a wavelength of 31.2 μ, what is the energy level of a boron impurity?

14. Suppose that the prism-shaped crystal in Exercise 11 is irradiated by a pulse of light such that 1.70×10^{13} photons are absorbed in the Ge crystal. Assuming a *quantum efficiency* of unity, that is, each photon absorbed produces one conduction electron, what happens to the resistance of the crystal following the irradiation?

15. In the absence of an external light source, a potential of 20 volts is placed across the long direction of the prism-shaped Ge crystal in Exercise 11. What is the drift velocity of an electron in such a case? What is the transit time?

16. A CdS crystal, $2 \times 2 \times 0.1$ mm, is used as a photodetector. The electrodes are arranged at the two ends so that the receiving area is 4 mm^2 and the contact area is 0.2 mm^2. Assume that electrons are the current carriers and that their mobility is 100 cm^2/volt-sec and lifetime is 10^{-3} sec. If the crystal is irradiated by violet light ($\lambda = 0.40\ \mu$) of 2 mv/cm^2 intensity, determine the following:

(a) The number of electron-hole pairs generated per second, assuming quantum efficiency of unity.
(b) The increase in the number of carriers in the crystal.
(c) The transit time for electrons in the crystal.
(d) The increase in conductivity in the crystal.
(e) The photocurrent produced if 100 volts are applied to the crystal.
(f) The gain factor.

17. Silicon, opaque when viewed with visible light, becomes transparent when viewed with infrared light. Why is this not true of iron? Quantitatively, what can be inferred about the band model of a crystal which is transparent to visible light? To ultraviolet light?

18. In describing trapping centers with the aid of the band model, the word *deep* state is used to denote a state far from the appropriate band edge, and *shallow* state for a state close to the appropriate band edge. Draw a band model for an *n*-type crystal containing both deep and shallow electron traps. Repeat for deep and shallow hole traps. How would a crystal containing deep and shallow states behave when irradiated with light of various energies?

19. The energy-band model for a *p*-type-semiconductor–metal contact with $\Phi_m < \Phi_s$ is shown in Fig. 20*B*. Make two drawings showing what happens to the energy-band models when a reverse bias and when a forward bias is applied to the contact.

20. The transition region in a *p-n* junction behaves as if it were an insulator that was inserted between a *p*-type and an *n*-type crystal. Using this model, draw an energy-band model showing the conduction and valence bands and the Fermi energy in the three crystals.

21. Describe, in terms of holes acting as the charge carriers, what happens at a *p-n* junction when a reverse bias is applied. Repeat for an applied forward bias.

22. Show a wiring diagram for a photovoltaic cell using a *p-n* junction. Show the polarity of the bias voltages and the direction of the currents.

23. Draw the energy-band diagram for two metals that have different work functions separated by a very thin vacuum gap. Show what happens when a voltage is applied across the gap so as to make the metal with the larger work function (*a*) positive and (*b*) negative.

24. With the aid of the energy-band model, explain the operation of a *p-n-p* transistor.

25. When the voltage gain observed in a point-contact transistor is compared with similar values predicted by theory, the measured value is smaller than the predicted one. Bardeen explained this discrepancy by suggesting that there are traps which are localized along the surface of the crystal. Suggest several physical models to explain the origin of these so-called *surface states*. Why should the existence of surface states decrease the gain when the crystal is used as a transistor?

13

Structure of semiconductors

Some of the most important properties of semiconductors were discussed in the previous chapter. It is the purpose of this chapter to describe the crystal structures of some typical semiconductor crystals and to indicate how their structures are related to the properties of these crystals. The most important role that the structure plays, of course, is in determining the energy-band model of a crystal. Because the band model of all crystals consists of essentially similar energy bands, the extent to which the available quantum states in each band are occupied determines whether a crystal is classified as a conductor, semiconductor, or insulator. In a metal, the available states in at least one band are only partly filled. Conversely, in an insulator, all bands must be either completely filled or completely empty and the uppermost filled band is separated by a forbidden-energy region from the lowermost empty band. A semiconductor is a special case of an insulator in which this energy gap is relatively narrow so that thermally excited electrons can transfer from states near the top of the filled valence band to unoccupied states at the bottom of the conduction band. These so-called conduction electrons can be generated in still another way, namely, when a crystal contains impurity atoms whose valence electrons have quantum states lying in the forbidden-energy band. Since these electrons require less energy to transfer to empty states in the conduction band, the same crystal can become conductive at lower temperatures, provided that it contains such impurity atoms. In fact, it is possible to distinguish between an *extrinsic* temperature range, in which the properties of a semiconductor are modified by the presence of impurities as imperfections in the structure, and an *intrinsic* range, in which the properties of a semiconductor are characteristic of pure ideal structure.

In addition to classifying a compound as a semiconductor, it is frequently of interest to decide whether a particular crystal has a real

potential for possible utilization in device applications. A discussion of
actual devices is considered to lie outside the scope of this book. At best,
such a discussion can be only a status report because new applications of
semiconductor properties are being constantly devised. Nevertheless,
certain fundamental properties are required for virtually all device
applications so that it is possible to assess the likely utility of a semiconductor material. These properties may be inherent in the pure material
or they may be "built" into the semiconductor by proper manufacture
of the crystals. For example, the conductivity of a crystal can be altered
by introducing foreign atoms into the structure either in substitution for
atoms normally present or in the interstitial positions of the normal
structure. Similarly, other kinds of imperfections can be introduced
in the crystal to modify its properties, for example, by creating electron
or hole traps, as discussed in Chapter 12. A few examples of how an
insulator crystal can be converted into a semiconductor by the introduction of imperfections are given in this chapter.

As discussed earlier in this book, many elements and compounds can
adopt more than one crystal structure. Because the structure determines
the band model, it is possible that the same element (or compound)

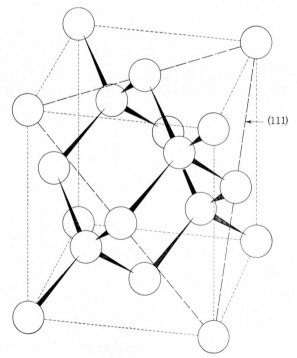

(111)

Fɪɢ. 1.   Bonding model of diamond structure.

behaves like a metal when it crystallizes in one form and like a nonmetal when it adopts another structure, for example, white and gray tin. Similarly, one polymorph may be an insulator and the other a semiconductor, for example, diamond and graphite. In all such cases, the structures of the semiconductor phases are described in this chapter.

The elements

Diamond structure. The elements carbon, silicon, germanium, and tin (gray) all crystallize with an identical crystal structure, the so-called diamond structure shown in Fig. 1. One of the interesting features of this structure is that normal to each a axis there is a glide plane whose glide components are $\dfrac{a}{4} + \dfrac{b}{4} \left(\text{or } \dfrac{b}{4} + \dfrac{c}{4} \text{ or } \dfrac{a}{4} + \dfrac{c}{4} \right)$. In fact, the glide operation is named after this structure the *diamond* glide d. (The space group of diamond is $Fd3m$.) The atoms in Fig. 1 are shown reduced in size so that the details of the structure can be better seen. Each atom is tetrahedrally coordinated by four like atoms, and the structure is most readily pictured as a stacking of sheets composed of continuously linked

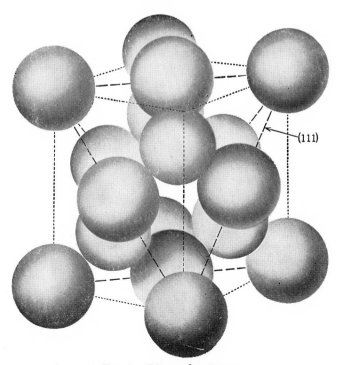

Fig. 2. Diamond structure.

"puckered" hexagonal rings of carbon atoms parallel to the ((111)) planes of the cubic crystal. This can be seen also in the dimensionally accurate drawing shown in Fig. 2, in which the top-front corner atom has been omitted from the drawing. The bonding between the atoms is predominantly covalent in character and is due to sp^3 hybrid formation. The electron-pair bonds are strongest in diamond crystals and weakest in gray tin. This can be inferred directly from the decrease in the width of the forbidden-energy region, as shown below.

	C (diamond)	Si	Ge	Sn (gray)	
Width of energy gap	7.0	1.09	0.72	0.08	eV

There are several ways to express the relation between the width of the forbidden-energy region and the bonding in the diamond structure. The essence of the explanation is that the strength of the forces binding the valence electrons to their respective nuclei decreases in the order diamond $\gg$ silicon $>$ germanium $>$ tin. The weaker this bonding becomes, the more metallike the properties become; that is, the valence electrons tend to resemble free electrons more and more.

It follows from the above that diamond is an insulator at all ordinary temperatures, while silicon, germanium, and gray tin are semiconductors. Germanium is an intrinsic semiconductor at room temperature while gray tin, being unstable at room temperature, is an intrinsic semiconductor below its transformation temperature. It is interesting to note that the unit cell dimensions of these crystals, as indicated below, show a steady increase that is due in part to the weaker binding and in part to the increased effective size of the atoms.

	C (diamond)	Si	Ge	Sn (gray)	
Cell edge a	3.56	5.42	5.62	6.46	Å
Interatomic separation	1.54	2.34	2.44	2.80	Å

Again note the rather abrupt change in going from carbon to silicon, whereas the cell edges and interatomic separations in the three semiconductors are more similar. The short interatomic distance in diamond also explains why diamond has such a high melting point, hardness, and other properties determined by bond strengths.

Of the four elements that crystallize with the diamond structure, tin can also crystallize to form the so-called white-tin structure described briefly in Chapter 11. In fact, this is the structure stable at room temperature, so that gray tin has to be crystallized at slightly lower temperatures. (The transformation temperature for tin is 13.2°C.) Similarly, carbon can crystallize with the diamond structure, the graphite structure, and another modification as well. Actually, carbon is somewhat unusual in that it can also exist in the solid state in a noncrystalline form called amorphous carbon or carbon black.

Graphite structure. The structure of the other common polymorphous form of carbon, graphite, is shown in Fig. 3. This modification of carbon is the stable phase at room temperature, very high pressures and temperatures being required to form diamond. Nevertheless, once formed, diamond is extremely stable at room temperatures also, because the transformation diamond → graphite is a reconstructive transformation involving a change in bond type. The hexagonal structure of graphite is somewhat similar to that of diamond in that it consists of a parallel stacking of layers comprised of carbon atoms forming hexagonal rings. Unlike the puckered ((111)) planes of diamond, the atoms in the (0001) planes of graphite all lie within the same plane. The interatomic distances in the plane are all equal (1.42 Å). The planes, however, are spaced fairly far apart, so that the shortest interatomic distance between the planes is 3.40 Å. This immediately suggests that

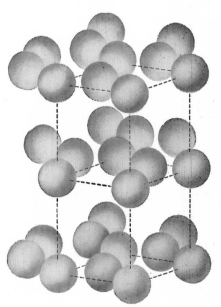

Fig. 3.   Graphite structure.

the bonding within the planes is different from the bonding between atoms of neighboring planes. It is believed that the carbon atoms lying in the (0001) plane form single electron-pair bonds with each other by means of sp^2 hybrids. The fourth electron (the ground state of a carbon atom is $1s^2 2s^2 2p^2$) either resonates between three atoms lying in the same plane (double-bond formation) or else forms a part-time bond with an atom in an adjacent layer. Note in Fig. 3 that only alternate atoms in a ring can do this since only alternate atoms have nearest neighbors in adjacent planes. Accordingly, the translation distance normal to these planes is equal to twice the interplanar spacing. ($c = 6.69$ Å, $a = 2.456$ Å.)

The physical properties of graphite can be readily explained in terms of this structure. Whereas the bonding within a layer is strong, between layers it is quite weak, so that graphite exhibits pronounced basal cleavage. The resulting flakiness of graphite crystals accounts for its usefulness as a lubricant and as the "lead" in pencils. The electrical and magnetic properties of graphite similarly show a marked difference when measured parallel and normal to the (0001) plane. For example, graphite can conduct parallel to the layers but not along the c axis. Careful calculations have shown that the conduction and valence bands actually touch at the corners of the Brillouin zone so that graphite can be considered to be a semiconductor with a vanishing energy gap along certain directions of the crystal. This metallike behavior is directly related to the resonance of the fourth electron of each carbon atom.

Recently, another modification of carbon has been reported. In this structure, the stacking of graphitelike layers is altered so that three layers are required to complete the stacking sequence along [0001] with the consequence that the hexagonal cell has $a = 2.45$ Å as before, but $c = \frac{3}{2} \times 6.696 = 10.044$ Å. By analogy to closest packings, this sequence is $...ABC...$ whereas the normal graphite sequence is $...AB....$ The third polymorph of carbon, therefore, is directly analogous to the diamond structure after the puckered (111) layers are flattened out and the interplanar separation is increased to 3.35 Å. For reasons that will become apparent below, it is sometimes convenient to choose a primitive rhombohedral cell to describe this form of carbon. ($a = 3.635$ Å and $\alpha = 39.5°$.)

Complex structures. The structures of arsenic, antimony, and bismuth are closely related to the third form of carbon described above. Their primitive rhombohedral cells differ in size as indicated below.

	As	Sb	Bi	C (3-layer graphite)	
Rhombohedral cell edge	4.123	4.498	4.736	3.635	Å
Rhombohedral angle	54.17	57.10	57.24	39.50	deg

The observed increase in the interatomic separations is responsible for the radically different physical properties. The bonding is predominantly covalent although it apparently has a semimetallic nature which increases in importance in the sequence from arsenic to bismuth. (Note again that the metallic nature increases as the interatomic separation increases or, conversely, as the bond strength decreases.) Other, less stable modifications of arsenic, antimony, and bismuth have been reported, but little is known about their properties.

Sulfur and selenium can exist in several polymorphous modifications and in an amorphous state. Basically, their structures consist of rings or chains in which each atom has two nearest neighbors, as predicted by the $8 - N$ rule, which suggests that the bonding is predominantly covalent in character. Orthorhombic sulfur has a large unit cell containing 16 eight-member sulfur rings. The high-temperature form of sulfur is monoclinic and contains forty-eight atoms in a unit cell. The polymorphous modifications of selenium are monoclinic and hexagonal, respectively. Red selenium is monoclinic and a virtual insulator like sulfur. The gray form of selenium has a small but measurable conductivity and can be safely classified as a semiconductor. Tellurium also has a structure composed of tellurium atom chains, and its structure is quite similar to that of gray selenium. The unit cell dimensions of the two crystals are compared below.

	Se (hexagonal)	Te (hexagonal)	
a	4.355	4.447	Å
c	4.949	5.915	Å

The atomic chains spiral about the c axis, and the interatomic distances along the chain direction are 2.32 Å for Se-Se, and 2.86 Å for Te-Te. Although tellurium is properly classified as a semiconductor, it has a very high room-temperature conductivity, only about 10^4 less than that of many metallic conductors.

Intermetallic compounds

General properties. The increased interest in semiconductors has led to the synthesis and study of a large number of crystals deemed suitable to semiconductor applications. Among these, there is a large group of crystals that are composed of two (possibly three) metals or metalloids arranged in a specific crystal structure. Most of these structures are quite simple and are, in fact, isostructural with the structures of entirely unrelated crystals. These so-called *intermetallic compounds* are analogous to other intermediate phases in alloy systems, with the distinction, however, that intermetallic compounds have more nearly covalent than metallic bonding; hence, they are usually semiconductors rather than metallic conductors. It is possible to classify these compounds according to their structure type:

1. *Sphalerite type.* The sphalerite structure (Fig. 4) is a derivative structure of diamond, obtained by replacing alternate carbon atoms with zinc and sulfur atoms, respectively. Consequently, it is a structure adopted by a number of AB-type compounds where A and B may come from the following columns of the periodic table: III-V, II-VI, or I-VII, respectively. Examples are AgSb, HgTe, InSb, CuBr, and InP. (Note that the average valency per atom is 4.)

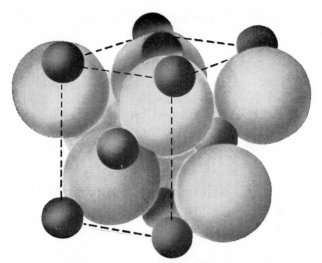

FIG. 4. Sphalerite (ZnS) structure.

2. *Fluorite type.*   These have the same structure as CaF_2 (Fig. 5), which is adopted primarily by AB_2 compounds formed from elements lying in the second and fourth columns of the periodic table.   Examples are Mg_2Si and Mg_2Sn.

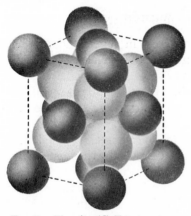

3. *Halite type.*   These have the same structure as NaCl (Fig. 6), which is adopted by AB compounds where A and B may come from columns II, IV, and VI of the periodic table, for example, SnTe, CaTe, and MgSe.

4. *Complex types.*   This category includes all the intermetallic compounds not already classified above. The structures of these compounds differ, depending on their composition. Examples are ZnSb (orthorhombic), Mg_3Sb_2 (hexagonal), and $AgTlTe_2$ (tetragonal).

FIG. 5.   Fluorite (CaF_2) structure.

The bonding in these compounds is predominantly covalent, as determined by the $8 - N$ rule.   Recently, a *semiconducting-bond* mechanism has been postulated which is a mixture of covalent- and metallic-bond types.   According to the proposed mechanism, the s and p shells of one atom must be completely filled (saturated covalent bond) whereas those of the other atom need not be completely filled (unsaturated covalent bond).   Metallic behavior is observed in these compounds only if two atoms having incomplete shells are nearest neighbors. This leads to a modification of the $8 - N$ rule to

$$\frac{n_e}{n_a} + b = 8 \tag{1}$$

where n_e is the number of valence electrons per formula unit; n_a is the number of elements from columns IV, V, VI, or VII of the periodic table; and b is the number of bonds formed by these elements with similar

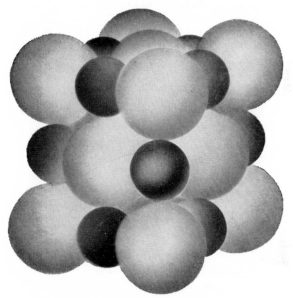

FIG. 6. Halite (NaCl) structure.

atoms. The applicability of this rule to some of the compounds described below is left to the exercises at the end of this chapter.

III-V compounds. The intermetallic compounds comprised of equal numbers of elements from the third and fifth columns of the periodic table are probably the first single group of intermetallic compounds to be considered for semiconductor applications. Certainly, these so-called III-V compounds have been studied most extensively. The reason for this interest is the similarity of these compounds to germanium and silicon, the two semiconductors best understood and most widely used at the present time. The similarity begins with their crystal structures. The III-V compounds crystallize with the sphalerite structure shown in Fig. 4. As can be readily seen, by comparison with Fig. 1, this is a simple derivative structure, derived from the diamond structure by the suppression of certain symmetry operations. Since the coordination number of each atom remains 4 (tetrahedral), it is reasonable to assume that, on an average, each atom also has four valence electrons. This suggests not only that the energy-band model of germanium and silicon is approximately correct for these compounds but also that their other properties should be similar. That this is approximately the case can be seen from the comparison of their crystal data given below.

	Si	AlP	Ge	GaAs	Sn	InSb	
Unit cell edge a	5.42	5.42	5.62	5.63	6.46	6.48	Å
Interatomic separation	2.34	2.34	2.44	2.44	2.80	2.80	Å
Energy gap (300°K)	1.09	2.5(?)	0.72	1.35	0.08	0.17	eV

The three intermetallic compounds listed above were selected because their constituent atoms bracket, in the periodic table, the element preceding them in the above table.

Actually, only the crystallographic dimensions show a very close agreement. There are several possible reasons for this. The primary reason, probably, is that the bonding in the intermetallic compounds has some ionic character because of the higher electronegativity of the elements in the fifth column. The interatomic forces differ in other ways also, but these differences are not too clearly understood. For example, germanium, like diamond, cleaves most readily along the octahedral ((111)) planes. This is a reflection of the layerlike structure of these crystals parallel to the ((111)) planes. Crystals of InSb and AlSb, on the other hand, cleave more readily along dodecahedral ((110)) planes. This may be owing to a relatively stronger electrostatic attraction along [[111]] than along [[110]] in these compounds. Other differences have been observed also. For example, the mobility of electrons in indium antimonide is 80,000 cm²/volt-sec at room temperature. This is such an extremely high value that the Hall effect in these crystals can be readily utilized in device applications. By comparison, the electron mobilities in germanium and silicon are 3600 and 300 cm²/volt-sec at room temperature. These differences, rather than the similarities, are the reason why the intermetallic compounds are being actively studied today.

Silicon carbide. Bluish-green crystals of silicon carbide were first synthesized at the end of the last century. Called carborundum, these crystals were found to have excellent abrasive properties and have been used as abrasives in tremendous quantities ever since. In the late 1920s, O. V. Losev, in Russia, observed that there were at least two kinds of SiC formed and called them Type I and Type II, respectively. He also found that the crystals were electroluminescent, Type I crystals emitting a greenish-blue light, whereas Type II crystals emitted, successively, orange, yellow, green, and violet light as the applied voltage was increased from 6 to 28 volts. Since then, it has been found that silicon carbide has other interesting semiconductor properties as well, and an intensive study of its photoconductivity, rectifying properties, Peltier effect, and other properties has followed. In the process, a large number of polymorphous modifications of SiC have been prepared, of which one is cubic and is called β-SiC while all the others are hexagonal and are commonly called α-SiC. Different values for the energy gap have been measured in both forms, depending on whether electrical conductivity or optical measurements were used. The energy-gap values for the alpha and beta modifications are given below.

	α-SiC (hexagonal)	β-SiC (cubic)	
E_g (electrical)	2.80	1.90	eV
E_g (optical)	6.0–6.2	6.0–6.2	eV

The difference between the values obtained from the two kinds of measurements can be explained by postulating an energy-band model containing "valleys" so that the minimum gap width corresponds to the electrical value and the maximum width exceeds the optical value. Such a picture is consistent with the observed luminescence properties which then can be explained in terms of trapping centers lying at different depths in the forbidden-energy region.

The designation β-SiC was given to the cubic modification because it has the same structure as sphalerite (β-ZnS), shown in Fig. 4. The length of the cubic cell edge is 4.34 Å so that the spacing between closest-packed layers of SiC is 2.512 Å ($= 4.349/\sqrt{3}$). The alpha or hexagonal

Table 1

SiC polytypes

Ramsdell's notation[†]	Hexagonal cell dimensions	
	a	c
4H	3.073 Å	10.053 Å $\approx$ 4 $\times$ 2.512 Å
6H	3.073	15.079 $\approx$ 6 $\times$ 2.512
15R	3.073	37.70 $\approx$ 15 $\times$ 2.512
21R	3.073	52.78 $\approx$ 21 $\times$ 2.512
33R	3.073	82.94 $\approx$ 33 $\times$ 2.512
51R	3.073	128.18 $\approx$ 51 $\times$ 2.512

† The numerical coefficient designates the number of layers in the stacking sequence (see the last column). The letter H denotes that the hexagonal cell is primitive and the letter R signifies that the hexagonal cell is centered, the primitive cell being rhombohedral.

modifications can then be described as different stacking sequences of closest-packed layers. In fact, because the various polymorphs differ only in their stacking period, the term *polytypes* instead of polymorphs has been proposed to describe them.

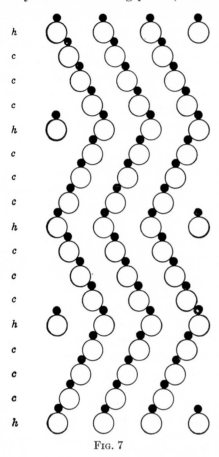

More recently, L. S. Ramsdell has proposed that the different types should be named according to the number of layers needed to complete the stacking sequence. Some of the polytypes and their unit cell dimensions are listed in Table 1. It should be noted that other classification schemes have been proposed also; however, Ramsdell's notation describes the structural features most succinctly. The fact that only one type of closest packing can have cubic symmetry whereas all others have hexagonal symmetry (Chapter 3) explains why only the alpha modification can exist in several polytypes.

The reason why the particular polytypes listed in Table 1 occur and not others is not fully understood. Nevertheless, a certain regularity in their structures can be observed. For example, all the stacking sequences consist of sets of three and two repeat units of which the sets of three occur most frequently. The occurrence of these so-called *zigzag sequences* can be seen best by considering the actual stacking sequences of some of the polytypes shown below.

FIG. 7

6H ...hcchcc...
15R ...hcchchcchchcchc...
33R ...hcchcchcchchcchcchcchchcchcchc...

The zigzag sequence in 6H, clearly, is 33; in 15R it is 32; and in 33R it is 3332. These sequences can be observed in sections parallel to $(11\bar{2}0)$, as shown in Fig. 7 for the 4H polytype. The silicon atoms in this figure are represented by open circles and the carbon atoms by black circles.

The polytype formed most frequently is 6H, with 15R being the second, and 4H the third most common type. The crystals appear to grow by means of the spiral-growth mechanism described in Chapter 7. In fact, spiral-growth steps can be observed quite easily on SiC crystals because the very large c values make the step heights normal to the growing (0001) faces readily visible. A number of investigators have suggested that screw dislocations are also responsible for the formation of the various polytypes. Recently, Mitchell has suggested that all the polytypes can be arranged in three groups whose structures can be derived from the three most common polytypes, 4H, 6H, and 15R, by screw dislocations having Burgers vectors of appropriate length. It turns out, however, that a fairly large number of polytypes remain that do not fit into this scheme. It should be noted that the polytype most commonly formed in the absence of impurities is 6H, whereas polytypes such as 51R and 141R and others occur when the melt contains a relatively large concentration of impurity atoms. This suggests that the impurities aid in the formation of dislocations which, in turn, lead to the formation of the more complex types.

Sulfides

Sulfides can be classified according to their crystal structure into three groups:

1. *Wurtzite and halite types.* These binary sulfides are covalently bonded and usually have stoichiometrically accurate compositions. The wurtzite type frequently can also crystallize with the sphalerite structure; however, the latter modification is not commonly used in semiconductor applications.

2. Other *binary sulfides.* The bonding in these sulfides is usually a mixture of covalent and ionic bonds with the result that it sometimes has a strong metallic character. The sulfides in this category are usually isostructural with simple AB- or AB_2-type compounds.

3. *Complex sulfides.* The sulfides in this category include those with more complicated structures as well as the ternary sulfides. The bonding in these sulfides can range from nearly pure covalent bonds to more complex mixed types.

The physical properties of sulfides probably include a wider assortment than can be found in any other single group of compounds. For example, there are sulfides that exhibit the properties of paramagnetism, diamagnetism, ferromagnetism, antiferromagnetism,[†] or ferrimagnetism.[†] On the basis of their composition, the sulfides that contain transition metals are of particular interest because they exhibit a large variation in prop-

---

[†] *Antiferromagnetism* and *ferrimagnetism* are described in the next chapter.

erties. Since sulfur, like selenium and tellurium, can exhibit semimetallic properties, the compositions of many sulfides resemble closely those of intermediate compounds in alloy systems. Because sulfides are not metals, however, this compositional variation merely accents the variety of properties that sulfides can and do have. Therein also lies one of their limitations for device applications. It is often extremely difficult to prepare materials that are either accurately stoichiometric or free of unintentionally included foreign atoms. Because of this, most naturally occurring sulfides cannot be used in careful investigations. On the other hand, the synthesis of sulfides is complicated by the relatively low vapor pressure of sulfur. Nevertheless, successively more attention is being turned toward investigating sulfide semiconductors because of their real potential utility.

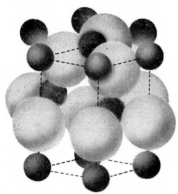

Wurtzite and halite types. Wurtzite is the name given to the hexagonal modification of zinc sulfide. The crystal structure of wurtzite is illustrated in Fig. 8 and, as can be seen by comparison with the sphalerite structure shown in Fig. 4, the two polymorphs differ only in the stacking sequence of

FIG. 8.   Wurtzite (ZnS) structure.

the sulfur tetrahedra layers. If the sequence is ...*AB*..., the hexagonal wurtzite structure results; if it is ...*ABC*..., then the cubic sphalerite or zinc blende structure results. Both structures have similar interatomic distances and, hence, binding energies, so that the energy gaps are also quite similar. The greater ease of preparing the hexagonal form of ZnS and particularly of CdS, the two most commonly used sulfides in this group, has focused attention on the wurtzite-type sulfides. The similarity of these sulfides can be seen from the information tabulated below.

	ZnS (hexagonal)	ZnS (cubic)	CdS (hexagonal)	Cds (cubic)	HgS (cubic)	
Interatomic separation	2.33	2.36	2.52	2.52	2.53	Å
Energy gap	3.55–3.70	3.60–3.64	2.38–2.48	...	...	eV

The variation in the energy-gap values listed above is due to variations in the methods used to determine the gap width. Note that, as in other semiconductors, the substitution of a heavier metal atom increases the interatomic separation and decreases the energy-gap width.

The similarity of the structures of the two polymorphous modifications has a very interesting consequence. The c/a ratio for both ZnS (1.63) and CdS (1.62) is very nearly that for an ideal hexagonal closest packing. Accordingly, it is not surprising that closest packings with other sequences can also occur. In the case of ZnS, a large number of different closest packings, having tens of layers in the stacking direction, have been reported. (Some of the ZnS polytypes are similar to the SiC polytypes discussed in the previous section.) None have so far been observed for CdS. This is not too surprising since the bonding in the heavier metal sulfide is weaker. Note that the stronger the bonding between nearest neighbors in these closest-packed structures, the more polytypes are formed. Thus SiC forms the strongest bonds and the most polytypes whereas closest-packed metals form the least. It may well be, however, that factors other than the bond mechanism determine polymorphism. For example, zinc sulfide has a much greater affinity for interstitial and substitutional impurities. As already shown in the case of silicon carbide, it is possible that the presence of impurities may be responsible for initiating the formation of the polymorphs in ZnS.

The sodium chloride or halite structure shown in Fig. 6 is adopted by several alkaline-earth and rare-earth sulfides. In addition, it is the structure of lead and tin sulfides, selenides, and tellurides. These compounds, like the zinc and cadmium sulfides, are particularly useful semiconductors because they are good photoconductors. It will be recalled that photoconductivity is the phenomenon whereby a semiconductor is rendered conducting when irradiated with electromagnetic radiation whose energy is sufficiently large to excite valence electrons to quantum states lying in the conduction band. For example, PbS, PbSe, and PbTe crystals can be used as detectors of infrared radiation. As in all such isomorphous semiconductors, the energy gap of the crystals decreases upon substitution of heavier atoms. In fact, it is possible to grow solid-solution crystals in which the energy gap varies continuously from one end of the crystal to the other, in direct proportion to the concentration gradient of the heaviest metal atom present. The variations in the energy-gap width of PbS, PbSe, and PbTe are compared below.

	PbS	PbSe	PbTe	
Interatomic separation	2.96	3.07	3.17	Å
Energy gap	0.40	0.31	0.25	eV

Binary sulfides. The sulfides in this category exhibit a variety of properties and hold forth great promise for future semiconductor applications. The sulfides whose already known properties suggest them for primary consideration are the compounds containing transition metals.

These sulfides crystallize in many different crystal structures, some of which are known and others are not. They bear certain resemblances to transition-metal oxides, and yet there are many more differences between their properties than there are similarities. This can be partially explained by comparing Pauling's electronegativity values, which are 2.5 for sulfur and 3.5 for oxygen. Accordingly, the bonding in sulfides has less ionic character than is present in the structurally related oxides. Furthermore, the sulfides often crystallize in two or more polymorphous modifications. Their stoichiometric compositions also do not bear a simple relationship to the number of valence electrons present. Thus, for example, perfectly stable sulfides can have compositions like FeS_2, Sb_2S_3, Co_3S_4, Cr_6S_7, CuS, Co_9S_8, Cu_9S_5, Ni_3S_2, Cu_2S, etc. This similarity to intermediate phases encountered in metal alloys is undoubtedly due to a resonance between covalent and ionic bonding, with the result that the valence electrons are not localized in the vicinity of individual atoms but tend to be shared in a way similar to the metallic bond. The true nature of the bonding, however, is not known at present.

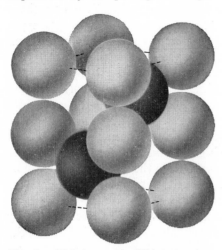

FIG. 9. Nickel arsenide (NiAs) structure. The dark spheres represent Ni and the light spheres As. Although not immediately apparent, note that the dark spheres are arrayed in a hexagonal closest packing. (This becomes more apparent if neighboring unit cells are considered.)

The properties of some of these sulfides have been investigated, and these compounds are briefly discussed below. CrS, CoS, FeS, and NiS have the nickel arsenide structure shown in Fig. 9. This structure consists of a sulfur hexagonal closest packing with the metal atoms occupying all the octahedral voids. In addition to their sulfides, the selenides, tellurides, stannites, and bismuthides of certain transition metals also crystallize with this structure. In fact, these compounds can be said to constitute a link with the true metal phases. The reason for the metallic nature of such compounds is partly the resonance between covalent and ionic bonding discussed above, and partly the increased coordination number of both kinds of atoms present, which also aids in the formation of unsaturated covalent bonds. (Sulfur has 6-fold coordination in the form of a trigonal prism.) This, in turn, is the probable reason why the nickel arsenide structure is stable over a fairly wide composition range. For example, FeS crystallizes with the nickel arsenide structure with an iron content that can vary from 43.8 to 50 atomic per cent. The crystal having the correct stoichiometric ratio of 50 atomic per cent Fe is antiferromagnetic. In the composition range 50–46½ atomic per cent Fe it is paramagnetic, and in the range 45–43.8 per cent Fe it is ferromagnetic. For intermediate compositions between these two ranges, iron sulfide has an anomalous magnetic behavior which is believed to depend on the arrangement of the cation vacancies in the FeS structure. The ordering of these vacancies is also believed to be the reason why iron sulfide adopts a structure that is different from the NiAs structure at certain compositions. Although at least two polymorphous forms of FeS are recognized, the elucidation of the exact nature of the polymorphism must await the determination of the exact crystal structures of these modifications. Similarly, nickel sulfide also crystallizes in a polymorphous modification, the so-called millerite structure, in which both nickel and sulfur have 5-fold coordination.

By comparison, MnS can crystallize with either the halite, sphalerite, or wurtzite structure, all of which are antiferromagnetic at room temperature. As the name implies, *antiferromagnetism* is a phenomenon that is inversely related to ferromagnetism and is caused by an antiparallel alignment of spin moments in neighboring atoms so that no net magnetization is possible. HgS can crystallize with either a hexagonal structure in the mineral cinnabar or with the sphalerite structure in the mineral metacinnabarite. The structures of SnS and GeS have different arrangements which can be derived, however, by suitably distorting the sodium chloride structure. The structures of PtS and PdS are of interest because the noble-metal atoms, in both structures, are coordinated by four sulfur atoms which are coplanar with the metal atoms. The structure of platinum sulfide is shown in Fig. 10, and the square bonds formed by platinum are clearly visible therein. These unusual bonds are formed by dsp^2 hybrids and are strongly covalent in character. It is reasonable to expect, therefore, that both of these crystals should prove to have interesting semiconductor properties.

Complex sulfides. Iron disulfide, FeS_2, crystallizes in two closely related structures as the minerals pyrite and marcasite. (See Fig. 2 of Chapter 1.) These compounds are of interest because they contain pairs of sulfur atoms that are very close to each other, almost as if they formed S_2 molecules in these compounds. The iron atoms in both structures have octahedral coordinations, and the pyrite structure can be likened to the halite structure shown in Fig. 6 by substituting Fe for Na and S_2 pairs for Cl. These compounds are more nearly insulators than semiconductors, however.

The structures of most other sulfides are more complex. The structures of $CuFeS_2$ and Cu_2FeSnS_4 and their derivation from the sphalerite structure have already been discussed in Chapter 4. Many other sulfides, including $CuFe_2S_3$, $CuSbS_2$, Cu_3SbS_3, Cu_3AsS_3, to name just a few, are similarly based on three-dimensional networks of sulfur tetrahedra. The structure of cubanite, $CuFe_2S_3$, is of some interest because

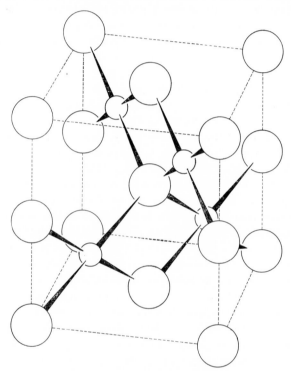

Fig. 10.   Bonding model of PtS structure.

the sulfur tetrahedra containing iron share a common edge. The resulting shortening of the Fe-Fe separation allows direct interactions between the spin moments of these atoms, with the result that cubanite is weakly ferromagnetic. A very large number of sulfides, such as the two polymorphs of Ag_2S or compounds like $7PbS \cdot 6Sb_2S_3$, are not discussed in this chapter because not only their semiconductor properties but also their crystal structures are not fully known. Sulfides, therefore, constitute one of the few remaining groups of solids that are relatively unexplored and unexploited.

Oxides

The similarity between transition-metal oxides and their sulfides has been pointed out in the previous section. In both cases, the crystal structures usually consist of either a hexagonal or cubic closest packing of anions in which the cations occupy either octahedral or tetrahedral voids. The differences between such pairs of compounds arise primarily because oxygen is more electronegative than sulfur. Consequently, the bonding in most metal oxides is predominantly ionic. (Some exceptions such as silicates, in which the bonding is believed to be 50 per cent covalent, are further discussed in Chapter 15.) Because the ionic bond is very strong and does not involve the sharing of electrons by two or more atoms, the electronic conductivity in ionic compounds is usually negligibly small. In this book, therefore, such compounds are classified as insulators. The transition-metal oxides, on the other hand, can become electronic conductors by having compositions that deviate from the stoichiometric ratio. One way that this can happen is through loss of oxygen by the crystal, with the result that the structure contains an excess of metal ions. To preserve charge neutrality, the extra electrons are usually located in the anion vacancies. These electrons occupy quantum states lying in the forbidden region so that the electrons can readily transfer to states lying in the conduction band. Some of these so-called *defect structures* are further discussed in this section.

Binary oxides. The oxides of some of the metals in the first long period are the only oxides belonging to this group that are discussed in this chapter. Iron and manganese form a series of compounds at different stoichiometric ratios, for example, FeO, Fe_2O_3, and Fe_3O_4, of which Fe_2O_3 is dimorphic, crystallizing with a structure similar to the ilmenite structure, described in the next section, or the spinel structure also described in the next section. The latter polymorph is called γ-Fe_2O_3 and is a defect structure having deficiency of iron. The monoxides of manganese, iron, cobalt, and nickel have the sodium chloride structure, and FeO usually has a deficiency of iron atoms. All these crystals become semiconductors when deviations from stoichiometry occur. The way that this can happen is described for the case of ZnO, NiO, and Cu_2O crystals below.

Stoichiometric zinc oxide is an insulator that crystallizes with the wurtzite structure, shown in Fig. 8, to form transparent needle-shaped crystals. As can be seen in Fig. 8, the structure contains large voids which can easily accommodate interstitial atoms. Consequently, it is virtually impossible to prepare really pure crystals so that the room-temperature resistivity of very carefully grown crystals ranges between 1 and 100 ohm-cm. When these crystals are heated, they tend to lose oxygen. In fact, if they are heated above 1000°C, they become yellowish in color following a brief annealing period at 1000°C. It is believed that the coloration is due to the diffusion of the zinc atoms left on the surface into the interstitial sites in the crystal. In order to test whether the excess zinc atoms actually do go into interstitial sites, other experiments have been conducted in which the "pure" crystals were placed in an atmosphere containing zinc vapor and heated to various temperatures, causing some of the vaporized zinc to diffuse into the crystal thereby. After such treatments, an increase in the conductivity of the crystal is observed. Although the processes occurring in both cases are undoubtedly similar, it is easier to see what happens when a crystal loses oxygen upon heating. In the crystal, oxygen exists in the form of O^{-2} ions but, when it escapes, it does so as neutral O atoms which pair up to form O_2 gas. Consequently each departing oxygen atom leaves two electrons behind. There are three ways that these excess electrons can be accommodated in the crystal. One possibility is that both electrons combine with a Zn^{+2} ion to form a neutral Zn atom according to the reaction

$$ZnO \rightarrow Zn^0 + O^0. \tag{2}$$

Alternatively, one or both of the electrons may occupy empty quantum states in the conduction band of the crystal and lead an existence that is essentially divorced from the zinc atoms. This can happen in two ways.

$$ZnO \rightarrow Zn^{+1} + O^0 + \ominus \tag{3}$$
$$ZnO \rightarrow Zn^{+2} + O^0 + 2\ominus \tag{4}$$

where $\ominus$ denotes a conduction electron.

Density measurements and radioactive tracer studies indicate that the excess zinc atoms enter interstitial sites in the crystal. The increased conductivity of the crystals implies that these zinc atoms are not electrically neutral. If the process in (2) is operative, this means that the conduction electrons come from initially neutral zinc atoms. Here, again, there are two possibilities, namely, that each interstitial zinc atom contributes, on an average, one or two electrons. It is unlikely, however, at the elevated temperatures at which the interstitials are created, that such neutral atoms are formed to any large extent. Hence, the conductivity must be explained by either (3) or (4). Because the ionic mobility is many orders of magnitude smaller than the electronic mobility, the conductivity can be considered to be due to the conduction electrons alone. This means that it should be possible to determine which of the two processes is operative from conductivity measurements at elevated temperatures. In the temperature range 500 to 700°C, it has been shown that the formation of Zn^{+1} ions predominates. At lower temperatures, the presence of additional impurities, inadvertently included in the original crystal, complicates the analysis of the conductivity data. In fact, recent Hall-effect measurements have shown that hydrogen and lithium donors behave just like interstitial zinc in increasing the conductivity. The name *electron-excess* semiconductors has been proposed for these crystals.

A related change in the conductivity is observed in transition metals crystallizing with the halite structure shown in Fig. 6. The atomic mechanism responsible for the conductivity, however, is different. Whereas it is observed that the conductivity of a nonstoichiometric ZnO crystal decreases when it is placed in an oxygen atmosphere at elevated temperatures, the conductivity of NiO, for example, increases under these conditions. The increase in the conductivity of nickel oxide, therefore, must be due to the absorption of oxygen by the crystal. Because the interstices in the halite structure are too small to accommodate the large oxygen atoms easily, it is most likely that the absorption of oxygen is accompanied by the formation of cation vacancies. In order to become an integral member of the NiO structure, each oxygen atom enters the crystal as an O^{-2} ion. Charge neutrality is preserved, therefore, by the creation of an equal number of Ni^{+2} vacancies. The electrons that combine with the absorbed oxygen to form O^{-2} ions must come from among the electrons already present in the crystal. This means that holes are created in the valence band of such a crystal. This is confirmed by Hall-effect measurements which show that the conductivity in NiO is primarily due to positive-current carriers. Because the motion of vacancies requires atomic movements, the mobility of holes is much greater than that of the vacancies and the observed current is produced by the holes.

A similar process is operative in Cu_2O. The conductivity of cuprous oxide, like nickel oxide, increases with increasing oxygen pressure. This means that the conductivity is due to an excess of oxygen atoms or, restating this, due to a deficiency of copper atoms. What apparently happens is that the copper atoms diffuse to the surface of the crystal where they recombine with oxygen atoms from the atmosphere. Each departing copper atom leaves behind a cation vacancy and a deficiency of one electron. The resulting hole can be trapped at such a vacancy and, as shown previously, can act just like a conduction electron when thermally excited. The name *electron-defect* semiconductor has been proposed for such crystals.

Complex oxides. The crystal structure of Fe_2O_3 is similar to that of the so-called ilmenite structure shown in Fig. 11 except that all the metal atoms are alike. The ilmenite structure (Fig. 11) is adopted by a large number of mixed transition-metal oxides, for example, $FeTiO_3$, $NiTiO_3$, $CoTiO_3$, and others. Because the relatively more stable titanium ion has a charge of $+4$, the other transition-metal ions are divalent in this structure so that the average metal valency is $+3$, the same as the valency of iron in Fe_2O_3. It is possible to substitute pairs of metal atoms in this structure in any ratio, provided only that the average valency of such pairs is $+3$ and that the usual rules governing substitutional solid solutions are obeyed, for example, $(Cu,Ti)_xFe_{2-x}O_3$. (See Chapter 4.) Although the conductivity in such crystals can be due to either a deficiency of oxygen atoms or a deficiency of metal atoms, depending on the composition, it has been shown that the crystals are usually p-type

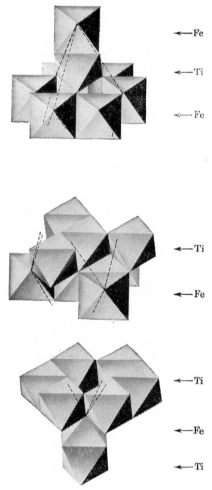

←—Fe

←—Ti

←—Fe

←—Ti

←—Fe

←—Ti

←—Fe

←—Ti

Fɪɢ. 11.   Ilmenite ($FeTiO_3$) structure.   The oxygen octahedra surrounding the metal atoms are shown for the unit rhombohedron.   Note that Fe^{+2} and Ti^{+4} segregate into alternate layers normal to the 3-fold axis.   [If all the metal atoms are the same, then this becomes the hematite (Fe_2O_3) or corundum (Al_2O_3) structure.]

semiconductors.   Thus they must be electron-defect semiconductors like NiO and Cu_2O.

A large number of oxides having the general formula AB_2O_4 crystallize with the spinel structure shown in Fig. 12.   The structure consists of oxygen atoms arranged in a cubic closest packing, the cubic unit cell containing thirty-two oxygen atoms. The metal atoms are distributed among the tetrahedral voids (A atoms) and octahedral sites (B atoms). The space group of a spinel is $Fd3m$, and the sixty-four available tetrahedral sites in this structure give rise to two sets of equipoints of rank 8

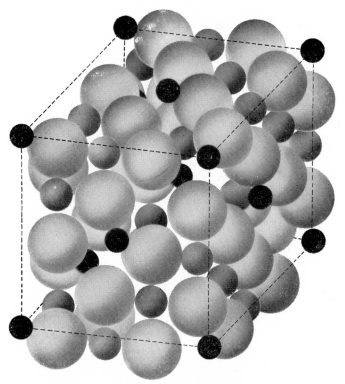

Fig. 12. Spinel ($MgAl_2O_4$) structure. The origin of the outlined unit cell has been placed in a tetrahedral void of the oxygen closest packing occupied by Mg.

and one set of equipoints of rank 48. Similarly, the thirty-two octahedral voids can be divided into two sets of equipoints of rank 16. If the origin of the unit cell is placed at one of the tetrahedral equipoints of rank 8, then the octahedrally coordinated B atoms occupy the equipoints given below. (See Fig. 12.)

A atoms in (a) $000;$ $\frac{1}{4}\frac{1}{4}\frac{1}{4};$ etc.

B atoms in (d) $\frac{5}{8}\frac{5}{8}\frac{5}{8};$ $\frac{5}{8}\frac{7}{8}\frac{7}{8};$ $\frac{7}{8}\frac{5}{8}\frac{7}{8};$ $\frac{7}{8}\frac{7}{8}\frac{5}{8};$ etc.

O atoms in (e) $xxx;$ $x\bar{x}\bar{x};$ $\bar{x}x\bar{x};$ $\bar{x}\bar{x}x;$ $\frac{1}{4}-x,\frac{1}{4}-x,\frac{1}{4}-x;$ $\frac{1}{4}-x,\frac{1}{4}+x,$
$\frac{1}{4}+x;$ $\frac{1}{4}+x,\frac{1}{4}-x,\frac{1}{4}+x;$ $\frac{1}{4}+x,\frac{1}{4}+x,\frac{1}{4}-x;$ etc.,

where $x = \frac{3}{8}$ for an ideal closest packing.

The distribution of the cations among the tetrahedral and octahedral sites is of interest. The spinel structure is adopted by a large number of crystals having a variety of atoms present in different ratios. Nevertheless, it is possible to divide these compounds into groups according to their composition, commonly called aluminates, $MeAl_2O_4$; ferrites, $MeFe_2O_4$; titanates, Me_2TiO_4; and so forth. The true nature of the bonding that exists between the atoms in these structures is subject to controversy; however, everyone agrees that it is predominantly ionic in character. As discussed below, the controversy is limited primarily to a few compounds in which it is believed that the bonding may be predominantly covalent in character. According to the compositional formula AB_2O_4, the total positive charge of the three cations must equal $+8$. It is possible to satisfy this condition by combinations of divalent and trivalent ions, or divalent and quadrivalent ions, etc. These are usually designated as 2-3 spinels, 2-4 spinels, and so forth. At first glance, it may appear that the natural distribution of cations in, say, a 2-3 spinel is to place the divalent ions in the tetrahedral sites and the trivalent ions in the octahedral sites. This is, indeed, the structure adopted by many compounds, such as $ZnFe_2O_4$, for example, and is called a *normal* spinel structure. It is also possible, however, to distribute the cations in another way. In $MgFe_2O_4$, for example, the tetrahedral sites are occupied by Fe^{+3} ions and the octahedral equipoints are statistically shared by Mg^{+2} and Fe^{+3} ions. Such an arrangement is called an *inverse* spinel structure and is best represented by the structurally correct formula $B(AB)O_4$.

The structure of magnetite, Fe_3O_4, is believed to be of this type. The structural formula, therefore, is written $Fe^{+3}(Fe^{+2}Fe^{+3})O_4$. Magnetite is a semiconductor at room temperature with a gap width of 0.05 eV. Unlike the other transition-metal oxides discussed above, the conductivity in Fe_3O_4 is not due to either cation or anion deficiencies. Instead, it is believed that the conductivity comes about by an exchange of electrons between Fe^{+3} and Fe^{+2} ions occupying octahedral sites in the spinel structure. Deviations from stoichiometry in Fe_3O_4 actually cause the conductivity to decrease. Furthermore, below 120°K, the conductivity decreases abruptly and, below 115°K, the gap width increases discontinuously to 0.10 eV. This is probably due to an ordering among the cations in the octahedral positions and a consequent decrease in the ease of electron exchange between them. This transformation causes the symmetry of Fe_3O_4 to become orthorhombic below $-158°C$.

By comparison, the mineral hausmannite, Mn_3O_4, is an insulator at room temperature. The crystal structure of hausmannite is quite similar to the cubic spinel structure except that two of the a axes of the pseudo cube are slightly shorter than the third so that the crystal is actually tetragonal ($c/a = 1.16$). Above 1025°C, the crystal structure becomes cubic, and the conductivity increases markedly. The tetragonal distortion of hausmannite and structurally related manganates such as $ZnMn_2O_4$ has been variously attributed to an ordering of Mn^{+2} and Mn^{+4} ions, assumed to be occupying octahedral sites in an inverse 2-4 spinel, and to the formation of covalent bonds in a normal 2-3 spinel. According to this postulate, the manganese atoms in octahedral sites are believed to form square dsp^2 hybrid bonds which tend to orient themselves parallel to each other. This has the effect of lengthening the Mn-O distance normal to the plane of the square bond and is believed to cause the tetragonal distortion.

Recent neutron diffraction experiments with structurally related cobalt and nickel manganates seem to support this view. Nickel atoms occupy octahedral sites and cobalt atoms occupy tetrahedral sites in the spinel structure. Because both of these metals are more stable in their divalent states, it is expected that, when divalent cobalt is substituted for divalent manganese in the tetrahedral sites, the tetragonal distortion should not be affected. Except for small variations in the c/a ratio, this is, indeed, the case in $(Mn_{\frac{2}{3}}Co_{\frac{1}{3}})Mn_2O_4$ and $CoMn_2O_4$. Conversely, when divalent nickel is substituted for the hybrid-forming manganese atoms in octahedral sites, it randomizes the orientation of these bonds sufficiently to destroy the tetragonal distortion. Consequently, $Mn(Ni_{\frac{1}{2}}Mn_{\frac{1}{2}})O_4$ and $Mn(NiMn)O_4$ have cubic symmetry. Similarly, $(Mn_{\frac{1}{2}}Co_{\frac{1}{2}})(NiMn)O_4$ is also cubic.

Suggestions for supplementary reading

Leonid V. Azároff, Formation, structure, and bonding of Ni–Co–Mn oxides having spinel-type structure, *Zeit. f. Krist.*, vol. 112 (1959), pp. 33–43.

R. C. Evans, *An introduction to crystal chemistry* (Cambridge University Press, London, 1948).

Richard S. Mitchell, A correlation between theoretical screw dislocations and the known polytypes of silicon carbide, *Zeit. f. Krist.*, vol. 109 (1957), pp. 1–28.

L. Pincherle and J. M. Radcliffe, Semiconducting intermetallic compounds, *Phil. Mag. Suppl.*, vol. 5 (1956), pp. 271–321.

F. C. Romeijn, Physical and crystallographic properties of some spinels, *Philips Research Repts.*, vol. 8 (1953), pp. 304–321.

A. F. Wells, *Structural inorganic chemistry*, 2d ed. (Oxford University Press, London, 1950).

Ajit Ram Verma, *Crystal growth and dislocations* [Buttersworth & Co. (Publishers) Ltd., London, 1953], pp. 100–112.

Exercises

1. Explain the relationship between interatomic distances in a crystal and the width of the forbidden-energy region in its energy-band model.

2. Using the modified $8 - N$ neighbor rule of relation (1), classify the following compounds as semiconductors or not, depending on whether they obey the modified rule: InSb, Mg_2Sn, SnS_2, CuS, Co_2S_3, AlP, and GaAs. (Assume that similar atoms do not form bonds with each other.)

3. Certain intermetallic compounds have the *antifluorite* structure in which the cation has 4-fold coordination and the anion 8-fold coordination. For what values of the radius ratio do you expect ionic compounds to adopt the fluorite structure? The antifluorite structure? The wurtzite structure?

4. Make a drawing of the structure of the $15R$ polytype of silicon carbide showing a cross section parallel to $(11\bar{2}0)$. What is the zigzag sequence in this structure?

5. Starting with the structure of the $6H$ polytype of SiC shown in Fig. 7, show how it can be altered by dislocations to give the $33R$ polytype. What is the zigzag sequence in a $33R$ polytype?

6. Why do you think it is that wurtzite containing excess zinc does not behave like an electron-excess semiconductor? (*Hint:* Compare the bonding of ZnS and ZnO.) What do you think the energy-band models of these two crystals are like?

7. Describe the step-by-step mechanism whereby excess oxygen atoms are absorbed by NiO, accompanied by the formation of Ni^{+2} vacancies. To begin, assume that neutral oxygen atoms are adsorbed on the surface of a stoichiometrically pure NiO crystal.

8. The phenomenon of *ferrimagnetism* is named after the ferrites in which it is often observed. It occurs whenever a larger number of ferromagnetic atoms have electrons with parallel magnetic moments than the number of antiparallel moments present. It is thus like ferromagnetism except that not all the moments are parallel. Suppose that the moments of all the Fe^{+3} ions in $NiFe_2O_4$ are parallel and those of Ni^{+2} are antiparallel. What is the relative orientation of the magnetic moments in the octahedral and tetrahedral sites if $NiFe_2O_4$ has the inverse spinel structure? Normal spinel structure?

9. Magnetite has the structural formula $Fe^{+3}(Fe^{+2}Fe^{+3})O_4$ at room temperature. Suppose that the divalent and trivalent iron atoms order at a lower temperature so that alternate atoms in the (001) plane are divalent. Show what would happen to the symmetry in this case. (See Fig. 12.)

14

Properties of insulators

The energy-band model of an insulator is not unlike that of a typical semiconductor except that the forbidden-energy region separating the conduction band from the valence band is much larger, of the order of several electron volts. Although insulator crystals may contain impurities, the prospective donor or acceptor states have energies that are sufficiently far removed from the band edges so that their contribution to conductivity at ordinary temperatures is negligibly small. As discussed elsewhere in this chapter, conductivity can occur by means of the diffusion of atoms, or, more correctly, ions, through the crystal. Ions have much lower mobilities than electrons so that the Hall effect, which is proportional to the charge-carrier mobility, is very much smaller for such crystals than for semiconductors. In fact, for purposes of classification, it is convenient to distinguish semiconductors from insulators on the basis of whether the Hall effect of the crystal can be measured or not.

Another way of describing an insulator is to note that the electrons are so tightly bound to the atoms that at ordinary temperatures they cannot be dislodged either by thermal vibrations or with ordinary fields. The negative and positive charges in each part of the crystal can be considered to be centered at the same point, and, since no conductivity is possible, the localized charges remain that way essentially forever. When an electric field is applied to the crystal, the centers of the positive charges are slightly displaced in the direction of the applied field and the centers of the negative charges are slightly displaced in the opposite direction. This produces local *dipoles* throughout the crystal, and the process of inducing such dipoles in the crystal is called *polarization*. The dipole moment induced in a unit volume of a polarized insulator can be considered as the average of the dipole moments of all the atoms in that unit volume, and the ratio of the induced dipole moment to the effective

379

field is called the *polarizability* of the atom.   It is possible that certain
groups of atoms (complex ions or molecules) already possess permanent
dipole moments.   In crystals containing such atomic groups, an external
field has the effect of orienting the dipoles parallel to the field direction.
In the absence of an external field, the dipoles are randomly oriented
because of their thermal motion so that the crystal has a zero net moment.
The polarization of these so-called *polar* crystals is strongly temperature-
dependent since, even in the presence of an applied field, thermal motion
tends to randomize the dipole orientations.   On the other hand, the
polarization of *nonpolar* crystals is independent of temperature since,
in the absence of an external field, no dipoles exist in the crystal.   The
temperature dependence of polarization, therefore, can be used to distinguish polar insulators from nonpolar insulators.

Electrical properties

Dielectric properties.   When a voltage V is applied to two parallel
metal plates, a charge whose magnitude is proportional to the voltage
develops on each plate according to

$$Q = CV. \tag{1}$$

Here C is called the *capacitance* of the parallel-plate capacitor and is
determined by the area of the plates A and the separation of the plates l.

$$C = \frac{\epsilon_0 A}{4\pi l} \tag{2}$$

where ϵ_0 is the *permittivity of empty space*.   Relation (2), therefore,
applies only if the two plates are separated by a vacuum.   Insertion of an
insulator or *dielectric* material between the plates increases the capacitance without altering the charge on the plates.   According to (1), therefore, this increase in the capacitance must be accompanied by a corresponding decrease in the potential difference between the plates.   When
all space between the two plates is filled by the dielectric material, the
capacitance is increased by a factor κ_e called the *dielectric constant* of the
material.   It is often convenient to express the increase in capacitance
by another factor ϵ, the *permittivity of the material*, since according to
elementary electrostatic theory

$$\epsilon = \frac{D}{\mathcal{E}} \tag{3}$$

where D is the *electric displacement* or *flux density* and $\mathcal{E}$ is the electric
field intensity.   The relationship between κ_e and ϵ is given by

$$\epsilon = \kappa_e \epsilon_0. \tag{4}$$

If cgs electrostatic units are used, $\epsilon_0 = 1$ and $\epsilon = \kappa_e$. If MKS units are used, however, $\epsilon_0 = \frac{1}{9} \times 10^{-11}$ farad/m.† Since the difference between the two systems of units involves the introduction of electric charge as a fundamental physical quantity, it is necessary to exercise care in applying these relations to actual calculations. The relations between these two systems are described further in Appendix 2. Because the magnitude of the dielectric constant κ_e is not affected by the units used, the cgs electrostatic units are used in this book, so that $\epsilon_0 = 1$.

The observed increase in the capacitance of a parallel-plate capacitor, when a dielectric material is inserted between the plates, is due to a decrease in the electric field inside the dielectric. This, in turn, is due to the electric field of the dipoles, which are induced inside the material, and can be expressed by a *polarization density* P which is defined as the total dipole moment induced in a unit volume of the material. If the capacitance of the vacuum capacitor is denoted C_{vac}, then the new capacitance is $C = \kappa_e C_{\text{vac}}$ and the decreased field in the presence of a dielectric is $\mathcal{E} = (1/\kappa_e)\mathcal{E}_{\text{vac}}$. The polarization density is a measure of the change in the capacitance (or field), so that

$$P = C_{\text{vac}} - C$$
$$= \frac{\mathcal{E}_{\text{vac}}}{4\pi} - \frac{\mathcal{E}}{4\pi} \qquad (5)$$
$$= (\kappa_e - 1)\frac{\mathcal{E}}{4\pi}$$

or, by rearranging the terms in (5),

$$\kappa_e = 1 + 4\pi\frac{P}{\mathcal{E}}$$
$$= 1 + 4\pi\chi_e \qquad (6)$$

where $\chi_e = P/\mathcal{E}$ is called the *electric susceptibility*.

The polarization density is determined by three factors:

1. The *electronic polarization* α_e produced by opposite displacements of negative electrons and positive nuclei within the same atoms

2. The *ionic polarizability* α_i produced by opposite displacements of positive and negative ions in the material

3. Contributions from the *permanent dipole moments* of complex ions or molecules whenever such permanent dipoles are present in the material

† Frequently, the factor $1/4\pi$ is included in ϵ_0 and omitted from the equations. In these cases $\epsilon_0 = 8.854 \times 10^{-12}$ farad/m in the MKS system of units. It is good practice, therefore, always to specify the units being used.

It is possible to express this analytically. Let the number of atoms or molecules per unit volume be N; then

$$P = N\left(\alpha_e + \alpha_i + \frac{\mu^2}{3kT}\right); \tag{7}$$

The electric susceptibility is then obtained by substituting (7) in (6):

$$\chi_e = \frac{\kappa_e - 1}{4\pi} = \frac{P}{\mathcal{E}} = N\left(\alpha_e + \alpha_i + \frac{\mu^2}{3kT}\right). \tag{8}$$

Note that the contribution to P, from the permanent dipoles present in the material, is temperature-dependent. It is thus possible to measure these dipole moments by observing the temperature dependence of the electric susceptibility. On the other hand, if no temperature dependence is observed, then it can be safely assumed that there are no permanent dipoles present.

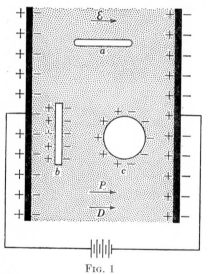

FIG. 1

So far the discussion has been quite general in that no restrictions have been placed on the nature of the dielectric material, that is, whether it is a gas, a liquid, or a crystalline substance. If attention is limited to crystals, it is necessary to take into account the influence, on an atom, of the internal field produced by the dipoles surrounding the atom as well as the influence of the externally applied field. Consider the parallel-plate capacitor shown in Fig. 1. A simple way to determine the value of the electric field inside the dielectric is to insert a test charge into an imaginary cavity in the dielectric and to calculate the force acting on such a charge. When the cavity is needle-shaped and oriented with its axis parallel to the field direction and the ends are very small relative to its length (cavity a in Fig. 1), the test charge placed inside such a cavity is acted on by the average field $\mathcal{E}$ so that the force on a charge q is $q\mathcal{E}$. If the cavity has a large surface normal to the field direction, say the disk-shaped cavity pictured in cross section by b in Fig. 1, then a bound charge appears on the two surfaces and the force acting on a test charge q inside such a cavity is

$$qD = q(\mathcal{E} + 4\pi P). \tag{9}$$

Here $4\pi P$ is the field due to the charge density P on the two surfaces of the disk-shaped cavity. Equation (9) expresses the fundamental relation between the three quantities D, $\mathcal{E}$, and P,

$$D = \mathcal{E} + 4\pi P. \tag{10}$$

The force on a test charge inside a spherical cavity (cavity c in Fig. 1) can be determined as follows: An enlarged view of the cavity is shown in Fig. 2. The charge density on a surface element dA of the sphere is equal to the normal component of the polarization times the surface element, that is, $P \cos \theta \, dA$. According to Coulomb's law, this charge element produces a force dF_r acting on the test charge q at the center of the sphere in the direction of r (Fig. 2).

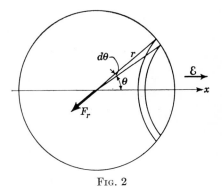

FIG. 2

$$dF_r = \frac{q_1 q_2}{r^2}$$

$$= \frac{qP \cos \theta \, dA}{r^2}. \tag{11}$$

The effect of the charge on the whole surface of the sphere can be calculated by considering the spherical ring shown in Fig. 2, whose area

$$dA = 2\pi r \sin \theta \, r d\theta = 2\pi r^2 \sin \theta \, d\theta,$$

and integrating over the whole sphere by integrating with respect to θ from 0 to π. Since it is desired to calculate the force in the direction of the electric field, $F_x = -F_r \cos \theta$, it can be calculated with the aid of (11).

$$dF_x = -q \frac{P \cos \theta}{r^2} 2\pi r^2 \sin \theta \, d\theta \cos\theta$$

$$F_x = -2\pi q P \int_0^\pi \cos^2 \theta \sin \theta \, d\theta. \tag{12}$$

This integral can be evaluated directly by making the substitution

$$z = \cos \theta \quad \text{and} \quad dz = -\sin \theta \, d\theta$$

so that

$$F_x = 2\pi q P \int_1^{-1} z^2 \, dz$$

$$= \frac{4\pi P}{3} q. \tag{13}$$

This force is called the *Lorentz force* because Lorentz was the first to show how to determine the local field $\mathcal{E}_{loc}$ acting on an atom in a dielectric material. This local field is the sum of four fields,

$$\mathcal{E}_{loc} = \mathcal{E}_1 + \mathcal{E}_2 + \mathcal{E}_3 + \mathcal{E}_4 \tag{14}$$

where $\mathcal{E}_1$ is the field intensity due to the charge density on the plates $D = \mathcal{E} + 4\pi P$.

$\mathcal{E}_2$ is the field intensity due to the charge density induced on the two sides of the dielectric opposite the plates. Since this contribution to the field is opposite in direction to that of the applied field (Fig. 1), it is equal to $-4\pi P$.

$\mathcal{E}_3$ is the field intensity at the center of a spherical cavity whose radius is large compared with the size of an atom but small compared with the size of the dielectric. According to (13),

$$\mathcal{E}_3 = \frac{F_x}{q} = \frac{4\pi P}{3}.$$

$\mathcal{E}_4$ is the field intensity at the center of a spherical cavity due to the dipoles of the atoms contained in that cavity. If the symmetry at the center of the sphere is cubic (as distinct from the crystal's symmetry), it can be shown that this term is equal to zero.

In the case of *dielectric isotropy*, therefore, substituting the above values in (14),

$$\mathcal{E}_{loc} = (\mathcal{E} + 4\pi P) + (-4\pi P) + \frac{4\pi P}{3} + 0$$

$$= \mathcal{E} + \frac{4\pi P}{3}, \tag{15}$$

the so-called *Lorentz field* is obtained. It has been assumed in the derivation of (15) that the region outside the sphere is a continuum having a dielectric constant κ_e. Note that the field intensity at the atom, that is, the Lorentz field, is larger than the applied field by an amount that is directly proportional to the polarization density.

It is now possible to relate the dielectric constant of an insulator to the polarizability of the atoms comprising it. The dipole moment of a single atom p is proportional to the local field, that is,

$$p = \alpha \mathcal{E}_{loc} \tag{16}$$

where α is the *electrical polarizability* of the atom. The total polarization of an insulator containing N atoms is

$$P = \sum_{i=1}^{N} n_i \alpha_i{}^i \mathcal{E}_{loc} \tag{17}$$

where n_i is the number of i atoms having polarizabilities α_i and acted on by local field $i\mathcal{E}_{loc}$.

In an insulator with dielectric isotropy, the local field inside the crystal is everywhere the same so that it can be taken outside the summation sign in (17). Substituting the Lorentz field (15) into (17) then gives

$$P = \left(\mathcal{E} + \frac{4\pi P}{3} \right) \sum_i n_i\alpha_i$$

or, after rearranging terms,

$$\frac{P}{\mathcal{E}} = \frac{\displaystyle\sum_i n_i\alpha_i}{1 - (4\pi/3) \displaystyle\sum_i n_i\alpha_i}. \tag{18}$$

By substituting the left side of (8) for $P/\mathcal{E}$ and rearranging terms, one obtains the *Clausius-Mosotti equation*

$$\frac{\kappa_e - 1}{\kappa_e + 2} = \frac{4\pi}{3} \sum_i n_i\alpha_i. \tag{19}$$

Equation (19) can be used to determine the electrical polarizabilities of the atoms if the dielectric constant is known. Conversely, the dielectric constants of new materials can be predicted from a knowledge of the individual polarizabilities of the atoms since, according to (19), the polarizabilities are additive. This relation is also valid for electronic polarizabilities α_e and dipolar polarizabilities α_d. If all these are taken into account, the Clausius-Mosotti equation (19) can be written

$$\frac{\kappa_e - 1}{\kappa_e + 2} = \frac{4\pi}{3} (N_i\alpha_i + N_e\alpha_e + N_d\alpha_d) \tag{20}$$

where N_i, N_e, and N_d are the total number of atoms in the crystal with ionic, electronic, and dipolar polarizabilities, respectively. It should be noted that the dipolar polarizability for permanent dipoles of moment μ is given by $\mu^2/3kT$ if the dipoles are completely free to align themselves with the field and by $2\mu^2/3\varphi$ if a so-called *activation energy* φ must be overcome before the dipoles can line up. This latter case is called *hindered rotation* of the dipoles.

Piezoelectricity. Consider a crystal having a centrosymmetric structure composed of positively and negatively charged ions as shown schematically in Fig. 3A. It will be recalled from Chapter 2 that such crystals must belong to one of the eleven centrosymmetric crystal classes. When a mechanical stress is applied to the crystal, the atoms are slightly

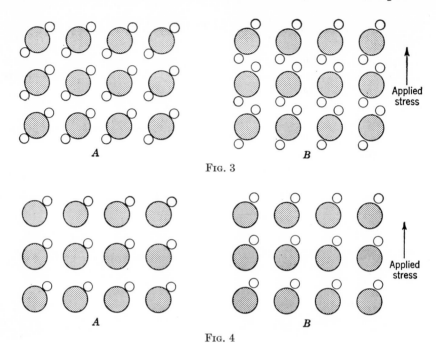

FIG. 3

FIG. 4

displaced, as shown in Fig. 3*B*. Since the ionic displacements are symmetrical about the symmetry centers, the charge distribution inside the crystal is not appreciably altered by the applied stress. On the other hand, if the acentric crystal whose structure is depicted in Fig. 4*A* is subjected to a mechanical stress, the ions are displaced in an asymmetric way (Fig. 4*B*) and electrical dipoles are produced in the crystal. This effect is called the *piezoelectric effect* and it is observed in crystals belonging to twenty of the twenty-one noncentrosymmetric crystal classes. Conversely, when an electric field is applied to a piezoelectric crystal, dipoles are induced in the crystal and the resulting small atomic displacements produce a mechanical strain. This is called the *inverse piezoelectric* effect. If an alternating field is applied to a piezoelectric crystal, the electric displacement also varies periodically. Generally, the displacement lags behind the applied field so that the two are not in phase. Since the amount of this phase difference depends on the frequency of the alternating field, at some frequency, called the *resonance frequency*, the two are exactly in phase. This effect, therefore, can be used to determine whether a crystal is piezoelectric and hence whether its structure is centrosymmetric or not. Alternatively, because the frequency range at which resonance occurs in most piezoelectric crystals is very sharp, such crystals (for example, quartz) can be used for frequency controls in radio transmitters and have also been used in electronic clocks.

In general, any mechanical stress can produce an electric polarization in a piezoelectric crystal; that is, it does not matter whether the stress is applied in compression, dilation, or shear. For example, consider a piezoelectric crystal placed between two metal plates, as shown in Fig. 5. If the crystal is compressed by an applied mechanical stress σ, a mechanical strain ε_m is produced in the crystal,

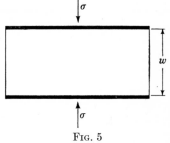

$$\varepsilon_m = \frac{\sigma}{E} = \frac{\Delta w}{w} \qquad (21)$$

Fig. 5

where E is Young's modulus. The applied stress also produces a polarization density P in the crystal which is proportional to the magnitude of the applied stress:

$$P = \eta\sigma \qquad (22)$$

where η is the *piezoelectric constant*. If the two plates are connected, that is, short-circuited, $\varepsilon = 0$ and, according to (10), the electric displacement

$$D = 0 + 4\pi P$$
$$= 4\pi\eta\sigma. \qquad (23)$$

On the other hand, if an electric field is applied to the crystal in Fig. 5 in the absence of an applied stress, then the induced strain is proportional to the applied field:

$$\varepsilon_m = \eta\varepsilon. \qquad (24)$$

Note that according to (3) the electric displacement D is also proportional to the applied field intensity. When both an external field and a stress are applied to the crystal, therefore, the electric displacement becomes

$$D = \kappa_e\varepsilon + 4\pi\eta\sigma \qquad (25)$$

and the internal strain

$$\varepsilon_m = \eta\varepsilon + \frac{\sigma}{E}. \qquad (26)$$

Ferroelectricity. The structures of some piezoelectric crystals are asymmetric in such a way that they are spontaneously polarized in the absence of an external field. The electric field produced by the permanent dipoles inside the crystal, however, is usually masked by charges on the crystal's surface or by twinning inside the crystal. Since, according to (7), the polarization due to permanent dipoles present inside an insulator is temperature-dependent, a change in the temperature of the crystal produces a change in its polarization which can be detected. This is called, therefore, the *pyroelectric effect*, and it turns out that crystals belonging to ten out of the twenty piezoelectric crystal classes exhibit this property. If it is possible to reverse the polarization direction of a pyroelectric crystal by applying a sufficiently intense external field, then the crystal is said to be a *ferroelectric* and the phenomenon of reversing the direction of polarity is called the *ferroelectric effect*. It should be noted that both piezoelectricity and pyroelectricity are inherent properties of a crystal, due, entirely, to its atomic arrangement or crystal structure. Ferroelectricity, on the other hand, is an effect produced in a pyroelectric crystal by the application of an external electric field.

The term *ferroelectricity* is applied to this phenomenon because it is quite similar to the phenomenon of ferromagnetism described in Chapter 10. Many ferroelectric crystals undergo a transformation at a certain temperature, frequently called the *Curie point*, above which they are no longer polar even though they may still have noncentrosymmetric structures. The dielectric constant of these crystals increases anomalously at these temperatures and, in general, behaves quite similarly to the Curie-Weiss law of ferromagnetism.

$$\kappa_e = \frac{C}{T - T_C} + \kappa_0 \tag{27}$$

where C is the so-called Curie constant, T_C is the transformation temperature, and κ_0 represents the contribution due to electronic polarization as distinct from the ionic contribution. When $T \simeq T_C$, $\kappa_e \gg \kappa_0$ and the electronic contribution can be neglected.

Below the transition temperature, ferroelectric crystals usually consist of multiple twins. Each twin individual is spontaneously polarized in a specific crystallographic direction; however, the directions of polarization of neighboring twins are different. Consequently, *ferroelectric domains* exist in the crystals, similar to the domain structure of ferromagnetic crystals, as illustrated in Fig. 6 which shows an electron micrograph of domains formed in a $BaTiO_3$ crystal. The free electric charges present on the surfaces of a uniformly polarized insulator produce a depolarizing field which makes such a uniformly polarized crystal unstable. The presence of adjacent domains having opposing directions of spontaneous polarization, on the other hand, serves to reduce the depolarizing field and stabilizes the crystal. As in the case of ferromagnetic domains, this energy is stored in the domain walls and an equilibrium condition is reached between the number and size of domains present and the thickness of the walls that separate them. On an atomic scale, there is a difference between ferroelectric and ferromagnetic domains. This is so because the crystal structure of a ferroelectric crystal undergoes considerable distortion below the Curie point, in a direction determined by the structure rather than by the applied field direction. (It will be recalled that magnetostriction depends on the relative field direction which can be arbitrarily chosen.) Consequently, the strains produced

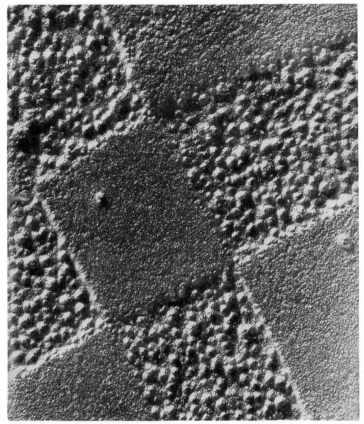

FIG. 6. Electron micrograph of the surface of a single crystal of $BaTiO_3$ showing ferroelectric domain pattern. (Photographed at a magnification of approximately 30,000 times by D. P. Cameron.)

by such a distortion play an even larger role in the behavior of ferroelectric domains than they do in the case of ferromagnetic domains.

As might be expected, by analogy to ferromagnetism, the presence of domains in a ferroelectric crystal produces a hysteresis in the polarization when an alternating electric field is applied. Consider the hysteresis loop of a typical ferroelectric crystal shown in Fig. 7. To start, assume that the crystal has equal numbers of domains with oppositely directed

polarizations.   When an electric field is applied parallel to a crystallographic direction, the domains whose polarization is more nearly parallel
to the field direction have a lower energy so that they grow in size at the
expense of the antiparallel domains.   As the field is increased, therefore,
the total polarization of the crystal increases rapidly (curve OA in Fig. 7)
until a saturation value is reached (AB) at which point the crystal is a
single domain.   This is usually accompanied by a distortion of the
crystal structure in the form of an elongation along the polarization
direction.   When the field later decreases to zero, a number of domains
retain their orientation parallel to this crystallographic direction so that

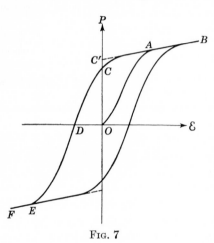

the polarization does not return to
zero.   This polarization is called
the *remnant polarization* and is
shown at C in Fig. 7.   If the line
AB is extrapolated backward to C',
then the polarization value of a
single domain at zero applied field
is obtained.   This is so because the
entire crystal acts as a single domain in the AB region.   Thus C'
represents the magnitude of the
spontaneous polarization of a single
domain.   When there are equal
numbers of oppositely directed,
spontaneously polarized domains in

FIG. 7

the crystal, its polarization again
becomes zero.   It is necessary, therefore, to apply a reverse field to the
crystal in order to reverse the polarization directions of a sufficient number of domains.   The magnitude of the field required to remove the
remnant polarization is called the *coercive field* and is indicated by D in
Fig. 7.   As the magnitude of the reverse field is increased further, the
saturation value of polarization in the reverse direction is reached (EF).
Reversing the field again then traces out the curve FEB, and so forth.
It follows from this discussion that an insulator crystal having a suitable
crystal structure can exhibit the ferroelectric effect only if the coercive
field required to reverse its polarization direction is not so large as to cause
electric breakdown of the crystal.   By comparison, ferroelectric crystals
having relatively low spontaneous polarizabilities are frequently used in
computers as memory cells, the direction of polarization indicating, say,
a plus or a minus sign.

    There are several groups of crystals that are known to be ferroelectrics.
The crystals typifying each group are rochelle salt, $NaK(C_4H_4O_6) \cdot 4H_2O$;
potassium dihydrogen phosphate, KH_2PO_4; barium titanate, $BaTiO_3$;
and guanidine compounds such as $C(NH_2)_3Al(SO_4)_2 \cdot 6H_2O$.   It should

be borne in mind that each of these groups contains a number of isomorphous or isostructural crystals all of which are ferroelectrics. As
already indicated, the property of ferroelectricity is related to the crystal
structure. So far it has not been possible, therefore, to devise a single
theory to explain this effect in different crystals, although several phenomenological theories have been proposed for rochelle salt and for
barium titanate. BaTiO₃ has the relatively simple perovskite structure
described in the next chapter so that its ferroelectric behavior is briefly
described below.

Above 393°K, barium titanate has the cubic perovskite structure shown
in Fig. 3 of Chapter 15 and it is not ferroelectric. By analogy to magnetic
terminology, it is said to be *paraelectric* at these temperatures. Below
393°K, the crystal structure becomes distorted by an elongation in the
polarization direction along one of the cube axes and a contraction at
right angles to it. The resulting structure is tetragonal ($c/a = 1.01$ at
room temperature) with the polarization direction parallel to [001].
Below room temperature ($\sim278°K$) another transformation takes place
resulting in a discontinuous change in the polarization direction parallel
to [110] in the original cubic structure. The resulting orthorhombic
structure is best described by taking a parallel to [110], b parallel to
[1$\bar{1}$0], and c parallel to [001] in the original cube. A third transformation
occurs at approximately 193°K, at which point the polarization direction
becomes [111] of the perovskite cube and the structure has rhombohedral
symmetry. The reasons for the stability of these various structures can
be explained by applying known principles of thermodynamics. The
result is a phenomenological theory which postulates that the local field
produced by the polarization increases at a faster rate than the elastic
restoring forces binding the ions in the crystal. The relative displacements of the titanium ions inside the oxygen octahedra coordinating
them are then stabilized at different positions in the three different structures. The resulting build-up in the local field's intensity is sometimes
called the *polarization catastrophy*.

It is of interest to observe what happens to the dielectric constant near
the transformation temperature. Assuming dielectric isotropy, (19)
can be written after rearrangement of terms†

$$\kappa_e = \frac{1 + (8\pi/3) \sum_i n_i\alpha_i}{1 - (4\pi/3) \sum_i n_i\alpha_i} \tag{28}$$

† This assumption is strictly valid only for the metal atoms in BaTiO₃. The
environment of oxygen atoms is not cubic; however, the effect of the dipoles in the
spherical cavity used in calculating the local field in (17) can be neglected for present
purposes.

where n_i is the number of i atoms having polarizabilities α_i. When $\sum_i n_i \alpha_i = \frac{3}{4}\pi$, the dielectric constant becomes infinite and P has some finite value and $\mathcal{E} = 0$ according to (18). This is the condition for the so-called polarization catastrophy described above.

For small deviations of the sum in (28) from its critical value, it is possible to substitute for $4\pi/3 \sum_i n_i \alpha_i$ the quantity $1 - \delta$, where $\delta \ll 1$.

Substituting in (28) then gives $\kappa_e \simeq 3/\delta$, and assuming that the deviation δ is temperature-dependent according to

$$\delta \simeq \frac{C}{3}(T - T_C) \qquad (29)$$

the Curie-Weiss law near the transition temperature

$$\kappa_e \simeq \frac{C}{T - T_C} \qquad (30)$$

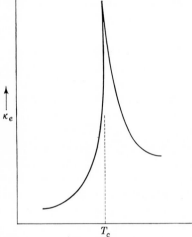

T_c

Temperature $\longrightarrow$

FIG. 8

is obtained. The plot in Fig. 8 shows the dependence of the dielectric constant on temperature in a ferroelectric crystal. This is another example of the so-called λ curve already discussed in Chapter 8 in connection with other crystallographic transformations such as specific heat, for example.

Ionic conductivity. As mentioned in the introduction to this chapter, when an electric field is applied to an ionic insulator an electric current may be produced. Since the number of electrons occupying quantum states in the conduction band of an insulator is negligibly small, it is necessary to postulate that the current is carried by positively or negatively charged ions, or both. Now, in a crystal in which all the ions occupy their appropriate equipoints or so-called *sites*, the motion of ions is not possible, since there is no way for an ion to move without leaving its proper site. It is necessary to conclude, therefore, that the current carriers are either interstitial ions or else vacant ionic sites. The mechanism whereby interstitial ions or vacant sites can be created has already been described in Chapter 5. It will be recalled from that chapter that ion vacancies are called *Schottky defects* and interstitial ions plus compensating ion vacancies are called *Frenkel defects*.

The generation of Schottky defects proceeds by the migration of, say, a positive ion to the surface of the crystal, thereby leaving a *positive vacancy* behind in the crystal. In order to preserve charge neutrality, it is necessary that a negative ion also migrate to the crystal's surface, creating a *negative vacancy* thereby. The result of the generation of such pairs of vacancies is that the volume of the crystal increases while its density decreases. On the other hand, a Frenkel defect is produced when an ion migrates into an interstitial position in the structure which is sufficiently far removed from the resulting vacancy so that direct recombination can be ruled out. This process does not disturb the macroscopic charge neutrality nor does it appreciably change the volume or the density of the crystal. It is thus possible to determine which of these two types of imperfections is present in a crystal by careful density measurements.

The process whereby ions or vacancies move through the crystal is called *ionic diffusion.* Suppose that a layer of radioactive sodium (Na^{23}) is deposited on one side of a sodium chloride crystal and the crystal is maintained at some elevated temperature for a finite period of time. It can be shown by subsequent sectioning of the crystal and measuring the radioactivity of successive sections that the radioactive sodium diffuses through the crystal in a regular way; that is, the concentration of Na^{23} atoms varies regularly with depth in the crystal. The diffusion process can be expressed analytically by *Fick's law* which states that the number of atoms crossing a unit area per unit time, that is, the flux of atoms, J, is proportional to the gradient of their concentration N. Considering diffusion in only one direction,

$$J = -D \frac{dN}{dx} \tag{31}$$

where D is the diffusion coefficient and the minus sign indicates that the flux is in a direction opposite to the direction of the gradient; that is, if the gradient increases to the right, diffusion proceeds to the left.

One usually distinguishes the diffusion of atoms normally present in the crystal from the diffusion of other kinds of atoms through the crystal by calling the former process *self-diffusion.* The atomic mechanisms whereby self-diffusion can occur are pictured in Fig. 9. Four distinct processes are possible:

A. Direct interchange between two atoms. Because of the need to displace neighboring atoms and, in the case of ionic compounds, the large repulsive forces between atoms of like charge, this mechanism requires a relatively large amount of energy.

B. Migration of an interstitial atom subsequent to formation of a Frenkel defect.

C. Atomic displacement into a neighboring vacancy subsequent to forma-

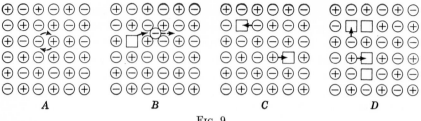

Fɪɢ. 9

tion of a Schottky defect. This is usually described as a *diffusion of vacancies* in the opposite direction.

D. *Diffusion of pairs of vacancies* by means of atomic movements into either of two adjacent vacancies. Since the pair moves by the motion of either vacancy, provided that the pair is not split up in the process, the energy required to move the pair is actually less than that required to move an isolated vacancy.

The energy required for any of the above processes to operate, that is, the sum of the energies of defect formation and subsequent migration, is called the *activation energy* of that process. Without distinguishing between the different processes, it has been observed that the temperature dependence of the coefficient of self-diffusion is related to the activation energy φ by

$$D = D_0 e^{-\varphi/kT} \tag{32}$$

where D_0 is a constant for the crystal.

The ionic conductivity due to monovalent ions of one sign, that is, positive or negative ions but not both, is

$$\sigma_{\text{ionic}} = eN\mu_{\text{ionic}} \tag{33}$$

where N is the number of ionic sites of one sign, and the mobility of these ions, according to Einstein, is

$$\mu_{\text{ionic}} = \frac{eD}{kT}. \tag{34}$$

Combining (33) and (34) and substituting (32) for D, the ionic conductivity is given by

$$\sigma_{\text{ionic}} = \frac{e^2 N}{kT} D$$

$$= \frac{e^2 N}{kT} D_0 e^{-\varphi/kT}. \tag{35}$$

Figure 10 shows an idealized plot of $\ln \sigma$ as a function of reciprocal temperature for an alkali halide crystal. According to (35), the slope of the straight line in such a plot can be used to determine the activation energy. As shown in Fig. 10, the curve consists of two straight-line portions; hence there are two activation energies for the two different temperature ranges. For sodium chloride, $\varphi_1 = 1.80$ eV in the high-temperature region, and $\varphi_2 = 0.77$ eV in the lower-temperature region.

The reason for the two slopes can be explained as follows: At high temperatures, the thermal energy is sufficiently great to create vacancies and the activation energy represents a sum of the energies required for vacancy generation and the motion of ions into the vacancies. At lower temperature, the thermal energy is only large enough to allow the migration of atoms into vacancies already present in the crystal. Recent experimental evidence has shown that these vacancies are primarily due

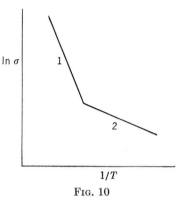

FIG. 10

to the inclusion of divalent metal atoms in substitution for the monovalent metal atoms in the crystal's structure. For each divalent metal thus incorporated in the crystal, a positive vacancy must be present nearby in order to maintain charge neutrality. Similarly to the case of semiconductors, the low-temperature conductivity is said to take place

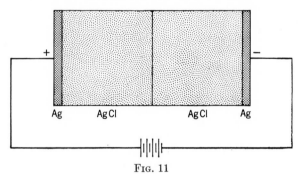

FIG. 11

in the extrinsic region, because the presence of divalent impurity atoms is required for conductivity to occur in this temperature region. On the other hand, the high-temperature conductivity is characteristic of the crystal and is called the intrinsic conductivity for this reason.

In view of the relatively small mobilities of ions, the Hall effect in these crystals is usually too small to be measured accurately, and it is not possible to determine the sign of the charge carriers by this means. It is possible to devise a simple alternative experiment for this purpose, however. Suppose that two identical crystals of silver chloride (AgCl) are placed between two silver electrodes and an electric field is applied, as shown in Fig. 11. Then the following situations are possible. If the electric current is carried by Ag^{+1} ions, they will move toward the negative electrode so that, after a while, the negative electrode is increased in size at the expense of the positive electrode. In this case, the salt acts merely as a conductor of positive ions and is not otherwise affected. If, on the other hand, the current is due to negative-ion migration, then they will collect on the positively charged electrode, where they will combine with the silver to form new AgCl. Thus, after a while, the positive

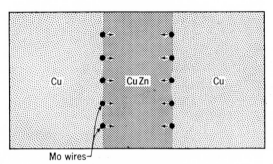

FIG. 12. Cu-CuZn-Cu diffusion couple. As the zinc diffuses out of the brass into the adjacent copper, the Mo wires move toward each other.

electrode will appear to have lost silver to the salt crystal adjacent to it which, concurrently, must increase in size. If both conduction processes are operative, an intermediate result should be obtained. It turns out that, in AgCl and in most alkali halides, the bulk of the current is carried by the metal ions. In barium and lead halides, conversely, the majority carriers are the negative halide ions.

It is interesting to note, in passing, that the self-diffusion in metals also proceeds predominantly by means of vacancies rather than through the migration of interstitials or the direct exchange between pairs of atoms. Suppose that a piece of brass (CuZn) is surrounded on two sides by copper and that wires of some relatively inert metal such as molybdenum are imbedded at the interfaces in the Cu-brass-Cu *diffusion couple* (Fig. 12). Upon subsequent heating of the sample to allow diffusion to occur, it is observed that zinc diffuses out of the brass and into the copper and the molybdenum wires on opposite sides of the brass core move toward each other. This is called the *Kirkendall effect*, and it is explained by postulating that the diffusion coefficient of zinc is greater than that of copper so that zinc diffuses out of the brass faster than copper can diffuse into the brass. The net flow of mass out of the brass, or, in other words, the net flow of vacancies into the brass causes it to decrease in size as evidenced by the motion of the wires. The Kirkendall effect has also been observed in Cu-Sn, Cu-Au, and other metal systems.

Electric breakdown. When an insulator is placed between two metal plates and a very large electric field is applied, a relatively large electric current may flow between the plates, provided that the electric field intensity exceeds a critical value. This process is called *electric breakdown* in an insulator. When the crystal is actually a semiconductor, the

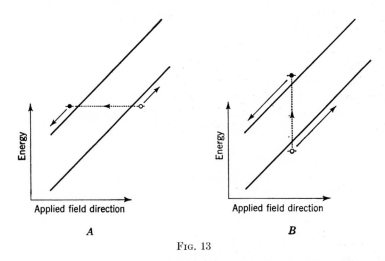

Fɪɢ. 13

breakdown can occur by two distinct processes. As described in Chapter 12, the application of an electric field skews the energy-band model, as shown in Fig. 13. If the applied field is sufficiently large, there exists a possibility that some of the electrons occupying states in the valence band can move into quantum states of like energy in the conduction band, as shown in Fig. 13*A*. This mechanism was first proposed by C. Zener and is called *Zener breakdown*. Another possible breakdown mechanism is shown in Fig. 13*B*. If a free electron gains more kinetic energy from the applied field than it loses in electron-atom collisions, then it is possible for it to lose this excess energy in a collision with a valence electron. This process results, therefore, in the production of an electron-hole pair, and now the two electrons can, in turn, produce four more conduction electrons, and so forth.† This rapid increase in the number of conduction electrons is called the *avalanche breakdown* and requires relatively high fields ($\sim10^5$ volts/cm in Ge).

The breakdown processes in true insulator crystals are not as well

† Actually, the holes also contribute to this process.

understood. Nevertheless, it is possible to distinguish five distinct processes:

1. *Thermal breakdown* is produced in insulators when heat is generated by the ionic currents faster than the crystal can dissipate it. Since the conductivity of heat in insulators occurs quite slowly, it is possible that temperatures in excess of the crystal's melting point can be attained in parts of the crystal. The resulting local melting of the crystal increases the ionic mobilities and electrical breakdown ensues.

2. *Electrolytic breakdown* can occur whenever conducting paths are present in the crystal. These paths form with the aid of imperfections in the crystal, such as dislocations, or along the dendritic or lineage structure interfaces discussed in Chapter 7.

3. *Dipole breakdown* may be caused in insulators either by polarizable atoms (molecules) or by permanent dipoles already present. When such dipoles surround a stressed region, they can produce local impurity or imperfection states lying in the forbidden-energy gap of the crystal. The much lower ionization potentials of electrons attached to dipoles then facilitate breakdown. When the breakdown occurs at the surface of a crystal, it is commonly called *flash-over*.

4. *Collision breakdown* is similar to the avalanche breakdown in semiconductors. Because of impurities in the crystal, there are some electrons available for conduction. When the energies of these electrons become sufficiently great they collide with other electrons, producing ever-increasing numbers of electrons and holes.

5. *Gas-discharge breakdown* can occur whenever the insulator contains occluded gas bubbles. For example, the silicate layers in a micacious crystal are frequently separated by thin adsorbed layers of air or other gases. Since the electric field required to ionize the gas ($\sim 10^4$ volts/cm) is much less than that required for electric breakdown in an insulator ($\sim 10^6$ volts/cm), the gas ionizes first, and the gas ions bombard the internal crystal surfaces, causing them to deteriorate, until complete electrical breakdown of the insulator occurs.

Optical properties

Refraction. Most insulator crystals are transparent to visible light. This is so because the energy gap separating the valence band from the conduction band is quite large. The energy of the incident light photons is too small, therefore, to excite any electrons from quantum states in the valence band to the higher energy states in the conduction band, and the photons are not absorbed by the crystal. When a light ray passes from air into such a crystal, its propagation direction usually is altered by a small amount. This phenomenon is called the *refraction* of light, and the angle of refraction r is related to the angle of incidence i (Fig. 14) according to *Snell's law*,

$$\frac{\sin i}{\sin r} = \frac{n_2}{n_1} \tag{36}$$

where n_1 is the *index of refraction* of air and n_2 is the index of refraction of the crystal. The index of refraction of vacuum is set equal to unity and the other indices are determined accordingly. Since the index of refraction of air then is 1.0003, air is frequently used as the reference standard instead. Usually some of the incident light is also reflected, and the angle of reflection equals the angle of incidence. Note that, if the index of refraction of the crystal n_2 is less than the index of the surrounding medium n_1, it is possible that for some value of the angle of incidence $(n_1/n_2) \sin i > 1$. Since $\sin r$ cannot exceed unity, none of the light is refracted; that is, all of it must be reflected. Thus, when the index of refraction of the

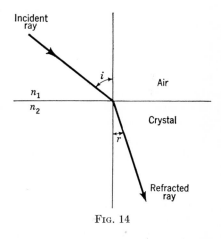

Fig. 14

first medium is less than that of the second medium, then, for angles of incidence greater than some critical value, *total reflection* occurs.

The physical reason for refraction is that light travels more slowly in a dielectric medium than in vacuum. The velocity of light in a dielectric is determined by the index of refraction, $v = c/n$, where c is the velocity of light in vacuum ($c = 2.998 \times 10^{10}$ cm/sec). Since light is a form of electromagnetic radiation, the retardation is due to the polarization of the atoms in such a way that the induced electric field opposes the electric field of the incident light. It can be shown that the dielectric constant of a dielectric crystal is equal to the square of its index of refraction so that the Clausius-Mosotti equation (19) can be written

$$\frac{n^2 - 1}{n^2 + 2} = \frac{4\pi}{3} \sum_i n_i \alpha_i \tag{37}$$

which is called the *Lorenz-Lorentz equation*. When n is very nearly equal to unity, so that $n^2 + 2 \simeq 3$, equation (37) becomes

$$n^2 = \kappa_e = 1 + 4\pi \sum_i n_i \alpha_i \tag{38}$$

which can be compared with (6). Multiplying both sides of (37) by M/D, where M is the molecular weight and D is the density,

$$\frac{M}{D}\frac{n^2 - 1}{n^2 + 2} = \frac{4\pi}{3}N_0\alpha \tag{39}$$

where N_0 is Avogadro's number and α is the polarizability of a molecule, so that (39) can be used to calculate the *molar polarizability* or the *molar refractivity*. This equation allows one to relate the index of refraction of a crystal to its structure.

Birefringence. The index of refraction of glasses and of crystals belonging to the isometric system is independent of the direction of propagation of the light. Such crystals are said to be optically *isotropic*. It is important, for the discussion in this section, to realize that, when light propagates along a certain direction, the electric field varies sinusoidally at right angles to the propagation direction. The electronic displacements and the resulting dipoles, therefore, are also orthogonal to the propagation direction. In tetragonal and hexagonal crystals, a light ray traveling parallel to c encounters an isotropic structure, since $a_1 = a_2$ in these crystals. (Note that this is just like a light ray traveling along a_3 in a cubic crystal.) A light ray traveling in a general direction, however, encounters an anisotropic structure so that it is not surprising that it travels with a different velocity. The c axis is, therefore, an optically unique axis in such crystals, and it is called the *optic axis*. Since there is only one unique direction in tetragonal and hexagonal crystals, they are called *uniaxial* crystals.

In order to study the properties of anisotropic crystals it is necessary to use plane-polarized light, that is, light whose electric field is constrained to alternate in a single plane containing the direction of propagation. The polarization direction is usually called the *vibration direction* of the light. When a ray of plane-polarized light traverses a uniaxial crystal parallel to the optic axis, then, regardless of the vibration direction of the electric field, the index of refraction is the same and is usually denoted ω. When a ray traverses the crystal along a direction which is normal to the optic axis, the index of refraction depends on the vibration direction of the electric field. If the vibration direction is also normal to the optic axis, then the index is, as before, ω. When the vibration direction is parallel to the optic axis, the index of refraction is different and is called ε. When the vibration direction lies between these two directions, then the light ray is split into two components whose electric fields are constrained to vibrate in directions respectively parallel and normal to the optic axis, as shown in Fig. 15. The component parallel to the optic axis has a vibration amplitude $\varepsilon \sin\phi$, and its propagation velocity is determined by ε while the amplitude of the other components is $\varepsilon \cos\phi$

and its velocity is determined by ω. The two indices of refraction ε and ω, therefore, are called the *principal indices of refraction* of a uniaxial crystal. If $\varepsilon > \omega$, the crystal is said to be *positive uniaxial*, and if $\varepsilon < \omega$, the crystal is said to be *negative uniaxial*.

Returning to Fig. 15, it is clear that, since the velocities of propagation of the two components are different, the two components emerge from the crystal with a relative *phase difference* whose magnitude depends not only on the relative propagation velocities (indices of refraction) but

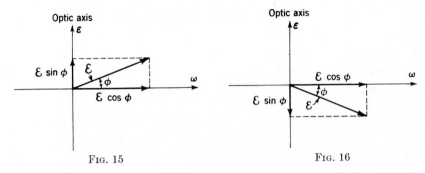

FIG. 15   FIG. 16

also on the thickness of the crystal. Suppose that the thickness of the crystal is such that one component is exactly one-half wavelength behind the other components; that is, they differ in phase by 180°. Then the emerging light has the two electric field components directed as shown in Fig. 16, and the resultant electric field is rotated by an amount 2ϕ from its original direction shown in Fig. 15. The phase of the component whose vibration direction is parallel to the optic axis is equal to $2\pi\nu t/v_\varepsilon$, where ν is the frequency of the incident light, t is the thickness of the crystal, and v_ε is its propagation velocity. Similarly, the phase of the other component is $2\pi\nu t/v_\omega$. The difference in phase δ, therefore, is

$$\begin{aligned}
\delta &= \frac{2\pi\nu t}{v_\varepsilon} - \frac{2\pi\nu t}{v_\omega} \\
&= \frac{2\pi\nu t}{c}(\varepsilon - \omega) \\
&= \frac{2\pi t}{\lambda}(\varepsilon - \omega)
\end{aligned} \tag{40}$$

since c/ν is the wavelength of the light in vacuum. Relation (40) can be used to determine the thickness of a so-called *half-wave plate* by setting $\delta = \pi$. Note that the relative phases depend on the frequency (wavelength) of the light.

Suppose that the incident light ray is neither parallel nor normal to the optic axis. For example, consider light incident at point A, in a direction which is normal to one of the natural cleavage faces of a calcite

rhombohedron, as shown in Fig. 17.   The incident light ray is observed
to split up into two rays.   This phenomenon is called *double refraction*.
One ray, designated the *O* ray in Fig. 17, traverses the crystal without
refraction according to Snell's law for normal incidence.   (When $i = 0°$,
sin $i = 0$, and sin $r = 0$.)   The other ray is refracted, however, and

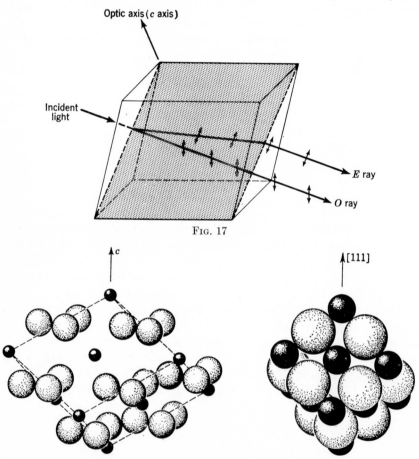

Fig. 17

Fig. 18.   Crystal structure of $CaCO_3$ compared with that of NaCl.   Only the Ca
atoms and CO_3 groups situated on the front faces of the calcite rhombohedron are
shown.   (The carbon atoms are hidden from sight by the much larger oxygen atoms.)

violates Snell's law.   For this reason it is called the *extraordinary ray E*
to distinguish it from the *ordinary ray O*.   Regardless of the vibration
direction of the incident light, the extraordinary ray is constrained to
vibrate in a plane containing the optic axis and the incident ray called
the *principal plane* (shaded plane in Fig. 17).   The ordinary ray, on the
other hand, is constrained to vibrate in a direction at right angles to the

principal plane. The relative velocities of the two rays are determined by the two principal indices of refraction, and the difference between these indices is used to measure the *birefringence* of a crystal.

Calcite, $CaCO_3$, is a negative uniaxial crystal (for the D line of sodium, $\lambda = 5893$ Å, $\varepsilon = 1.486$, and $\omega = 1.658$) whose relatively large birefringence (0.172 for Na D) can be easily understood when its crystal structure is considered. The structure of calcite resembles that of a NaCl cube tipped so that its [111] direction is parallel to the c axis of calcite (Fig. 18). Note that the CO_3 groups form triangles whose planes are oriented normal to the c axis which is parallel to the optic axis of this

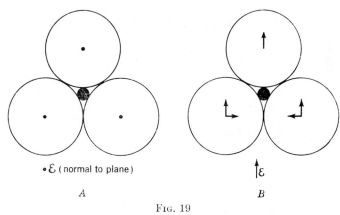

$\bullet \, \mathcal{E}$ (normal to plane)

$\uparrow \mathcal{E}$

A　　　　　　　　　　　　*B*

Fig. 19

crystal. The large difference between the indices of refraction, for light vibrating parallel to and light vibrating normal to the optic axis, is due to this orientation of the carbonate groups. Consider a carbonate group consisting of three oxygen atoms lying at the corners of an equilateral triangle and the carbon atom at its center, as shown in Fig. 19. When the vibration direction of the electric field is normal to the plane of the triangle (Fig. 19A), the oxygen atoms are polarized so that the induced dipoles are also normal to the plane of the triangle. Their direction is such that it opposes the direction of the external field. Each dipole, therefore, tends to depolarize its neighboring oxygen dipoles. When the vibration direction of the field is parallel to the plane of the triangle, then two of the induced dipoles tend to reinforce the third and, simultaneously, the third dipole tends to reinforce the other two. This can be seen from the induced field directions indicated by small arrows in Fig. 19B. Although the fields in two adjacent oxygen atoms oppose each other, it can be shown that the average increase in the induced electric field intensity exceeds the average depolarizing field intensity. Accordingly, a light ray vibrating in the plane of the CO_3 groups in calcite is retarded more than a light ray vibrating in a direction normal to the plane.   Since the optic axis of calcite is normal to the plane of the CO_3 groups and since the index of refraction is inversely proportional to the propagation velocity, $\varepsilon < \omega$, and calcite is optically negative.

Crystals belonging to the orthorhombic, monoclinic, and triclinic systems have two optic axes and are called *biaxial* crystals.   There are three mutually perpendicular vibration directions and three indices of refraction called α, β, and γ.   These directions of vibration bear definite relations to the crystallographic symmetry of a biaxial crystal and the magnitudes of the indices of refraction are intimately related to its structure.   Many examples of such relationships can be found among the silicates whose structures are briefly discussed in the next chapter.   For example, Table 1 lists the refractive indices of quartz which has a three-

Table 1
Birefringence of silicates
(Na D line $\lambda = 5893$ Å)

Mineral	Indices of refraction	Birefringence
Quartz	$\varepsilon = 1.553,\ \omega = 1.544$	$\varepsilon - \omega = 0.009$
Hornblende	$\alpha = 1.629,\ \beta = 1.642,\ \gamma = 1.653$	$\gamma - \alpha = 0.024$
Muscovite	$\alpha = 1.561,\ \beta = 1.590,\ \gamma = 1.594$	$\gamma - \alpha = 0.033$

dimensional network structure, hornblende which has a double-chain structure, and muscovite which has a sheet structure.   As expected from their structures, the birefringence of quartz is much smaller than that of the more anisotropic structures of hornblende and muscovite. Note that the birefringence of biaxial crystals is determined by the numerical difference between the largest and the smallest index.

It should be obvious from the above discussion that the optical properties of crystals are strongly structure-sensitive.   In fact, it turns out that the refractive indices of all transparent crystals are as unique as fingerprints.   This immediately suggests that refractive-index determinations can be used as a routine analytical tool for identifying such crystals.   Mineralogists realized this long before the physical causes of the refraction of light were fully understood and have compiled extensive reference tables for just this purpose.   In this connection, it should be noted that x-ray diffraction diagrams of crystals are also related to crystal structure and can be used in an analogous way for identification purposes.   Moreover, x-ray diffraction has the advantage that the crystals need not be transparent.   Both methods of analysis, nevertheless, are in widespread use today.

Color centers.   As already noted, most insulator crystals are transparent to visible light.   Occasionally, however, these crystals appear to be colored. It is believed that the color of a crystal is due to the selective absorption of some component of the visible spectrum by certain imperfections, called *color centers*, which are present in the crystal. These imperfections may be interstitial impurity atoms such as transition-metal ions. Alternatively, they may be vacancies in the structure produced by deviations from stoichiometry so that there are present excess positive ions accompanied by negative vacancies, or excess negative ions accompanied by positive vacancies. Thus, when excess Zn is present in ZnO it takes on a yellow color, whereas excess lithium in LiF turns the crystal pink and excess potassium in KCl makes the crystal appear violet.

When an alkali halide crystal is heated in an atmosphere containing an excess of the alkali metal vapor, the excess metal atoms deposit on the crystal's surface. Halogen ions then may diffuse to the surface where they combine with the metal atoms which have become ionized by losing a valence electron. This electron, in turn, can diffuse into the crystal until it encounters a negative-ion vacancy with which it combines. A similar end result is obtained when an excess of the alkali metal is incorporated in the crystal during its growth. The quantum state of such a trapped electron lies somewhere in the forbidden-energy region. The exact energy value of this state depends only on the environment of the vacancy, that is, the crystal structure, and not on the metal atom from which the electron originally came. It does not matter, therefore, whether the excess metal present in the crystal is the same as the metal normally present in the host crystal or not. When the crystal is irradiated with white light, some component of this light has the appropriate energy to excite the trapped electron to a higher-lying quantum state, so that it becomes absorbed by the crystal in the process. Although the process of absorption by these so-called *F centers* is only approximately understood, it is believed that the electron is excited to another quantum state also lying in the forbidden region. Actually, a range of energies can excite this electron so that an *absorption band*, called the *F band*, is observed. It has been shown that the total absorption is directly proportional to the number of excess metal atoms in the crystal, that is, the number of *F* centers produced. The *F* absorption band is not symmetrical about a central energy value but has a tail on the short-wavelength side. This tail is believed to be due to electronic transitions to quantum states having higher energies but still lying below the bottom of the conduction band. The name *K* band has been proposed for this section of the absorption-band spectrum.

As might be expected, the excited electrons should be able to contribute to electrical conductivity since they now occupy quantum states close to the bottom of the conduction band. Photocurrents are indeed observed; however, it is necessary that electrons flowing to the positive electrode be replaced by other electrons injected into the crystal by the negative electrode, so that space charges do not build up inside the crystal. Alternatively, in the absence of an external electric field, it is reasonable to expect that the excited electrons can return to their ground state by the emission of a photon of light. Luminescence is actually observed in additively colored alkali halides; however, it is necessary to maintain the crystals at low temperatures so that the electrons are not thermally excited to quantum states in the conduction band.

It is possible to produce halide crystals containing excess halogen ions. Such excess ions are accompanied by positive-ion vacancies which serve to trap holes quite similarly to the way the anion vacancies trapped the electrons. In order to distinguish the color centers thus produced, they are called *V centers*. It turns out that the absorption spectra of crystals containing *V* centers show several absorption maxima so that there is apparently more than one kind of transition possible. These absorption maxima are usually designated V_1 bands, V_2 bands, etc.

A curious effect is observed when a crystal already containing *F* centers is irradiated at elevated temperatures by light that is absorbed by these *F* centers. The absorption of the *F* band is gradually decreased following such an irradiation (this process is called *bleaching*), and a new absorption band lying on the long-wavelength side of the *F* band appears. This new band is called the *F' band* and it is believed to be produced in the following way. Some electrons that are excited by the incident light become "free" electrons by absorbing thermal energy. These electrons subsequently can combine with other *F* centers. This produces an *F' center* which is believed to be an *F* center that contains two electrons. As expected from this model, when a crystal containing *F'* centers is irradiated by light that is absorbed by these centers, *F* centers are produced in turn. Since the energy of this light is less than that necessary to excite electrons trapped in *F* centers, the reversible effects described above are consistent with the energy-band model proposed to explain them.

It is possible to produce color centers in still another way. When a crystal is irradiated with high-energy radiation in the form of x-rays, γ-rays, or neutrons, color centers are also produced. The process in this case first consists of the production of recoil electrons by the incident radiation, followed by the interaction of these electrons with valence electrons to produce electron-hole pairs. Consequently, such irradiated crystals usually contain both *F* and *V* centers. Unlike the stoichiometrically deficient crystals, however, the crystals that are colored by radiation can be easily bleached by reirradiating the crystals with visible light or by annealing them. This is so because the excited electrons and holes ultimately recombine with each other. Although not discussed here, other types of color centers have also been observed; however, their nature is not well understood.

Magnetic properties

Exchange interactions. The fundamental magnetic properties of most crystals, namely, paramagnetism and diamagnetism, have already been discussed in Chapter 10. It is suggested that the reader review this material prior to reading this section. It has also been pointed out in that chapter that certain crystals, notably iron, nickel, and cobalt crystals, are ferromagnetic. The property of ferromagnetism arises whenever the magnetic moments, due to the spins of the valence electrons of atoms in the crystal, align themselves parallel to each other in the absence of an external magnetic field. In these crystals there is an *exchange interaction* between the spin moments of neighboring atoms. This exchange interaction is similar to covalent-bond formation in hydrogen, as was first suggested by Heitler, and is due to the overlap of the outer electron orbitals of two adjacent atoms. Because the exchange forces decrease rapidly with increasing distance between the atoms, only nearest-neighbor interactions need be considered. Also note that the exchange interaction between the outer electron spin moments is much stronger than that between the magnetic moments of the atoms (ions). Consequently, ionic interactions can be neglected.

In the discussion of the ferromagnetism of the iron-group elements in Chapter 10, the sign of the exchange interaction was assumed to be positive, which is the correct sign for parallel orientations of spin moments. It is possible for the sign to be negative, however, which is the case when the spin-moment directions in adjacent atoms are antiparallel, that is, when they point in diametrically opposite directions. This is the case, for example, when two adjacent atoms have incomplete s and p shells. For atoms having incomplete $3d$ and $4f$ shells, the exchange interaction may be either positive or negative, depending on whether the spin moments are parallel or antiparallel.

Antiferromagnetism. The paramagnetic susceptibility χ_p, according to the Curie law, is

$$\chi_P = \frac{C}{T} = \frac{M}{H} \tag{41}$$

where C is the Curie constant
$\quad T$ is the absolute temperature
$\quad M$ is the total magnetization
$\quad H$ is the magnetic field strength.

When calculating the effect of the exchange interaction, it is convenient to make use of the so-called *molecular-field* approximation introduced by P. Weiss. The molecular field or *Weiss field h* is proportional to the field acting on an atom (or molecule) due to the other atoms in the surrounding crystal structure. For a positive interaction, $h = \gamma M$, where γ is a positive constant, so that the effective field acting on an atom is

$$H_{\text{effective}} = H + \gamma M. \tag{42}$$

Substituting the effective field for H in the right side of (41) gives

$$M = \frac{C}{T}(H + \gamma M). \tag{43}$$

Remembering that $\chi = M/H$, divide both sides of (42) by H so that

$$\chi = \frac{C}{T} + \gamma \frac{C}{T}\chi$$

and

$$\chi\left(1 - \gamma \frac{C}{T}\right) = \frac{C}{T}$$

and, finally,

$$\chi = \frac{M}{H} = \frac{C}{T - \gamma C} = \frac{C}{T - \Theta} \tag{44}$$

where $\Theta = \gamma C$ is called the *Curie temperature*. Below this temperature, there is a magnetic field present inside the crystal even though no external field is applied; that is, there exists spontaneous magnetization in the crystal. This is the phenomenon of ferromagnetism. For comparison,

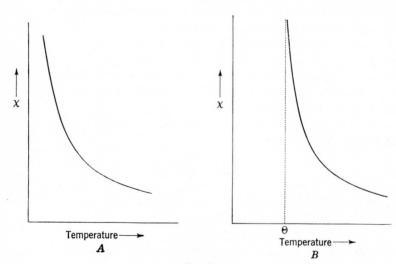

Temperature ⟶

A

Temperature ⟶

B

Fɪɢ. 20

the susceptibilities in (41) and (44) are plotted as a function of temperature in Fig. 20A and B.

For a negative exchange interaction, $h = -\gamma M$, and (44) becomes

$$\chi = \frac{M}{H} = \frac{C}{T + \gamma C} = \frac{C}{T + \Theta} \tag{45}$$

where Θ now is called the *asymptotic* Curie temperature because the transition from paramagnetic to antiferromagnetic behavior occurs not at Θ but at another temperature T_N called the *Néel temperature.* The reason for this is discussed below.

As already stated, a negative exchange interaction results from antiparallel spin moments in adjacent atoms. In a crystal, this means that alternate atoms have their spin moments oriented parallel to each other but adjacent atoms do not. It is convenient to picture such an arrangement by considering the atoms to be arranged on two interpenetrating sublattices† so that the spin moments of atoms in one sublattice array have an opposite sense from the spin moments of atoms in the other sublattice array.‡ Below the transition temperature, the spin moments of both sublattice arrays are ordered, as shown diagrammatically in Fig. 21, and no spontaneous magnetization is possible, since the moments exactly cancel when summed over the entire crystal. Above the transition temperature, the order disappears because of thermal motion of the electrons, and the paramagnetic behavior of the crystal can be described by describing the behavior of the atoms in the two sublattice arrays separately. Denoting the two sublattice arrays by the subscripts A and B, respectively, it follows from (43) that

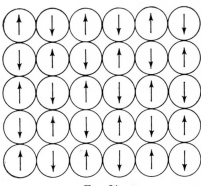

Fig. 21

† Recently it has been shown that the 230 space groups can be extended to include *antisymmetry* operators which have the property of repeating a white motif into a black motif and the black one back into a white motif. (Actually several such repetitions are possible before the cycle is completed.) These so-called *color space groups* include the symmetry groups of all possible arrangements of parallel and antiparallel spin directions and should prove very useful in the study of ferromagnetic and antiferromagnetic crystals.

‡ As might be expected, the counterpart of antiparallel spin moments in antiferromagnetic crystals can be found in *antiferroelectric* crystals in which the dipoles of adjacent atoms are oriented antiparallel with respect to each other. Antiferroelectricity has actually been observed in $PbZrO_3$ crystals.

$$M_A = \frac{C'}{T}(H - \alpha M_A - \beta M_B) \qquad (46)$$

and

$$M_B = \frac{C'}{T}(H - \alpha M_B - \beta M_A) \qquad (47)$$

where α is the interaction parameter for two atoms having like spin moments (AA or BB) and β is the interaction parameter for two unlike atoms.

The total magnetization is the sum of partial magnetizations like (46) and (47) so that

$$
\begin{aligned}
M &= M_A + M_B \\
  &= \frac{C'}{T}[(H - \alpha M_A - \beta M_B) + (H - \alpha M_B - \beta M_A)] \\
  &= \frac{C'}{T}[2H - (\alpha + \beta)(M_A + M_B)] \\
  &= \frac{2C'}{T}[H - \tfrac{1}{2}(\alpha + \beta)M].
\end{aligned} \qquad (48)
$$

Letting $C = 2C'$ and rearranging terms,

$$\chi = \frac{M}{H} = \frac{2C'}{T + C'(\alpha + \beta)} = \frac{C}{T + \tfrac{1}{2}C(\alpha + \beta)} = \frac{C}{T + \Theta} \qquad (49)$$

which is the same as relation (45) already encountered above.

The transition or Néel temperature is determined by equations (46) and (47) since it is the temperature for which M_A or M_B has a finite value in the absence of an external magnetic field. Setting $H = 0$ and eliminating M_A and M_B in these two simultaneous equations, a quadratic equation is obtained whose positive root gives the Néel temperature:

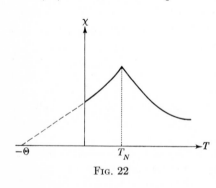

Fig. 22

$$
\begin{aligned}
T_N &= (\beta - \alpha)C' \\
    &= \tfrac{1}{2}(\beta - \alpha)C.
\end{aligned} \qquad (50)
$$

This is the temperature at which a kink in the magnetic susceptibility curve occurs, as shown in Fig. 22. Similar anomalous behavior can be observed at this temperature in the specific heat and the thermal coefficient of expansion of antiferromagnetic materials.

Ferrimagnetism.   Ferromagnetism is observed in many crystals that contain the iron-group elements, including the oxides, sulfides, and other compounds formed by these metals.   For a material such as magnetite, Fe_3O_4, which contains Fe^{+2}, Fe^{+3}, and O^{-2} ions, it can be shown that the total saturation moment is 14 Bohr magnetons per formula weight, if positive exchange interactions, that is, parallel spin moments, are assumed. The measured value, however, is 4.08 Bohr magnetons. This discrepancy was explained by L. Néel who showed that some of the exchange interactions actually are negative even though the crystals are ferromagnetic. Negative exchange interactions are necessary to explain the ferromagnetism of a large group of compounds having the spinel structure described in Chapter 13 and, by analogy to the name *ferrite*, given to all such compounds that contain iron, this phenomenon is called *ferrimagnetism*.

Néel accounted for the low magnetic susceptibility of Fe_3O_4 by assuming that the spins of the Fe^{+3} ions are antiparallel to each other, thus canceling each other's contribution to the total magnetization. The resultant moment, therefore, is due to the magnetic moments of the Fe^{+2} ions which have a net moment of 4 Bohr magnetons. This value agrees quite well with the measured value. As discussed in Chapter 13, the distribution of the iron atoms in the structure of Fe_3O_4 is such that the Fe^{+3} ions are divided equally among the octahedral and tetrahedral equipoints, filling the latter entirely. Thus the magnetic moments in Fe_3O_4 can be pictured to be distributed as shown in Fig. 23 which indicates schematically the ionic positions relative to a closest-packed oxygen layer. Note that the metal ions are separated by oxygen ions so that the interaction between them is indirect. It can be shown that this so-called *superexchange* interaction is strongest for a collinear configuration Me-O-Me and weakest when the two Me-O bonds form right angles with each other.

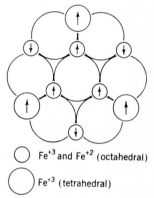

○ Fe^{+3} and Fe^{+2} (octahedral)

○ Fe^{+3} (tetrahedral)

Fig. 23. Spin directions in Fe_3O_4. Fe^{+3} ions in tetrahedral sites and in octahedral sites have antiparallel spins. The net magnetization is due to Fe^{+2} ions in octahedral sites.

Magnetic resonance. As discussed in Chapter 10, the paramagnetic behavior of crystals is explained by the cooperative alignment of electronic magnetic moments parallel to an external magnetic field. In some respects, therefore, paramagnetism is similar to the orientation of electric dipoles in insulators, by an external field, as discussed in this chapter. These two effects, however, differ in one important way. Whereas the induced dipole field opposes the external electric field, the induced magnetic field aids the external magnetic field.

Suppose that a paramagnetic crystal is placed in a magnetic field whose direction is parallel to, say, the z axis.   In the presence of such a field, the energy levels of the electrons split, as shown in Fig. 24 (Zeeman

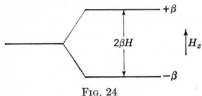

FIG. 24

effect).   The difference in the energy of the two levels, $2\beta H$, is sometimes written

$$\Delta E = g\beta H \qquad (51)$$

where g is called the *spectroscopic splitting factor* or, simply, the *g* factor and is equal to 2.0 for electron spins.   The energy that the electrons absorb can also be expressed by $\Delta E = h\nu$.   It follows from this that when the external field alternates with a frequency ν such that

$$h\nu = g\beta H \qquad (52)$$

the field can induce transitions between adjacent levels and the crystal absorbs energy.   When such energy absorption occurs, the phenomenon is called resonance or, more specifically, *paramagnetic resonance*.   Note in (52) that there are two ways that resonance can come about; either the frequency is varied while the field strength H is maintained constant or the frequency is held constant and the field strength is varied.

There are essentially two ways in which an external magnetic field can interact with the electrons in a crystal because the spin moments of the electrons in a crystal are affected by the magnetic field created by the moments of surrounding electrons.   The strength of this internal field, acting on a single electron, ranges from a couple of hundred up to a thousand gauss.   The effect that such a magnetic field has is that it causes the spin moments to precess about the field direction.   At normal temperatures, the thermal motion of the electrons produces constant fluctuations in the internal field so that it assumes random directions. This, in turn, means that the spin moments precess about random directions and no net magnetization results.   The effect of applying an external field, therefore, depends on its strength relative to the internal field. Suppose that the external field is much weaker than the internal field. Such a field can only influence the net field direction inside a crystal so that the precession directions of the spin moments are altered slightly to conform with the direction of the external field.   Thus the interaction is between the external field and the spin system of the crystal.   It produces a net magnetization in the direction of the applied field and is commonly called the *spin-spin* interaction.   Another type of mechanism becomes operative when the applied field strength is larger than that of the internal field.   The stronger field requires that all the spin moments align either parallel or antiparallel to the external field direction.   Suppose that the magnitude of such a field is varied slightly.   Since the direction along which the spin moments must align remains unchanged. the only way that the magnetization can vary is for the relative numbers of parallel and antiparallel moments to change. These two mechanisms are not unlike the two ways in which ferromagnetic domains can align themselves in an external magnetic field. It will be recalled from Chapter 10 that, in a weak field, favorably oriented domains grow in size by small changes in the orientations of spin moments along domain walls, whereas, in strong fields, the spins within entire domains can simultaneously reorient themselves. The ease with which such complete reversals in spin direction can occur depends on the crystal structure. Accordingly, such an interaction between a strong field and a nonferromagnetic crystal is frequently called the *spin-lattice* interaction.†

The role of different atoms in crystals is primarily determined by their electrons rather than by their nuclei, because the nuclei are relatively immobile. It is true, however, that the atomic nucleus has an angular momentum and, associated with it, a magnetic moment that can interact with an external field. The torque of the force acting on the nucleus acts at right angles to its angular momentum and cannot change the magnitude of the angular momentum. Instead, it causes the angular-momentum vector to precess about the direction of the applied field (similarly to the precession of a gyroscope). The precession induced by a magnetic field is called the *Larmor precession,* and the angular frequency of the precession is called the *Larmor frequency.* In addition to causing the Larmor precession, the external magnetic field produces a splitting of the energy levels of the atom (Zeeman effect). Transitions between these levels are determined by the selection rules which allow transitions only between adjacent levels. If an alternating magnetic field has a frequency equal to the Larmor frequency, its energy is just right for transitions to take place and resonance can occur. This phenomenon is called *nuclear magnetic resonance* (NMR) and for a field strength of 10^4 gauss occurs at radio frequencies of 1 to 50 megacycles. The width and structure of the resonance absorption curves is determined by interactions between magnetic moments of neighboring atoms. Since this interaction is, in turn, determined by the crystal structure, nuclear magnetic resonance can be used to study structural features in crystals. For example, metal isotopes can be located in a crystal's structure and used to study such phenomena as order-disorder transformations in crystals.

Quite similarly, it is possible to locate isolated electrons in crystals. The resonance phenomenon for electrons occurs at frequencies that are a

† This mechanism is more correctly called a *spin-structure* interaction. This is another example of the incorrect popular use of the word lattice, since the exchange interaction takes place with the crystal structure and not with the imaginary lattice.

thousand times larger than those used in NMR because the mass of an electron is a thousand times smaller than the mass of a nucleus. The name given to this phenomenon is *electron paramagnetic resonance* (EPR), and it can be used to study isolated electrons such as occur at F centers where an electron is trapped in a negative vacancy. The width and structure of the resonance absorption curves in EPR are due to the atomic environment of the electron and can be used to study the nature of the trapping center.

A related effect is observed when a semiconductor is placed in a steady magnetic field. The conduction electrons (or holes) in the crystal are caused to travel in spiral orbits about the magnetic field direction. If the radius of their orbit is r, the centrifugal force acting on an electron moving with a velocity v is

$$F = \frac{m^* v^2}{r}. \tag{53}$$

At the same time, the electron feels a force due to the applied field, the so-called Lorentz force

$$F = \frac{evH}{c}. \tag{54}$$

At equilibrium, the two forces just balance:

$$\frac{m^* v^2}{r} = \frac{evH}{c}$$

and the angular frequency of the electron is

$$\omega = \frac{v}{r} = \frac{eH}{m^* c}. \tag{55}$$

Next, suppose that an alternating field is introduced at right angles to the steady field H. When the frequency of the alternating field is $\nu = \omega/2\pi$, then resonance absorption takes place and the effect is called *cyclotron resonance* by analogy to the spiral orbits executed by electrons accelerated in the magnetic fields of a cyclotron.

Cyclotron resonance requires alternating fields in the radio-frequency range. It is very useful for measuring the effective mass of electrons or holes, as can be seen from equation (55). In fact, it is one of the most effective ways of determining the band structure of semiconductors. This is so because it is possible to determine the effective mass as a function of direction in a crystal by changing the orientation of the crystal relative to the applied field direction.

Suggestions for supplementary reading

Walter G. Cady, *Piezoelectricity* (McGraw-Hill Book Company, Inc., New York, 1946).

Paul F. Kerr, *Optical mineralogy*, 3d ed. (McGraw-Hill Book Company, Inc., New York, 1959).

Humboldt W. Leverenz, *An introduction to luminescence in solids* (John Wiley & Sons, Inc., New York, 1950).

Solid-state electronics issue, *Proc. IRE*, vol. 43 (1955), p. 1738.

Charles P. Smyth, *Dielectric behavior and structure* (McGraw-Hill Book Company, Inc., New York, 1955).

Ernest E. Wahlstrom, *Optical crystallography* (John Wiley & Sons, Inc., New York, 1943).

Aldert van der Ziel, *Solid state physical electronics* (Prentice-Hall, Inc., Englewood Cliffs, N.J., 1957), pp. 475–525.

Suggestions for advanced reading

Adrianus J. Dekker, *Solid state physics* (Prentice-Hall, Inc., Englewood Cliffs, N.J., 1957), pp. 133–210; 483–519.

Arthur R. von Hippel, *Dielectric materials and applications* (John Wiley & Sons, Inc., New York, 1957).

Charles Kittel, *Introduction to solid state physics*, 2d ed. (John Wiley & Sons, Inc., New York, 1956), pp. 157–206; 477–503.

Exercises

1. Two parallel plates, 10×15 cm in area, are separated by sodium nitrate, $\kappa_e = 5.2$, and are permanently connected to a 250-volt battery.

(a) What is the capacitance of this capacitor?
(b) What is the charge on the plates?
(c) What is the induced dipole moment per unit volume in the dielectric?
(d) What is the electric field intensity in the dielectric?

2. A capacitor is constructed from two concentric metal spheres whose radii are 3 and 4 cm, respectively. The space separating the two spheres is completely filled with sulfur, $\kappa_e = 4.0$. What is the capacity of this spherical capacitor?

3. Consider the parallel-plate capacitor in Fig. 1. Why must the ends of the needle-shaped cavity be small? Assuming that the ends have an area of 4 mm², what is the force acting on a test charge placed into such a cavity?

4. What is the dipole moment of a NaCl molecule in a vapor? Assume that the molecule consists of Na^{+1} and Cl^{-1} ions separated by 2.5 Å.

5. The resonance frequency of a piezoelectric crystal is given by

$$f_0 = \frac{v}{2w} = \frac{1}{2w} \sqrt{\frac{E}{D}}$$

where v is the velocity of sound in crystal
w is the width of crystal
E is Young's modulus
D is the density of crystal.

What is the resonance frequency of a quartz crystal 2.5 mm wide? What must be the size of a crystal to be useful in the frequency control of oscillators in the kilocycle range? In the megacycle range? Is quartz suitable for use in both ranges? (Look up the values of density and Young's modulus in a handbook.)

6. Consider the piezoelectric crystal shown in Fig. 5.

(a) When the electrodes are not connected to each other, what is the open-circuit voltage when a stress σ is applied?

(b) What is the mechanical strain in this case?

(c) What is the electrical polarization in this case?

(d) How do these quantities compare with the case of short-circuited electrodes?

7. Assume that only Na^{+1} contributes to the ionic conductivity in NaCl. If the measured conductivity of NaCl at $600°K$ is 10^{-6} mho/cm, what is the value of the diffusion coefficient per unit area for sodium in NaCl? ($a_{NaCl} = 5.63$ Å.)

8. Why is the ionic mobility in alkali halides small? Why is the electronic mobility also small in these crystals?

9. It is often convenient to represent the optic properties of a crystal by drawing a prolate or oblate spheroid whose major and minor axes are the indices of refraction. Make a sketch of this so-called *indicatrix* for a uniaxial positive and negative crystal.

10. Consider the principal planes of the two indicatrices in Exercise 9.

(a) Show the vibration directions and relative wave fronts of the ordinary and extraordinary rays for light incident at 30° to the optic axis of a uniaxial positive crystal whose indices of refraction are $\varepsilon = 2.5$, $\omega = 1.5$.

(b) Repeat above for light incident at 40° to the optic axis of a uniaxial negative crystal for which $\varepsilon = 1.8$, $\omega = 2.0$.

11. Na D light ($\lambda = .5893\mu$) passes through a uniform wedge of quartz ($\varepsilon = 1.553$, $\omega = 1.544$). At what thickness of the edge will the phase difference $\delta = \pi$ for light traveling parallel to $[11\bar{2}0]$?

12. Using the Lorenz-Lorentz equation, calculate the two refractive indices of calcite by assuming that the molar refractivity in calcite is equal to the sum of the ionic refractivity of Ca^{+2} ($R = 1.99$) and of the carbonate groups ($R_\varepsilon = 8.38$, $R_\omega = 11.32$). Why do you think that the calculated ratio ε/ω is the same as the measured ratio $1.486/1.658$ but the actual magnitudes are different?

13. Make separate sketches showing the energy-band model of a crystal containing the following:

(a) F centers.

(b) F and F' centers.

(c) F and V centers.

14. Make a sketch of an antiferromagnetic crystal having the CsCl structure. Assume that the two different kinds of atoms have antiparallel spin moments and indicate this by arrows in the two sublattice arrays. Indicate the antiferromagnetic unit cell in this crystal. Is the symmetry of the crystal changed if differences in the spin moments are considered?

15. $ZnFe_2O_4$ is antiferromagnetic. Assuming that zinc atoms occupy the tetrahedral voids in the spinel structure, suggest a model that explains the antiferromagnetism in zinc ferrite.

16. An alkali halide crystal contains some divalent metal impurities. List and describe some of the imperfections present in such a crystal and by what resonance arrangements one could study these imperfections.

17. When an EPR experiment is performed on a ferromagnetic crystal, the g factor determined is several times larger than its free-electron value of 2.0. It has been shown that if the field H in relation (52) is replaced by $(BH)^{\frac{1}{2}}$, where $B = H + 4\pi M$, the g factor has more nearly the free-electron value. For example, g then equals 2.2 in Fe_3O_4. At what frequencies do you think this so-called *ferromagnetic resonance* can be observed? (Assume that $H \sim 5000$ oersteds.)

15

Structure of insulators

Following the classification scheme adopted in this book, all those compounds that are not conductors, namely, all nonmetals, can be subdivided into two groups. The nonmetals in one group can conduct electricity in readily measured amounts via electronic conduction and are called semiconductors. The nonmetals in the second group, called insulators, can conduct electricity only by the ionic conduction process described in the previous chapter, since their electronic conductivity is negligibly small. This does not mean that all these compounds find use as dielectric materials but rather that their electrical resistivity is normally very high ($\sim 10^{15}$ ohm-cm). This group contains by far the largest number of known inorganic compounds. It is possible, therefore, to discuss only a very small number of compounds representative of this group. Accordingly, the following plan is adopted in this chapter. The crystal structures of the elements not as yet described are first discussed. It turns out that the only elements in this category that are important in solids are the halogens. Because these elements form an important group of compounds called halides, the structures of halides are also briefly reviewed. The oxides of metals not discussed in Chapter 13 are considered next. This group includes the silicates which are of particular interest because they compose the bulk of the earth's crust. It is obviously not possible to consider the thousands of different silicates individually, so that only their common structural features are described. Finally, the structural arrangements found in another important class of solids not discussed elsewhere in this book, namely, glasses, are briefly considered.

Halogens and halides

The crystal structures of the inert gases and oxygen and of elements heavier than bismuth are not described in this book because the former are gases at ordinary temperatures and the heavy elements are too little used and too incompletely known to warrant discussion here. This leaves the elements fluorine, chlorine, bromine, and iodine unaccounted for. These elements are strongly electronegative, as shown below, and tend to form negative ions by the addition of one electron.

	F	Cl	Br	I
Electronegativity	4.0	3.0	2.8	2.5

Alternatively, since they each have seven electrons in the unfilled shell, a halogen can form one electron-pair bond in covalently bonded crystals. It is also possible for the halogens to act as singly charged positive ions in certain compounds.

Fluorine and chlorine are gases at ordinary temperatures. Below $-185°C$, chlorine crystallizes with a tetragonal structure containing pairs of chlorine atoms in molecules of Cl_2, as evidenced by Cl-Cl distances of 1.82 Å within a molecule and 2.52 Å between molecules. Bromine is also a gas at room temperature and crystallizes below $-150°C$ in an ortho-rhombic structure containing Br_2 molecules. The same crystal structure is adopted by iodine, which is the only element in this series to crystallize at room temperature. The interatomic distances within each molecule and the separations between molecules found in these crystals are compared with the intramolecular separations in these molecules in their vapors below.

	Separation within a molecule	Separation between molecules	Separation within molecules in vapor
Br	2.27	3.30	2.28 Å
I	2.70	3.54	2.65 Å

The large electron affinities of the halogens suggest that these elements prefer to form ionic compounds. The crystal structures of the halides range from simple alkali halides, having either the halite structure shown in Fig. 6 of Chapter 13 or the cesium chloride structure shown in Fig. 1 of this chapter, to considerably more complex structures in such compounds as $TlAlF_4$ and $Na_5Al_3F_{14}$. The halogens also sometimes form compounds with oxygen. Such compounds are called *oxyhalides*, for example, CaO_2Cl_2, MoO_2Br_2, and $Sb_4O_5Cl_2$. Some of these compounds, for example, calcium hypochlorite, CaO_2Cl_2, contain complex ions of the form ClO^{-1} in which the halogen ion has an effective positive charge of $+1$.

Returning to the simpler alkali halides, it will be recalled from Chapter 8 that the structure with which a particular halide crystallizes is determined by the relative radius ratio of the ions. It follows from the discussion in that chapter that only those crystals for which this ratio has values between 0.414 (octahedral coordination) and 0.732 (cubic coordination) should crystallize with the halite structure. It turns out, however, that all alkali halides except CsCl, CsBr, and CsI adopt the NaCl structure at room temperature. This is very surprising, particularly since the radius ratio for KF, RbF, and CsF is 0.98, 1.09, and 1.24, respectively, indicating that the coordination number for both ions should be 8. It is not as yet possible to explain this anomaly theoretically

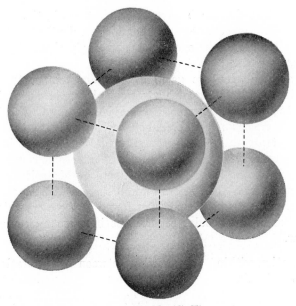

Fig. 1.   Cesium chloride (CsCl) structure.

because the cohesive energies that have been calculated for both structural arrangements indicate that the cubically coordinated CsCl structure is preferred. It may be that secondary effects such as van der Waals forces, however, actually make the halite structure more stable.

When mixed halides are formed, for example, by the addition of limited amounts of divalent metals, the crystals can become conductive. The presence of divalent metals in a crystal requires that an equal number of monovalent atoms be missing so that charge neutrality is preserved. The resulting cation vacancies provide a mechanism whereby the cations in the crystal can move about. This process is called diffusion and, as described in the previous chapter, when an external electric field is applied, it leads to ionic conductivity. The mobility of the ions is much smaller than the electronic mobilities encountered in semiconductors so that it is not possible to measure the Hall effect. Also, the total ionic conductivity is relatively small. The electronic conductivity is limited to even smaller values in these crystals because the number of conduction electrons in an ionic crystal, as well as their mobility, is very small.

Oxides

Perovskite type. Some of the halides containing alkali metals, for example, $KMgF_3$, crystallize with the perovskite structure shown in Fig. 2. The potassium and fluorine ions form closest-packed planes in

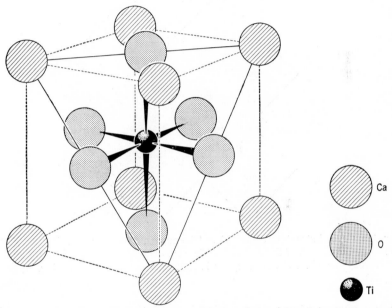

FIG. 2. Perovskite ($CaTiO_3$) structure. The atoms are reduced in size for clarity.

this structure normal to the [[111]] directions of the cube so that the resulting structure can be thought of as a cubic closest packing of such sheets containing a magnesium atom in the octahedral void at the center of each unit cube. Perovskite is the mineral name of the oxide whose composition is $CaTiO_3$ and whose structure consists of similar closest-packed sheets of calcium and oxygen atoms containing titanium at the centers of the unit cubes. A large number of oxides crystallize with this structure, for example, $SrTiO_3$, $BaZrO_3$, $BaTiO_3$, and others. Some of these compounds also crystallize in several polymorphous modifications having slightly distorted perovskite-type structures. For example, barium titanate can transform to a tetragonal, orthorhombic, or rhombohedral modification at lower temperatures. In each case, the displacive transformation is accomplished by a shift in the titanium atom positions. This is best seen by considering Fig. 3, which shows the perovskite structure when the origin of the cube is placed at the position of a titanium atom. Because the polymorphs of, say, $BaTiO_3$ have interesting ferroelectric properties related to their structures, they are considered in some detail below.

Consider the oxygen octahedra coordinating each titanium atom, as shown in Fig. 3. The titanium atom can shift in its position relative

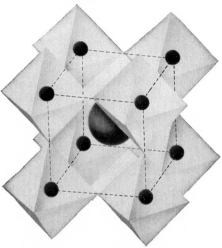

Fig. 3. Crystal structure of $BaTiO_3$. The oxygen octahedra coordinating Ti^{+4} are shown at the corners of the unit cell. Note that the large Ba^{+2} ion is coordinated by twelve oxygens since the Ba-O array is that of a cubic closest packing. (See also Fig. 2.)

to the oxygen atoms surrounding it, and the oxygen atoms can shift relative to the barium atom at the center of the cube. In the tetragonal distortion of $BaTiO_3$, it turns out that the titanium atom moves toward an oxygen atom while the oxygen atoms move in the opposite direction by about the same amount, as shown by the projection of the structure on (100) in Fig. 4A. By comparison, a much more drastic displacement of ions occurs in the tetragonal modification of $PbTiO_3$, as shown in the projection on (100) in Fig. 4B. In lead titanate, both the oxygen and titanium ions are placed in the same direction relative to the lead atoms; however, the displacement of the titanium ions is three times smaller. The axial ratio c/a is 1.04 in $BaTiO_3$ and 1.06 in $PbTiO_3$, and both crystals contain electrical dipoles parallel to [001] produced by the relative shifts of the positive titanium and negative oxygen ions. These crystals are, therefore, said to be polarized along the c axis. When a sufficiently strong electric field is applied parallel to the c axis, it is possible to reverse the direction of the polarization, that is, the relative displacements of the ions. By analogy to the reorientation of magnetic dipoles in ferromagnetic crystals, this phenomenon is called ferroelectricity.

Below room temperature, a further shifting of the atoms occurs so that dipoles are produced along the [110] direction. This produces an orthorhombic structure in which the a and b axes are parallel to the [110] and [1$\bar{1}$0] directions and the c axis does not change its direction. Finally, below 193°K, another shift occurs so that the polarization direction is

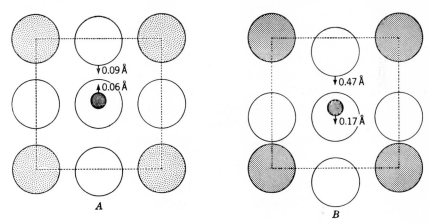

FIG. 4

parallel to [111] and a rhombohedral structure results. All these polymorphs of barium titanate are also ferroelectric.

Borates. Boron is quite unlike the other elements in the third column of the periodic table. In fact, it is far more similar to silicon when it comes to compound formation. Similarly to silicates, the fundamental unit in the so-called borates is a complex ion. In this case, it is $[BO_3]^{-3}$, which consists of three oxygen atoms lying at the corners of an equilateral triangle containing the boron atom at its center. The atoms are coplanar according to *Zachariasen's rule*, which states that the complex MX_2 is collinear and MX_3 is coplanar if $v = 2p$, or $v = 3p$, respectively. Here v is the total number of valency electrons in the group and p is the number of valency electrons in the inert gas that follows X in the periodic table. The borate ions can combine in various ways to give simple borates like CaB_2O_4 or complex ones like $Mg_7Cl_2B_{16}O_{30}$. It is for this reason that the possible structure types of borates are of interest.

The possible borate structures can be classified according to the number of oxygen atoms each BO_3 group shares with another BO_3 group, as follows:

1. *No* oxygen atoms are shared. Thus the $[BO_3]^{-3}$ ions exist as separate groups in these crystals and act like typical complex ions, say the carbonate ion. An example of these so-called *orthoborates†* is the mineral hambergite, Be_2OHBO_3.

2. *One* oxygen atom is shared. The sharing of one oxygen atom by two borate triangles produces a pair complex $[B_2O_5]^{-4}$. This form of complex ion occurs in *pyroborates,†* for example, $Mg_2B_2O_5$.

3. *Two* oxygen atoms are shared. This requires that a *chain* complex be formed in which adjacent triangles share corners. (Pauling's rules forbid the sharing of edges by triangles.) The structural formula of these so-called *metaborates†* is $[BO_2]^{-1}$, and an example of this complex is found in CaB_2O_4.

4. *Two and one-half* oxygen atoms are shared. This type of sharing comes about when alternate triangles in a *double chain* share two and three oxygen atoms, respectively. The structural formula of this complex is $[B_4O_7]^{-2}$, and it is believed to exist in common borax, $Na_2B_4O_7 \cdot 10H_2O$.

5. *Three* oxygen atoms are shared. Since the borate triangle contains only three oxygen atoms, this is the maximum sharing possible. The resulting complex is a *sheet* in which adjacent triangles share corners. It is not necessary, however, for the triangles to be mutually coplanar. The resulting crystal has the formula B_2O_3, and such crystals have actually been synthesized although this oxide more commonly forms a glass.

The structural units and the valence of the respective complexes are easily determined with the aid of Table 1. It is, of course, possible to conceive of other complexes consisting of a finite number of borate triangles. Such complexes actually occur; for example, potassium pentaborate, $KH_4B_5O_{10} \cdot 2H_2O$, contains double rings formed by borate triangles. One of the boron atoms in this complex, however, has tetrahedral coordination so that this complex does not fit into the scheme outlined in Table 1.

Silicates. It is interesting to note that the earth's crust is composed of approximately $62\frac{1}{2}$ atomic per cent oxygen, 21 per cent silicon, $6\frac{1}{2}$ per cent aluminum, and 10 atomic per cent of all the remaining elements. The three major constituents occur primarily as silicate crystals or glasses in which the aluminum atoms either substitute for silicon in the silicon tetrahedra or else are octahedrally coordinated in the voids between the silicon tetrahedra. (The dual role that aluminum can have

† The prefixes *meta*, *ortho*, and *pyro* are derived from the names given to the acids **from** which the salts are supposed to form. The relationship between them is that

$$\text{meta} + H_2O = \text{ortho} \qquad HBO_2 + H_2O = H_3BO_3$$
$$2 \text{ ortho} - H_2O = \text{pyro} \qquad 2H_3BO_3 - H_2O = H_4B_2O_5$$

in silicates became known only when the actual crystal structures of silicates had been determined.) It is not surprising, in view of the abundance of silicates, that they are utilized in many types of construction materials used in building houses, bridges, and roads. Silicates are the main ingredients of brick, mortar, sand, cement, and so on as well

Table 1
Borate structural units

No. of oxygens shared	Structural unit	Charge compensation	Structural formula
0		B + 3 0 | -6 $\overline{\quad -3 \quad}$	$[BO_3]^{-3}$
1		B + 6 0 | -10 $\overline{\quad -4 \quad}$	$[B_2O_5]^{-4} = [BO_{\frac{5}{2}}]^{-2}$
2		B + 3 0 | -4 $\overline{\quad -1 \quad}$	$[BO_2]^{-1}$
$2\frac{1}{2}$		B + 12 0 | -14 $\overline{\quad -2 \quad}$	$[B_4O_7]^{-2} = [BO_{\frac{7}{4}}]^{-\frac{1}{2}}$
3		B + 6 0 | -6 $\overline{\quad 0 \quad}$	$[B_2O_3]^{0}$

as most naturally occurring rocks. Also, most gems and semiprecious stones are silicates.

The number of silicates in existence is so large that even the ones that already have been identified form a rather voluminous catalog. Nevertheless, the basic features of all silicates are quite similar. The fundamental building units are $[SiO_4]^{-4}$ complex ions in which the four oxygen atoms coordinating the central silicon atom are disposed at the corners of a regular tetrahedron. The silicon tetrahedra are frequently so arranged that the oxygen atoms actually form a closest packing. The other metal atoms present then occupy some of the remaining interstices.

Because of their structural similarities, it is possible to devise a general plan for the structures of silicates, similar to the one outlined for borates in the previous section. Many examples of each of the different structure types are known although many more silicates remain to be classified. In the following discussion, the mineral names of a number of silicates are listed without further amplification. These names will be old friends to mineralogists but are probably unknown to other readers. Because the structural features of the minerals rather than their names are of interest to the purpose of this book, they are not discussed further here. It should be borne in mind that the differences in silicate structures are reflected in differences in their physical properties such as cleavage, for example. All the silicate structures determined to date fall into one of the following categories:†

1. *No* oxygen atoms are shared. The resulting $[SiO_4]^{-4}$ groups, called *individuals*, are found in the *orthosilicates:* olivine, $(MgFe)_2SiO_4$; chondrodite, $Mg_5(SiO_4)_2(OH)_2$; garnet, $Fe_3Al_2(SiO_4)_3$; and others. Because of the random orientations of the individual tetrahedra, these crystals have virtually no natural cleavage planes.

2. *One* oxygen atom is shared. The sharing of one oxygen atom by two silicon tetrahedra produces *pairs* with the formula $[Si_2O_7]^{-6}$ found, for example, in hemimorphite, $Zn_4Si_2O_7(OH)_2 \cdot H_2O$, which is an important zinc ore. Like the silicates containing single individuals, the *pyrosilicates* containing pairs do not have pronounced cleavage planes because the pairs are usually randomly oriented.

3. *Two* oxygen atoms are shared. When two oxygen atoms are shared the structural unit is a *single chain* with the formula $[SiO_3]^{-2}$. These chain structures are commonly found in the pyroxenes like enstatite, $MgSiO_3$, or diopside, $CaMg(SiO_3)_2$, and the infinitely long single chains, therefore, are commonly called *pyroxene chains*. It is also possible for the chains to close upon themselves; that is, it is possible that they form rings. Three-member rings are found in benitoite, $Ba_3TiSi_3O_9$, and six-member rings occur in beryl, $Be_3Al_2Si_6O_{18}$. These so-called *beryl rings* lie in sheets but they are bonded to each other between sheets as tightly as they are within the sheets so that the cleavage is poor. Nevertheless, the cleavage in most *metasilicates* is more pronounced than in the silicates belonging to the first two categories.

4. *Two and one-half* oxygens are shared. This combination is obtained by having alternate tetrahedra in a *double chain* share two and three oxygen atoms, respectively. The formula of the resulting complex is

† A number of synthetic silicates have been prepared recently under extremely high pressures. As might be expected, these silicates have much denser structures. It is interesting to note, however, that Pauling's rules are not violated in these compounds; that is, the silicon tetrahedra share corners only.

$[Si_4O_{11}]^{-6}$, and these double chains are found in all amphiboles and are called *amphibole chains* for that reason. The minerals tremolite, $(OH)_2Ca_2Mg_5(Si_4O_{11})_2$, and hornblende, $Ca_2Mg_2(OH)_2(Si_4O_{11})_2$, are examples of the amphibole group. The aluminum atoms in hornblende occur in tetrahedral positions normally occupied by silicon, which is the reason for combining the two metals inside the parentheses in the formula. As might be expected, amphiboles exhibit reasonably good cleavage because the double chains tend to align parallel to each other.

5. *Three* oxygen atoms are shared. Similarly to the borates, the sharing of three corners by the tetrahedra produces infinite *sheets*. There are different ways in which the tetrahedra can form such sheets, for example, by the joining of two out of three unshared corners in six-member rings or alternatively in eight-member and four-member rings. The structural formulas of all sheets are the same, namely, $[Si_2O_5]^{-2}$. Six-member rings forming an infinite sheet are found in the micas and clays, for example, in muscovite, $KAl_2(OH)_2(Si_3Al)O_{10}$, and montmorillonite, $(AlMg)_8(Si_4O_{10})_3(OH)_{10} \cdot xH_2O$. The sheet structures cleave very easily because the sheets usually are bonded to each other by forces much weaker than the forces bonding the atoms within a sheet.

6. *Four* oxygen atoms are shared. When all four corners are shared by the tetrahedra, infinite three-dimensional *networks* are formed. This is the structure of the three polymorphous forms of Si_2O: quartz, tridymite, and cristobalite. Each of these forms has, in addition, two or more high-temperature polymorphs.

A large number of silicates crystallize with structures that are related to the network structures of SiO_2. Quartz has the densest structure of the three so that only relatively small atoms can fit into the unoccupied interstices, for example, lithium atoms to form eucryptite, $Li(SiAl)O_4$. The more open structure of tridymite and cristobalite can accommodate larger atoms, for example, sodium in the high-temperature structure of tridymite to form nepheline, $Na(SiAl)O_4$. It is not surprising that the common rock-forming minerals, the *felspars*, which also have network structures, can and do accommodate many different atoms in their interstices. For example, continuous solid solutions are possible between orthoclase, $K(Si_3Al)O_8$, and celsian, $Ba(Si_2Al_2)O_8$, or between albite, $Na(Si_3Al)O_8$, and anorthite, $Ca(Si_2Al)O_8$. In each of these solid solutions, the substitution of a divalent ion in the interstices must be accompanied by the substitution of an aluminum atom for a silicon atom in a tetrahedron. Variations in the structure of these networks are also possible. Thus the networks can contain tunnels, as in the *zeolites* analcite, $Na(AlSi_2)O_6 \cdot H_2O$, and leucite, $K(AlSi_2)O_6$, or they can form cages around large voids, as in the *ultramarines* such as sodalite, $Na_8(Al_6Si_6)O_{24} \cdot Cl_2$.

The various structural units that can be built out of silicon tetrahedra are illustrated in Table 2 in which the silicon units are drawn in projection on the tetrahedral faces. As can be seen in this table, as more tetrahedra are combined into a single structural unit, the net valence of the unit

Table 2
Silicate structural units

No. of oxygens shared	Structural unit	Charge compensation	Structural formula
0		Si $+4$ 0 $\dfrac{\quad -8}{-4}$	$[SiO_4]^{-4}$
1		Si $+8$ 0 $\dfrac{\quad -14}{-6}$	$[Si_2O_7]^{-6} = [SiO_{7/2}]^{-3}$
2		Si $+4$ 0 $\dfrac{\quad -6}{-2}$	$[SiO_3]^{-2}$
$2\frac{1}{2}$		Si $+16$ 0 $\dfrac{\quad -22}{-6}$	$[Si_4O_{11}]^{-6} = [SiO_{11/4}]^{-3/2}$
3		Si $+8$ 0 $\dfrac{\quad -10}{-2}$	$[Si_2O_5]^{-2} = [SiO_{5/2}]^{-1}$
4	Three-dimensional network	Si $+4$ 0 $\dfrac{\quad -4}{0}$	$[SiO_2]^{0}$

decreases from -4, in the individual unit, to 0, in the three-dimensional network. It is, of course, possible to conceive of other structural units as well. Up to the present time, however, no such units have been found to exist in crystals. Because of the more random nature of the structures of glasses, such different units can be supposed to exist in glasses. It is not possible to speak of the exact structure of glasses, however, because of the inability of present methods to determine such structures in detail since they are not periodic.

Glasses

The present concept of the structures of glasses is that they consist of random three-dimensional networks in which the formation of chains or sheets is not impossible. However, it is not necessary to postulate the presence of specialized units in order to explain the observed properties of glasses. The structure of a typical silicate glass is schematically shown in Fig. 5. The exact composition of glasses can vary tremendously although they must contain predominantly oxygen, silicon, boron, and aluminum, which are the network-forming atoms. Table 3 lists a few of the more common glasses and their compositions. As can be seen in this table, in addition to the so-called *network formers*, the different glasses can contain varying amounts of other oxides called *network modifiers* because they serve to change or modify the basic properties of the glass.

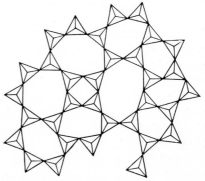

FIG. 5. Schematic representation of arrangement of SiO_4 tetrahedra in a glass. The relatively large irregular openings can accommodate various ions.

The strongest bonds in these glasses are the Si-O bonds in the silicon tetrahedra. The absence of any symmetry in the structure, however,

Table 3
Composition of common glasses†

	Network formers			Network modifiers				
	SiO_2	B_2O_3	Al_2O_3	Na_2O	K_2O	MgO	CaO	PbO
Fused silica	99.8	. . .	. . .	. . .	. . .	0.1	0.1	
Vycor	96	3	1					
Pyrex	80	14	2	3.5	0.5			
Soda-silica	72	. . .	1	20	. . .	3	4	
Lead-silica	63	. . .	1	8	6	. . .	1	21

† The compositions are expressed as weight per cent of the constituent oxides because it is not possible to distinguish structural complexes in glasses.

allows the strength of the bond to vary from one tetrahedron to the next. (The *average* Si-O distance in glasses is 1.62 Å which is very similar to the 1.60 Å separation found in crystals.) Consequently, there does not exist a single temperature at which all the bonds are broken simultaneously. When heated, glasses soften gradually, therefore, rather than melt abruptly the way crystals do. In fact, it is possible to think of a glass as a liquid which has been cooled rather rapidly so that the atoms have not had a chance to rearrange themselves in a symmetrical manner before their motion was arrested. This is different from the state of a supercooled liquid, to which glasses have sometimes been likened, because a supercooled liquid has very definite properties at fixed pressures and temperatures whereas the properties of compositionally identical glasses are determined primarily by their previous thermal history. Thus a glass is best likened to a liquid whose viscosity has increased upon cooling until it became so large that the liquid, in effect, became a solid. Furthermore, given sufficient time, the atoms tend to adopt the more symmetrical and more stable crystalline structure even while in the highly viscous state of a glass. This process of crystallization from a solid glass is called *devitrification*.

In addition to the network modifiers, glasses can contain fluorine or sulfur in substitution for oxygen atoms. For example, beryllium difluoride can form a glass consisting of a three-dimensional network of $[BeF_4]^{-2}$ tetrahedra. Moreover, glasses can contain a variety of cations which can influence the optical properties of the glass such as its color, index of refraction, or absorption coefficient. Similarly, the addition of boron oxide to fused silica decreases its high-temperature stability because the B-O bonds are weaker. Concurrently, it minimizes the tendency of fused silica to devitrify so that such glasses as Pyrex are better suited to withstand repeated heating and cooling cycles. Unlike crystals, the determining factor in the structural composition of glasses is the requirement of electrical neutrality as distinct from a definite stoichiometric ratio.

Silicate glasses. As can be seen in Table 3, the vitreous form of silica has the composition SiO_2. In agreement with the above described laws for the structures of silicate crystals, it is reasonable to expect that silica glass consists of some type of network of silicon tetrahedra. The interatomic distances in each tetrahedron in a glass are virtually the same, on an average, as similar interatomic distances in crystals; however, small local variations are very likely. By analogy to crystals, therefore, it can be assumed that each silicon atom is tetrahedrally coordinated by four oxygen atoms while each oxygen atom is bonded to two silicon atoms. If other metal oxides are added to the silica glass, then the total number of oxygen atoms present in the glass is increased to a larger number than twice the number of silicon atoms present. Consequently, some of the oxygen atoms can be bonded to only one silicon atom and must pick up additional bonds of total strength $+1$ from some of the other metal atoms present. These metal atoms are assumed to be ions which are randomly distributed among the various voids in the silicon-oxygen network. Thus the "structure" of vitreous $CaSiO_3$ or $PbSiO_3$ consists of silicon tetrahedra arranged in chains or rings around the modifier ion, the chains or rings being linked to each other through shared oxygen atoms to form a kind of three-dimensional network.

Borate glasses. The vitreous form of B_2O_3 appears to be actually more stable than the crystalline form only recently synthesized. Like vitreous silica, it consists of a random network of boron atoms each triangularly coordinated by three oxygen atoms. When glasses are formed by combining silica with boric oxide, the structural arrangement is a combination of the two network types. Each silicon is tetrahedrally coordinated by four oxygen atoms; each boron is triangularly coordinated by two of the cations. On the other hand, when an alkali-earth oxide is added to such a glass, some of the boron atoms change over from a triangular coordination to a tetrahedral one. This produces an interesting change in the thermal expansion coefficient of the glass, which has been called the *boric oxide anomaly*. When SiO_2 is added to boric oxide, the bonding in the silicon tetrahedra serves to tie together more strongly the planar boron triangles in the three-dimensional network so that a regular decrease in the thermal expansion coefficient of the glass is observed. Similarly, when Na_2O is added to boric oxide, some of the boron atoms change to tetrahedral coordination so that, again, the network structure is more tightly bonded and the expansion coefficient decreases. A type of saturation effect sets in, however, at about 13 per cent of Na_2O. The reason for this is that, at this composition, the number of additional oxygen atoms introduced by the addition of Na_2O is quite large and the Na^{+1} ions are able to saturate the extra O^{-2} ions without requiring any more boron atoms to assume 4-fold coordination. In fact, an increase in the soda content above 13 per cent again starts to increase the thermal expansion coefficient, indicating that the tetrahedrally coordinated boron atoms tend to revert to the triangular coordination in which they are more stable.

Other glasses. According to thermodynamic considerations, a glass is stable only when its energy is less or equal to the energy of the corresponding crystal structure. It follows from this that glasses can be formed only by compounds tending to form network-type structures in crystals. The only element known to exist as a glass is selenium, although sulfur also exists in a modification quite similar to a glass. This form is the so-called plastic sulfur. It will be recalled that both of these elements crystallize with structures composed of chains and rings so that the glassy state can be pictured simply as a disordered array of these atomic groupings. Similarly, certain compounds crystallizing in structures composed of discrete groups can form glasses. In addition to SiO_2, BeF_2, and B_2O_3 already cited, it is expected that GeO_2, P_2O_5, As_2O_5,

Sb_2O_5, P_2O_3, As_2O_3, Sb_2O_3, and similar oxides may form glasses. Actually GeO_2 and P_2O_5 form glasses fairly easily. The P-O distance in lime-phosphate glasses is 1.57 Å as compared with 1.55 Å in crystalline phosphates. The phosphorus atoms are tetrahedrally coordinated but the total number of oxygen atoms present in all phosphate glasses is always somewhat in excess of twice the number of phosphorus atoms. Thus, there are always some oxygen atoms present that are bonded to only one phosphorus atom.

Physical properties. The distinguishing property of all glasses is that they undergo a continuous decrease in viscosity when heated rather than the abrupt melting stage encountered in crystals. This is, of course, because of the randomness of their structural arrangements. Furthermore, since the bonding in these compounds is predominantly ionic, any observed electrical conductivity must be due to ionic conduction. It can be shown that the network-forming ions are too tightly bound to contribute to the conductivity which is, therefore, due primarily to the diffusion of the modifier metals present. Like all the properties of glasses, the electrical conductivity depends strongly on the previous thermal history of the glass.

When viewed with visible light, glasses behave just like any isotropic medium. The isotropy is due, of course, to the randomness in the structural arrangement. The index of refraction depends, however, on the previous thermal history of the glass. If a glass has been stressed, then some type of preferred orientation effects takes place in the immediate vicinity of the induced strains and a local anisotropy results. This can be easily seen when a glass that has been prestressed by, say, heating followed by rapid cooling is viewed between crossed polarizers. The randomness of the structure of a glass actually allows the glass to absorb a considerable amount of strain without breaking. Recently, such prestressed glasses have been developed, and these glasses are remarkably strong. In addition, such glass has the interesting property that, when it is subjected to an abrupt impact, the glass shatters into a very large number of tiny particles, literally pulverizing instead of breaking into several large pieces.

Suggestions for supplementary reading

E. U. Condon, Physics of the glassy state, *Am. J. Phys.*, vol. 22 (1954), pp. 43–53; 132–142; 224–232; 310–317.

R. C. Evans, *An introduction to crystal chemistry* (Cambridge University Press, London, 1948).

Linus Pauling, *The nature of the chemical bond*, 2d ed. (Cornell University Press, Ithaca, N.Y., 1957).

J. E. Stanworth, *Physical properties of glass* (Oxford University Press, London, 1950).

B. E. Warren, The basic principles involved in the glassy state, *J. Appl. Phys.*, vol. 13 (1942), pp. 602–610.

A. F. Wells, *Structural inorganic chemistry*, 2d ed. (Oxford University Press, London, 1950).

Exercises

1. What is the lattice of the cesium chloride structure shown in Fig. 1? Why is it *not* body-centered cubic?

2. If the radius ratio for 12-fold coordination is unity, what prevents a simple ionic AB compound having atoms of equal size from adopting a crystal structure in which each ion is coordinated by twelve unlike ions? What structure types do you know that do have 12-fold coordination?

3. Is the perovskite structure shown in Fig. 2 centrosymmetric? Are the tetragonal, orthorhombic, and rhombohedral distortions of this structure centrosymmetric? Are there any directions in the undistorted perovskite structure along which the structure is polar; that is, when the structure is viewed along this direction, does it look different when viewed from opposite sides?

4. Make a sketch of the double-ring complex you think may exist in the structure of $KH_4B_5O_{10} \cdot 2H_2O$. What is the net valence of this complex?

5. The glassy form of P_2O_5 contains phosphorus in tetrahedral coordination. Assuming that phosphor tetrahedra can be used to build structures similar to silicon tetrahedra, prepare a table similar to Table 2 showing the structural complexes possible and their net valences. Look up the structures of some phosphates to see if such complexes actually occur.

6. What internal process can make a glass appear to be colored when it is viewed with white light?

7. Why should the addition of Na_2O in excess of 13 per cent to a boric oxide glass decrease the number of tetrahedrally coordinated boron atoms?

Appendix 1
Physical constants

Symbol	Constant	Magnitude
m	mass of an electron	9.108×10^{-28} g
AMU	$\frac{1}{16}$ of mass of oxygen atom	1.600×10^{-24} g
. . . . .	mass of hydrogen atom	1.008 AMU
. . . . .	1 gram equivalent	8.987×10^{20} ergs
. . . . .	1 AMU equivalent	9.311×10^{2} MeV
. . . . .	1 MeV equivalent	1.783×10^{-27} g
eV	1 electron volt	1.606×10^{-10} esu
MeV	1 million electron volts	1.606×10^{-4} esu
h	Planck's constant	6.628×10^{-27} erg-sec
N_0	Avogadro's number	6.025×10^{23} AMU/g (or molecules/mole)
k	Boltzmann's constant	1.380×10^{-16} erg/°K
R	Rydberg (gas) constant	8.317×10^{7} erg/mole $\times$ °K
e	charge of one electron	4.803×10^{-10} esu
e/m	charge/mass of one electron	5.269×10^{17} esu/g
c	velocity of light	2.998×10^{10} cm/sec
Å	Ångstrom unit	10^{-8} cm $= 10^{-10}$ m
β	Bohr magneton	9.284×10^{-21} erg/gauss

Appendix 2
Conversion units

The equations of Maxwell express the basic relations of electromagnetic theory. The conversion of units from the cgs to the MKS system, therefore, can be best seen in terms of these equations.

MKS	cgs	
$B = \kappa_m\mu_0 H$ (1 weber = 10^8 maxwells) $I = \sigma\mathcal{E}$ (σ ohm^{-1}m^{-1}) $D = \kappa_e\epsilon_0\mathcal{E}$ $c = 2.998 \times 10^8$ m/sec $\mu_0 = 10^{-7}$ henry/m $\epsilon_0 = 10^7/c^2$ farads/m	$B = \kappa_m H$ (1 maxwell = 1 gauss-cm^2) $I = \sigma\mathcal{E}$ (σ ohm^{-1}cm^{-1}) $D = \kappa_e\mathcal{E}$ $c = 2.998 \times 10^{10}$ cm/sec	
	esu	emu
1 coulomb 1 amp (1 coulomb/sec) 1 volt	$= 3 \times 10^9$ escoulombs $= 3 \times 10^9$ esamperes $= \frac{1}{300}$ esvolt	$= \frac{1}{10}$ abcoulomb $= \frac{1}{10}$ abamperes $= 10^8$ abvolts
1 joule = 1 volt $\times$ 1 coulomb $= 10^7$ ergs	1 erg = 1 esvolt $\times$ 1 escoulomb $= 10^{-7}$ joule	1 erg = 1 abvolt $\times$ 1 abcoulomb $= 10^{-7}$ joule

κ_m and κ_e are dimensionless and have the same value in both systems.
1 eV $\simeq 4.803 \times 10^{-10}$ escoulomb $\times \frac{1}{300}$ esvolt $\simeq 1.601 \times 10^{-12}$ erg.

Appendix 3
Atomic radii

Ionic radii. As discussed in Chapter 4, ionic radii are usually determined by subdividing the cation-anion separation in crystals by some means. Because the bonding in, say, alkali halides is not purely ionic, however, different values are obtained for different compounds. For example, the radius of Li^{+1} calculates as follows:

> 0.68 Å from Li-F
> 0.76 Å from Li-Cl
> 0.78 Å from Li-Br
> 0.82 Å from Li-I

Pauling derived a set of *crystal radii* by assuming that the radius of O^{-2} is 1.40 Å. He further deduced certain crystal radii from the so-called univalent radii according to (see Chapter 4)

$$R_{\text{crystal}} = R_{\text{univalent}} \, z^{-2/(n-1)}. \tag{1}$$

A list of Pauling's crystal radii is given in Table 1.

Ahrens used the radius of F^{-1} ($=1.33$ Å) instead of oxygen to determine the radii of a number of cations. Using these as standards, he deduced the radii of the other cations by employing their ionization potentials I in the relation

$$R_{\text{cation}} = \frac{K}{I^n} \tag{2}$$

where K has a constant value for each element considered and n is assumed to have the same value for all the elements. He then used the pairs of ions Mn^{+2} and Mn^{+7} and Tl^{+1} and Tl^{+3} as calibration ions. The cation radii deduced by Ahrens are listed in Table 2. Because of the procedure used in deriving their values, these radii are correct, strictly speaking, only for cations having 6-fold coordination.

Covalent radii. When atoms form electron-pair bonds with each other, the interatomic separation depends on the number of electron-pair bonds formed. In the case of hybrid-bond formation, it also depends on the types of orbitals used. For example, the interatomic separation for two carbon atoms is as follows:

> 1.542 Å when single bonds are formed
> 1.330 Å when double bonds are formed
> 1.204 Å when triple bonds are formed

Similarly, the radius of covalently bonded nickel depends on the orbitals used, as follows:

1.21 Å if octahedral d^2sp^3 orbitals are used
1.22 Å if square dsp^2 orbitals are used
1.23 Å if tetrahedral sp^3 orbitals are used

As can be seen from the above, it is not possible to assign a single radius to cover all cases of covalent bonding. Moreover, it should be remembered that most atoms do

Table 1
Crystal radii of Pauling† (in Ångstroms)

−4	−3	−2	−1	0	+1	+2	+3	+4	+5	+6	+7
...	...	...	H 2.08	He‡ 0.93	Li 0.60	Be 0.31	B 0.20	C 0.15	N 0.11	O 0.09	F 0.07
C 2.60	N 1.71	O 1.40	F 1.36	Ne‡ 1.12	Na 0.95	Mg 0.65	Al 0.50	Si 0.41	P 0.34	S 0.29	Cl 0.26
Si 2.71	P 2.12	S 1.84	Cl 1.81	A‡ 1.54	K 1.33	Ca 0.99	Sc 0.81	Ti 0.68	V 0.59	Co 0.52	Mn 0.46
....	....	....	....	....	Cu 0.96	Zn 0.74	Ga 0.62	Ge 0.53	As 0.47	Se 0.42	Br 0.39
Ge 2.72	As 2.22	Se 1.98	Br 1.95	Kr‡ 1.69	Rb 1.48	Sr 1.13	Y 0.93	Zr 0.80	Nb 0.70	Mo 0.62	
....	....	....	....	....	Ag 1.26	Cd 0.97	In 0.81	Sn 0.71	Sb 0.62	Te 0.56	I 0.50
Sn 2.94	Sb 2.45	Te 2.21	I 2.16	Xe‡ 1.90	Cs 1.69	Ba 1.35	La 1.15	Ce 1.01			
....	....	....	....	....	Au 1.37	Hg 1.10	Tl 0.95	Pb 0.84	Bi 0.74		

† Linus Pauling, *The nature of the chemical bond*, 2d ed. (Cornell University Press, Ithaca, N.Y., 1948), p. 346.
‡ Univalent radii.

not form purely covalent bonds in crystals. Nevertheless, a number of elements appear to have very nearly the same radii in a number of crystals in which they are believed to be covalently bonded. Table 3 lists such radii for a number of elements. These radii are appropriate, strictly speaking, only when the atoms have tetrahedral coordination.

Metallic radii. Probably the simplest radii to determine are those of metal elements. These can be determined by halving the known $Me\text{-}Me$ distances in the metal crystals. Nevertheless, two problems arise in this connection. First of all, the interatomic separations are usually not the same for different allotropic modifications. Secondarily, in the case of noncubic metals, there are two or more interatomic dis-

Table 2
Ionic radii of cations† (in Ångstroms)

Ac^{+3}	1.18	Cs^{+1}	1.67	Mn^{+2}	0.80
				Mn^{+3}	0.66
Ag^{+1}	1.26	Cu^{+1}	0.96	Mn^{+4}	0.60
Ag^{+2}	0.89	Cu^{+2}	0.72	Mn^{+7}	0.46
Al^{+3}	0.51	Dy^{+3}	0.92	Mo^{+4}	0.70
				Mo^{+6}	0.62
Am^{+3}	1.07	Er^{+3}	0.89		
Am^{+4}	0.92			N^{+3}	0.16
		Eu^{+3}	0.98	N^{+5}	0.13
As^{+3}	0.58				
As^{+3}	0.46	F^{+7}	0.08	Na^{+1}	0.97
At^{+7}	0.62	Fe^{+2}	0.74	Nb^{+4}	0.74
		Fe^{+3}	0.64	Nb^{+5}	0.69
Au^{+1}	1.37				
Au^{+3}	0.85	Fr^{+1}	1.80	Nd^{+3}	1.04
B^{+3}	0.23	Ga^{+3}	0.62	Ni^{+2}	0.69
Ba^{+2}	1.34	Gd^{+3}	0.97	Np^{+3}	1.10
				Np^{+4}	0.95
Be^{+2}	0.35	Ge^{+2}	0.73	Np^{+7}	0.71
		Ge^{+4}	0.53		
Bi^{+3}	0.96			O^{+6}	0.10
Bi^{+5}	0.74	Hf^{+4}	0.78		
				Os^{+6}	0.69
Br^{+5}	0.47	Hg^{+2}	1.10		
Br^{+7}	0.39			P^{+3}	0.44
		Ho^{+3}	0.91	P^{+5}	0.35
C^{+4}	0.16				
		I^{+5}	0.62	Pa^{+3}	1.13
Ca^{+2}	0.99	I^{+7}	0.50	Pa^{+1}	0.98
				Pa^{+5}	0.89
Cd^{+2}	0.97	In^{+3}	0.81		
				Pb^{+2}	1.20
Ce^{+3}	1.07	Ir^{+4}	0.68	Pb^{+4}	0.84
Ce^{+4}	0.94				
		K^{+1}	1.33	Pd^{+2}	0.80
Cl^{+5}	0.34			Pd^{+4}	0.65
Cl^{+7}	0.27	La^{+3}	1.14		
				Pm^{+3}	1.06
Co^{+2}	0.72	Li^{+1}	0.68		
Co^{+3}	0.63			Po^{+6}	0.67
		Lu^{+2}	0.85		
Cr^{+3}	0.63			Pr^{+3}	1.06
Cr^{+6}	0.52	Mg^{+2}	0.66	Pr^{+4}	0.92

Table 2 (*Continued*)

Pt^{+2}	0.80	Se^{+4}	0.50	Ti^{+3}	0.76
Pt^{+4}	0.65	Se^{+7}	0.42	Ti^{+4}	0.68
Pu^{+3}	1.08	Si^{+4}	0.42	Tl^{+1}	1.47
Pu^{+4}	0.93			Tl^{+3}	0.95
Ra^{+2}	1.43	Sm^{+3}	1.00	Tm^{+2}	0.87
Rb^{+1}	1.47	Sn^{+2}	0.93	U^{+4}	0.97
		Sn^{+4}	0.71	U^{+6}	0.80
Re^{+4}	0.72	Sr^{+2}	1.12	V^{+2}	0.88
Re^{+7}	0.56			V^{+3}	0.74
				V^{+4}	0.63
Rh^{+3}	0.68	Ta^{+5}	0.68	V^{+5}	0.59
		Tb^{+3}	0.93	W^{+4}	0.70
Ru^{+4}	0.67	Tb^{+4}	0.81	W^{+6}	0.62
S^{+4}	0.37				
S^{+6}	0.30	Tc^{+7}	0.56	Y^{+3}	0.92
				Yb^{+3}	0.86
Sb^{+3}	0.76	Te^{+4}	0.70		
Sb^{+5}	0.62	Te^{+6}	0.56	Zn^{+2}	0.74
Sc^{+3}	0.81	Th^{+4}	1.02	Zr^{+4}	0.79

† L. H. Ahrens, The use of ionization potentials, Part 1.   Ionic radii of the elements, *Geochim. et Cosmochim. Acta*, vol. 2 (1952), pp. 155–169.

Table 3
Tetrahedral covalent radii† (in Ångstroms)

	Be	B	C	N	O	F
	1.06	0.88	0.77	0.70	0.66	0.64
	Mg	Al	Si	P	S	Cl
	1.40	1.26	1.17	1.10	1.04	0.99
Cu	Zn	Ga	Ge	As	Se	Br
1.35	1.31	1.26	1.22	1.18	1.14	1.11
Ag	Cd	In	Sn	Sb	Te	I
1.53	1.48	1.44	1.40	1.36	1.32	1.28
Au	Hg	Tl	Pb	Bi		
1.50	1.48	1.47	1.46	1.46		

† A. F. Wells, *Structural inorganic chemistry*, 2d ed. (Oxford University Press, London, 1950), p. 50.

tances that occur in the same crystal. Moreover, these metals do not necessarily have the same radii in alloys that they have in the elemental crystals. The radii listed in Table 4, therefore, represent a range of values that are most commonly observed. As in the case of ionic and covalent radii discussed above, the calculation of interatomic separations by simple addition of the values in Table 4 gives only approximately accurate results.

Table 4
Metallic radii (in Ångstroms)

Li 1.52	Be 1.1–1.14	B ~1.0	C 0.71–0.77						
Na 1.85	Mg 1.60	Al 1.43	Si 1.17	P 1.09					
K 2.31	Ca 1.97	Sc 1.60–1.65	Ti 1.44–1.47	V 1.31	Cr 1.25	Mn 1.23–1.48	Fe 1.24	Co 1.25	Ni 1.24
Cu 1.28	Zn 1.33–1.45	Ga 1.22–1.40	Ge 1.22	As 1.25–1.57	Se 1.16–1.73		Ru 1.32–1.35	Rh 1.34	Pd 1.37
Rb 2.46	Sr 2.15	Y 1.80–1.83	Zr 1.58–1.61	Nb 1.43	Mo 1.36	Tc 1.35–1.36	Os 1.34–1.36	Ir 1.35	Pt 1.38
Ag 1.44	Cd 1.49–1.64	In 1.62–1.69	Sn 1.40–1.59	Sb 1.45–1.68	Te 1.43–1.73				
Cs 2.63	Ba 2.17	La 1.36–1.87	Hf 1.57–1.60	Ta 1.43	W 1.37	Re 1.37–1.38			
Au 1.44	Mg 1.50	Tl 1.70–1.73	Pb 1.75	Bi 1.55–1.74	Po 1.64–1.67				
			Th 1.80	Pa 1.60–1.62	U 1.50				

Appendix 4
Space-group symbols

No. of space† group	Schoenflies symbol	Standard‡ full symbol	No. of space† group	Schoenflies symbol	Standard‡ full symbol
1	C_1^1	$P1$	24	$D_2^9 = V^9$	$I2_12_12_1$
2	C_i^1	$P\bar{1}$	25	C_{2v}^1	$Pmm2$
			26	C_{2v}^2	$Pmc2_1$
3	C_2^1	$P112$	27	C_{2v}^3	$Pcc2$
4	C_2^2	$P112_1$	28	C_{2v}^4	$Pma2$
5	C_2^3	$I112$	29	C_{2v}^5	$Pca2_1$
6	C_s^1	$P11m$	30	C_{2v}^6	$Pnc2$
7	C_s^2	$P11b$	31	C_{2v}^7	$Pmn2_1$
8	C_s^3	$I11m$	32	C_{2v}^8	$Pba2$
9	C_s^4	$I11b$	33	C_{2v}^9	$Pna2_1$
10	C_{2h}^1	$P11\dfrac{2}{m}$	34	C_{2v}^{10}	$Pnn2$
			35	C_{2v}^{11}	$Cmm2$
11	C_{2h}^2	$P11\dfrac{2_1}{m}$	36	C_{2v}^{12}	$Cmc2_1$
			37	C_{2v}^{13}	$Ccc2$
12	C_{2h}^3	$I11\dfrac{2}{m}$	38	C_{2v}^{14}	$Amm2$
			39	C_{2v}^{15}	$Abm2$
13	C_{2h}^4	$P11\dfrac{2}{b}$	40	C_{2v}^{16}	$Ama2$
			41	C_{2v}^{17}	$Aba2$
14	C_{2h}^5	$P11\dfrac{2_1}{b}$	42	C_{2v}^{18}	$Fmm2$
			43	C_{2v}^{19}	$Fdd2$
15	C_{2h}^6	$I11\dfrac{2}{b}$	44	C_{2v}^{20}	$Imm2$
16	$D_2^1 = V^1$	$P222$	45	C_{2v}^{21}	$Iba2$
17	$D_2^2 = V^2$	$P222_1$	46	C_{2v}^{22}	$Ima2$
18	$D_2^3 = V^3$	$P2_12_12$	47	$D_{2h}^1 = V_h^1$	$P\dfrac{2}{m}\dfrac{2}{m}\dfrac{2}{m}$
19	$D_2^4 = V^4$	$P2_12_12_1$			
20	$D_2^5 = V^5$	$C222_1$	48	$D_{2h}^2 = V_h^2$	$P\dfrac{2}{n}\dfrac{2}{n}\dfrac{2}{n}$
21	$D_2^6 = V^6$	$C222$			
22	$D_2^7 = V^7$	$F222$	49	$D_{2h}^3 = V_h^3$	$P\dfrac{2}{c}\dfrac{2}{c}\dfrac{2}{m}$
23	$D_2^8 = V^8$	$I222$			

No. of space† group	Schoenflies symbol	Standard‡ full symbol
50	$D_{2h}^4 = V_h^4$	$P\,\dfrac{2}{b}\,\dfrac{2}{a}\,\dfrac{2}{n}$
51	$D_{2h}^5 = V_h^5$	$P\,\dfrac{2_1}{m}\,\dfrac{2}{m}\,\dfrac{2}{a}$
52	$D_{2h}^6 = V_h^6$	$P\,\dfrac{2}{n}\,\dfrac{2_1}{n}\,\dfrac{2}{a}$
53	$D_{2h}^7 = V_h^7$	$P\,\dfrac{2}{m}\,\dfrac{2}{n}\,\dfrac{2_1}{a}$
54	$D_{2h}^8 = V_h^8$	$P\,\dfrac{2_1}{c}\,\dfrac{2}{c}\,\dfrac{2}{a}$
55	$D_{2h}^9 = V_h^9$	$P\,\dfrac{2_1}{b}\,\dfrac{2_1}{a}\,\dfrac{2}{m}$
56	$D_{2h}^{10} = V_h^{10}$	$P\,\dfrac{2_1}{c}\,\dfrac{2_1}{c}\,\dfrac{2}{n}$
57	$D_{2h}^{11} = V_h^{11}$	$P\,\dfrac{2}{b}\,\dfrac{2_1}{c}\,\dfrac{2_1}{m}$
58	$D_{2h}^{12} = V_h^{12}$	$P\,\dfrac{2_1}{n}\,\dfrac{2_1}{n}\,\dfrac{2}{m}$
59	$D_{2h}^{13} = V_h^{13}$	$P\,\dfrac{2_1}{m}\,\dfrac{2}{m}\,\dfrac{2}{n}$
60	$D_{2h}^{14} = V_h^{14}$	$P\,\dfrac{2_1}{b}\,\dfrac{2}{c}\,\dfrac{2_1}{n}$
61	$D_{2h}^{15} = V_h^{15}$	$P\,\dfrac{2_1}{b}\,\dfrac{2_1}{c}\,\dfrac{2_1}{a}$
62	$D_{2h}^{16} = V_h^{16}$	$P\,\dfrac{2_1}{n}\,\dfrac{2_1}{m}\,\dfrac{2_1}{a}$
63	$D_{2h}^{17} = V_h^{17}$	$C\,\dfrac{2}{m}\,\dfrac{2}{c}\,\dfrac{2_1}{m}$
64	$D_{2h}^{18} = V_h^{18}$	$C\,\dfrac{2}{m}\,\dfrac{2}{c}\,\dfrac{2_1}{a}$
65	$D_{2h}^{19} = V_h^{19}$	$C\,\dfrac{2}{m}\,\dfrac{2}{m}\,\dfrac{2}{m}$
66	$D_{2h}^{20} = V_h^{20}$	$C\,\dfrac{2}{c}\,\dfrac{2}{c}\,\dfrac{2}{m}$
67	$D_{2h}^{21} = V_h^{21}$	$C\,\dfrac{2}{m}\,\dfrac{2}{m}\,\dfrac{2}{a}$
68	$D_{2h}^{22} = V_h^{22}$	$C\,\dfrac{2}{c}\,\dfrac{2}{c}\,\dfrac{2}{a}$
69	$D_{2h}^{23} = V_h^{23}$	$F\,\dfrac{2}{m}\,\dfrac{2}{m}\,\dfrac{2}{m}$
70	$D_{2h}^{24} = V_h^{24}$	$F\,\dfrac{2}{d}\,\dfrac{2}{d}\,\dfrac{2}{d}$
71	$D_{2h}^{25} = V_h^{25}$	$I\,\dfrac{2}{m}\,\dfrac{2}{m}\,\dfrac{2}{m}$
72	$D_{2h}^{26} = V_h^{26}$	$I\,\dfrac{2}{b}\,\dfrac{2}{a}\,\dfrac{2}{m}$

No. of space† group	Schoenflies symbol	Standard‡ full symbol
73	$D_{2h}^{27} = V_h^{27}$	$I\,\dfrac{2}{b}\,\dfrac{2}{c}\,\dfrac{2}{a}$
74	$D_{2h}^{28} = V_h^{28}$	$I\,\dfrac{2}{m}\,\dfrac{2}{m}\,\dfrac{2}{a}$
75	C_4^1	$P4$
76	C_4^2	$P4_1$
77	C_4^3	$P4_2$
78	C_4^4	$P4_3$
79	C_4^5	$I4$
80	C_4^6	$I4_1$
81	S_4^1	$P\bar{4}$
82	S_4^2	$I\bar{4}$
83	C_{4h}^1	$P4/m$
84	C_{4h}^2	$P4_2/m$
85	C_{4h}^3	$P4/n$
86	C_{4h}^4	$P4_2/n$
87	C_{4h}^5	$I4/m$
88	C_{4h}^6	$I4_1/a$
89	D_4^1	$P422$
90	D_4^2	$P42_12$
91	D_4^3	$P4_122$
92	D_4^4	$P4_12_12$
93	D_4^5	$P4_222$
94	D_4^6	$P4_22_12$
95	D_4^7	$P4_122$
96	D_4^8	$P4_32_12$
97	D_4^9	$I422$
98	D_4^{10}	$I4_122$
99	C_{4v}^1	$P4mm$
100	C_{4v}^2	$P4bm$
101	C_{4v}^3	$P4_2cm$
102	C_{4v}^4	$P4_2nm$
103	C_{4v}^5	$P4cc$
104	C_{4v}^6	$P4nc$
105	C_{4v}^7	$P4_2mc$
106	C_{4v}^8	$P4_2bc$
107	C_{4v}^9	$I4mm$
108	C_{4v}^{10}	$I4cm$
109	C_{4v}^{11}	$I4_1md$
110	C_{4v}^{12}	$I4_1cd$
111	$D_{2d}^1 = V_d^1$	$P\bar{4}2m$
112	$D_{2d}^2 = V_d^2$	$P\bar{4}2c$
113	$D_{2d}^3 = V_d^3$	$P\bar{4}2_1m$
114	$D_{2d}^4 = V_d^4$	$P\bar{4}2_1c$
115	$D_{2d}^5 = V_d^5$	$P\bar{4}m2$
116	$D_{2d}^6 = V_d^6$	$P\bar{4}c2$
117	$D_{2d}^7 = V_d^7$	$P\bar{4}b2$

No. of space group	Schoenflies symbol	Standard full symbol	No. of space group	Schoenflies symbol	Standard full symbol
118	$D_{2d}^8 = V_d^8$	$P\bar{4}n2$	145	C_3^3	$P3_2$
119	$D_{2d}^9 = V_d^9$	$I\bar{4}m2$	146	C_3^4	$R3$
120	$D_{2d}^{10} = V_d^{10}$	$I\bar{4}c2$	147	C_{3i}^1	$P\bar{3}$
121	$D_{2d}^{11} = V^{11}$	$I\bar{4}2m$	148	C_{3i}^2	$R\bar{3}$
122	$D_{2d}^{12} = V^{12}$	$I\bar{4}2d$	149	D_3^1	$P312$
123	D_{4h}^1	$P\frac{4}{m}mm$	150	D_3^2	$P321$
			151	D_3^3	$P3_112$
124	D_{4h}^2	$P\frac{4}{m}cc$	152	D_3^4	$P3_121$
			153	D_3^5	$P3_212$
125	D_{4h}^3	$P\frac{4}{n}bm$	154	D_3^6	$P3_221$
			155	D_3^7	$R32$
126	D_{4h}^4	$P\frac{4}{n}nc$	156	C_{3v}^1	$P3m1$
			157	C_{3v}^2	$P31m$
127	D_{4h}^5	$P\frac{4}{m}bm$	158	C_{3v}^3	$P3c1$
			159	C_{3v}^4	$P31c$
128	D_{4h}^6	$P\frac{4}{m}nc$	160	C_{3v}^5	$R3m$
			161	C_{3v}^6	$R3c$
129	D_{4h}^7	$P\frac{4}{n}mm$	162	D_{3d}^1	$P\bar{3}1\frac{2}{m}$
130	D_{4h}^8	$P\frac{4}{n}cc$	163	D_{3d}^2	$P\bar{3}1\frac{2}{c}$
131	D_{4h}^9	$P\frac{4_2}{m}mc$	164	D_{3d}^3	$P\bar{3}\frac{2}{m}1$
132	D_{4h}^{10}	$P\frac{4_2}{m}cm$	165	D_{3d}^4	$P\bar{3}\frac{2}{c}1$
133	D_{4h}^{11}	$P\frac{4_2}{n}bc$	166	D_{3d}^5	$R\bar{3}\frac{2}{m}$
134	D_{4h}^{12}	$P\frac{4_2}{m}nm$	167	D_{3d}^6	$R\bar{3}\frac{2}{c}$
135	D_{4h}^{13}	$P\frac{4_2}{m}bc$	168	C_6^1	$P6$
			169	C_6^2	$P6_1$
136	D_{4h}^{14}	$P\frac{4_2}{m}nm$	170	C_6^3	$P6_5$
			171	C_6^4	$P6_2$
137	D_{4h}^{15}	$P\frac{4_2}{n}mc$	172	C_6^5	$P6_4$
			173	C_6^6	$P6_3$
138	D_{4h}^{16}	$P\frac{4_2}{n}cm$	174	C_{3h}^1	$P\bar{6}$
			175	C_{6h}^1	
139	D_{4h}^{17}	$I\frac{4}{m}mm$			$P\frac{6}{m}$
140	D_{4h}^{18}	$I\frac{4}{m}cm$	176	C_{6h}^2	$P\frac{6_3}{m}$
141	D_{4h}^{19}	$I\frac{4_1}{a}md$	177	D_6^1	$P622$
			178	D_6^2	$P6_122$
142	D_{4h}^{20}	$I\frac{4_1}{a}cd$	179	D_6^3	$P6_522$
			180	D_6^4	$P6_222$
			181	D_6^5	$P6_422$
143	C_3^1	$P3$	182	D_6^6	$P6_322$
144	C_3^2	$P3_1$	183	C_{6v}^1	$P6mm$

No. of space† group	Schoenflies symbol	Standard‡ full symbol	No. of space† group	Schoenflies symbol	Standard‡ full symbol
184	C_{6v}^2	$P6cc$	207	O^1	$P432$
185	C_{6v}^3	$P6_3cm$	208	O^2	$P4_232$
186	C_{6v}^4	$P6_3mc$	209	O^3	$F432$
187	D_{3h}^1	$P\bar{6}m2$	210	O^4	$F4_132$
188	D_{3h}^2	$P\bar{6}c2$	211	O^5	$I432$
189	D_{3h}^3	$P\bar{6}2m$	212	O^6	$P4_332$
190	D_{3h}^4	$P\bar{6}2c$	213	O^7	$P4_132$
191	D_{6h}^1	$P\dfrac{6}{m}\dfrac{2}{m}\dfrac{2}{m}$	214	O^8	$I4_132$
			215	T_d^1	$P\bar{4}3m$
192	D_{6h}^2	$P\dfrac{6}{m}\dfrac{2}{c}\dfrac{2}{c}$	216	T_d^2	$F\bar{4}3m$
			217	T_d^3	$I\bar{4}3m$
193	D_{6h}^3	$P\dfrac{6_3}{m}\dfrac{2}{c}\dfrac{2}{m}$	218	T_d^4	$P\bar{4}3n$
			219	T_d^5	$F\bar{4}3c$
194	D_{6h}^4	$P\dfrac{6_3}{m}\dfrac{2}{m}\dfrac{2}{c}$	220	T_d^6	$I\bar{4}3d$
			221	O_h^1	$P\dfrac{4}{m}\bar{3}\dfrac{2}{m}$
195	T^1	$P23$			
196	T^2	$F23$	222	O_h^2	$P\dfrac{4}{n}\bar{3}\dfrac{2}{n}$
197	T^3	$I23$			
198	T^4	$P2_13$	223	O_h^3	$P\dfrac{4_2}{m}\bar{3}\dfrac{2}{n}$
199	T^5	$I2_13$			
200	T_h^1	$P\dfrac{2}{m}\bar{3}$	224	O_h^4	$P\dfrac{4_2}{n}\bar{3}\dfrac{2}{m}$
201	T_h^2	$P\dfrac{2}{n}\bar{3}$	225	O_h^5	$F\dfrac{4}{m}\bar{3}\dfrac{2}{m}$
202	T_h^3	$F\dfrac{2}{m}\bar{3}$	226	O_h^6	$F\dfrac{4}{m}\bar{3}\dfrac{2}{c}$
203	T_h^4	$F\dfrac{2}{d}\bar{3}$	227	O_h^7	$F\dfrac{4_1}{d}\bar{3}\dfrac{2}{m}$
204	T_h^5	$I\dfrac{2}{m}\bar{3}$	228	O_h^8	$F\dfrac{4_1}{d}\bar{3}\dfrac{2}{c}$
205	T_h^6	$P\dfrac{2_1}{a}\bar{3}$	229	O_h^9	$I\dfrac{4}{m}\bar{3}\dfrac{2}{m}$
206	T_h^7	$I\dfrac{2_1}{a}\bar{3}$	230	O_h^{10}	$I\dfrac{4_1}{a}\bar{3}\dfrac{2}{d}$

† This space-group number is the same as the designation used in *International tables for x-ray crystallography*, vol. 1, where a complete description can be found.

‡ The symmetry elements are listed in the order *abc*, and the *z*-axis unique setting is used in the monoclinic system.

INDEX

447